This is essentially a complete course in theoretical physics for the first year graduate and advanced undergraduate level. The author first explains the fundamental ideas and principles of physics in the simplest and most intuitive terms, and then shows how these ideas can be developed into the most elaborate formalisms of contemporary theories. The method of exposition is to start with the most fundamental concepts and ideas, and to explain them thoroughly before the introduction of a new idea becomes necessary. The reader will be surprised to see how little is required to reproduce the whole of modern physics when approached by this powerful technique. Paramount importance is given to the idea of relativity; almost all the other concepts are developed in close relationship with relativity. All in all, five basic ideas are employed: relativity; causality; the positive definiteness of energy; the quantum nature of energy; the equivalence of inertial and gravitation mass. Simple but illustrative problems and their solutions are provided at the end of the book. Each chapter ends with a concise summary of its contents.

RELATIVITY AND MODERN PHYSICS

A Blaisdell Book in the Pure and Applied Sciences

BERNARD T. FELD, *Massachusetts Institute of Technology*
WILLIS LAMB, *Yale University*

CONSULTING EDITORS

INTRODUCTION TO THE
Theory of Relativity
AND THE
Principles of Modern Physics

HÜSEYIN YILMAZ

BLAISDELL PUBLISHING COMPANY

A Division of Ginn and Company

NEW YORK · TORONTO · LONDON

DEDICATED

TO

Professor Philip M. Morse

TEACHER AND FRIEND

PREFACE

Many scientists have the impression that the theory of relativity is already a closed subject. This is completely erroneous. The recent discovery of the violation of space-inversion (1957), the accurate measurements of the velocity of light by MASER techniques (1958), the measurement of the gravitational red shift by Mössbauer rays (1960), the proof of the local isotropy of space (1960), and planned experiments on the Lense-Thirring effect, on parallel displacement, on gravitational waves, etc., indicate that the subject is under constant inquiry. On the theoretical side the achievement of a relativistic formulation of quantum field theory (1948), the steady state theory of the universe (1948), progress on the quantization of general relativity (1954–60), and the recent relativistic S-matrix and dispersion relations approach to dynamics (1959) are evidences of continual research and development. Therefore, one of our primary aims in this book is to present the theory of relativity as a living subject.

Another point, which is often overlooked, is the profound influence of the theory of relativity on the early development and the present form of quantum theory. Although a non-relativistic quantum mechanics for electrons can be developed without reference to Einsteinian relativity, it cannot be consistently generalized to include positrons, photons, and mesons and it leaves the logical background completely obscure. The intimate relationship of relativistic ideas to all the fundamental principles of modern physics and the intense light they shed on the nature of our world has been invaluable in the development of present-day physics. Therefore, a second aim of this book will be the presentation of material in close relationship to relativity. We do not claim completeness of treatment or finality in mathematical rigor.

To emphasize the physical background, the chapters start with extremely simple situations and lead step by step to the most advanced concepts of relativity and of field theory. As an aid in practicing the ideas and the computational techniques developed, simple but illustrative problems and their solutions are provided for each chapter of the book.

The units used in some chapters of the book are $c = \hbar = 1$ or $c = G = 1$ but c, $\hbar$, and G appear explicitly in most formulas since this is felt to be useful and to result in greater clarity.

It is a great pleasure to acknowledge the support and encouragement of Dr. Howard McMahon president of Arthur D. Little, Inc., and Dr. Leonard S. Sheingold of Sylvania Electric Company. I am also indebted to several friends and colleagues, and to my secretaries and students for the sincere help I received while the manuscript was in progress during the past few years. Special thanks are due to Ruth H. Harris for graciously typing and to John Jasperse for critically reading the final manuscript.

Cambridge, Massachusetts
April, 1964

HÜSEYIN YILMAZ

CONTENTS

INTRODUCTION

At the present stage of our understanding the physical world seems to reveal itself to us through certain abstract statements we call principles. Some of these principles are general in that they refer to all physical phenomena, whereas others have to do only with limited classes. For example, the principle of conservation of energy is general and refers to all processes, whereas the principles of gauge invariance and of charge conservation are restricted to those phenomena in which the electromagnetic field plays a part. The general principles which the physical world seems to obey are very few in number. In fact, at present only five are known. They are: (1) the principle of relativity (symmetries of space-time geometry plus the covariance of natural laws); (2) the principle of causality; (3) the principle of positive definiteness of energy; (4) the quantum nature of action; (5) the principle of equality of inertial and gravitational mass. The present book is developed mainly around these general principles with intent to indicate that very little is required to arrive at man's present knowledge about the world in which he lives. A principle should not be considered as something absolutely necessary or true. It should be regarded only as a convenient way of summarizing the results of large numbers of observations made by a particular method and subsequently used as the basis for a theory aimed at predicting the outcome of other observations to be made by the same method. A system of observation may be compared to our complex of sensory perceptions by means of which we try to perceive and determine the state of the physical world. Such a system of perception is useful for our survival and evidently that is why it is evolved. Visual perception provides us with a crude image of the state of the world at a particular time. This image changes as the state of the world changes but, as such, it is not predictive. We can extend these perceptions into the past by recording the successive images into a memory and by extrapolation of the stored perceptions into the future. Our power of memory and successful extrapolation of what is in the memory constitute the predictive behavior of living beings. The reverse process of singling out a future sense perception and following the intermediate perceptions leading to it is an interpolation in time and is characteristic of the purposeful behavior of living beings. Some of the predictive powers are so necessary that they are fixed as reflexes. For instance, should an object approach the eye with a certain speed, reflexively we will close our eyes. Most predictive processes, however, take place at a higher level and involve logical argumentation in extrapolation. This is apparently necessary because the exterior happenings depend also on variables which we do not perceive directly. Thus, for a given force a lead ball will accelerate less than one of aluminum precisely the same size and appearance. The difference, of course, lies in the unperceived (visually) element of mass of the two balls. We must assign to them different properties mentally if we are to know their future position and speed. Doubtlessly, a fully predictive faculty is needed, which at our present stage of evolution is not present in reflexive or instinctive form. Thus, we go to great pains of logical argumentation and mathematical computation to produce mentally an image of a future perception from a given set of present and past perceptions. The scientific form of this activity is to calculate the outcome of a future observation from a given set of initial and boundary conditions. In this sense, man's science is a system of refined and extended perceptions. Thus, it is not surprising that his views evolve in time, similar to the evolution of perception devices, from simpler to higher forms and power. He improves, sometimes completely changes his methods of observation with a related change in the logical structure of his theory. For example, the passage from the Newtonian theory of space-time measurements to Einsteinian relativity is marked by new definitions of length and time consistent with the finite velocity of transmittal of information. In a sense, this is an evolution in our way of observation similar to the evolution of our perception mechanism. It is perfectly possible that a particular way of observation may be incapable of detecting certain physical objects or characteristics, leaving the observable world essentially incomplete. In elementary perception, we have an example of this possibility in color vision. In the course of its evolution, the human eye adopted only a small portion of the spectrum and therefore detects only a small range of frequencies. If we relied solely on this device of observation, as a seventeenth-century physicist might have done, we would be forced to impose certain conditions on electromagnetic theory in order to exclude all other frequencies. Such a condition might not be consistent with relativity or quantum mechanics, thus possibly necessitating a completely different foundation for the theory. Similarly, the eye sees only three independent variables in a light distribution, namely, brightness, hue, and saturation, creating the false impression that light distributions have only these three characteristics. Light distributions have, in general, an infinite number of independent variables of which the human eye detects only three. It is possible to construct super color machines which see four, five, or any number of different qualities. The normal human eye would be considered color blind compared to these machines, just as we classify as color blind those people who perceive a smaller number of independent qualities than normal. Bees seem to perceive an extended number of qualities, including polarization. A theory of light based on man's device of visual observation, the eye, would be so limited in its scope as to be hardly of any value. Thus, this method of detection and observation was duly replaced by sensitive instruments which, themselves, have other properties as well, and theories were adapted to the findings and the particular properties of these instruments. The basic fact remains, however, that this is still a particular form of perception and is subject to change at any time into an even more suitable and comprehensive system of instrumentation and theory. It is along these lines that we must try to understand the epistemology of our subject in this book. The principles introduced should not be taken as the properties of the exterior world alone but as the properties of the world plus our observation complex. In this sense, a physical principle is analogous to the so-called principle of color constancy in color perception. Clearly, this is not a property of the exterior light distributions alone; a photographic camera does not show it. Yet, the eye could not possibly have evolved this law if the exterior light distributions did not have a property which allowed its evolution. We usually think that laws are there for us to discover. This is not quite so; our active creation of a conceptual framework through which facts acquire meaning is an integral part of science and theory.

RELATIVITY AND MODERN PHYSICS

1

GALILEAN RELATIVITY

1.1. Introductory Remarks

Some time ago, I took my little niece for her first train ride. She was fascinated by the huge station and asked innumerable questions. We settled in a seat and in a few minutes were on our way. As we sped by the houses and the trees, my niece looked out the window and asked, "Why are the houses and trees going so fast? I told her that the houses and trees were not moving at all, but that we, together with the train, were moving. It was difficult for her to accept this. She continued to say that the trees and houses were moving very fast. Finally, a fellow passenger convinced her by saying that the trees and houses could not move because they do not have legs or wheels.

A few hours later, we entered a sizable station. Soon after we stopped, a train on the next track started to move. Watching from the window, my little niece declared that we were already on our way. It was again very hard for us to explain to her that we were standing still, but that the other train was moving. She did not believe this until we pointed out, through another window, that the walls, the electric lights, and the clock in the station were standing still. We gave her a very poor lesson, for the theory of relativity teaches us that my niece was not wrong.

Precisely the same thing happened in the history of science. Thousands of years ago when our ancestors looked up at the sky, they saw the sun, the moon, and the stars moving (Figure 1.1). To them, the earth was a solid immovable body, the base for everything in their lives. Legends were created on this basis and great religions were founded. Great scientific theories were constructed, as well. Ptolemy, the Greek astronomer, advanced his theory of the motions of the heavens and the heavenly bodies about 200 A.D. According to him, the earth was the center of the universe. The sun moved around the earth once a day, and the moon approximately once a day, but slightly slower. The planets also rotated around the earth once a day, but their motion was not on a perfect circle. Superimposed on their circular motion was a smaller circular motion which made their trajectories epicycles. Thus, the motion of the planetary system was similar to a gear works. The whole heavens in its turn, with the stars fixed in it, rotated regularly around the earth once a day or almost once a day. This theory prevailed under the name of the Ptolemaic System until the time of Copernicus, Galileo, and Kepler. In 1532, Copernicus advocated the theory of a stationary sun with the small earth revolving around it (Figure 1.1). The earth and the other planets together represented a family, all rotating about the sun. Galileo supported this theory with his astronomical discoveries. It was so difficult for the people of that time to believe this new theory that Galileo was condemned to death by the Inquisition for defending it. Fortunately, Galileo was very old at the time, and he had a good friend in the court. His punishment was commuted to life imprisonment, and later he was released. It is sometimes claimed that on the very day he was condemned to death, Galileo looked up at the sky

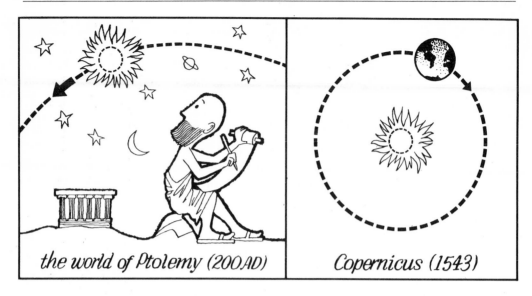

the world of Ptolemy (200AD)   Copernicus (1543)

FIGURE 1.1   (a) *The world of Ptolemy and* (b) *the world of Copernicus.*

outside the courtroom, then looked down at the earth and said, "I feel under my feet that the earth moves around the sun.

Actually, Galileo did not feel anything under his feet, nor has any other man ever felt the earth move under his feet. The theory of relativity teaches us that such feeling is impossible. It also teaches us that the great battle between the Ptolemaic System and the Copernican System was unnecessary. Galileo's condemnation by the court was certainly nonsense. So was Galileo's defense, because the Copernican and the Ptolemaic systems are basically equivalent to each other. The actual question was merely a matter of convenience in description. How can this be? *It is possible because of the principle of relativity.*

In a sense, the principle of relativity is nothing new. It was known to Galileo, Leibniz, and Newton. However, it was known in such a restricted and hidden form that its full discovery took 300 years. In the following three sections, we present the Galilean or classical relativity principle, that is, the principle of relativity inherent in Newtonian mechanics.

1.2. Principle of Galilean Relativity

Consider a train at rest near a building. Suppose there is a group of children inside the car (as shown in Figure 1.2a) and that they are experimenting by dropping an apple from a height. The apple, of course, falls to the point B, just beneath the point A from which the apple was dropped. If a woman on the balcony of the house drops an apple, this apple also falls to a point F, just below the point D from which it was dropped.

Now consider a uniformly moving train (Figure 1.2b). Let the woman on the balcony drop another apple from the same point D at the instant when the point F is just below D, that is, when D and F are on the same vertical line. Where will the apple fall? Of course, during the apple's descent, the train will move forward, and the apple will hit a different point F'. Let us now return to the children inside the train. Suppose that they had marked the points A and B while the coach was still at rest. Now suppose that they repeat the same apple-dropping experiment in the uniformly moving train. If they drop the apple from the same point A, where will it fall? The answer to this question is not so easy. It requires a good knowledge of mechanics (or much experience at dropping apples on trains). For the time being we will give the result of such an experiment without any explanation: The apple will always hit the same point B that it hit originally when the train was at rest. It does not fall forward or backward, as the apple falling from the balcony does. If you do not believe this, put your heavy suitcase just above your head next time you are on a uniformly moving train and let it go; see on whose head it lands (Figure 1.3). Before you perform this experiment, however, don't forget to reserve a bed in the hospital for yourself!

Thus, the apple dropped by the woman on the balcony hits a different point on the train when the coach is in uniform motion, while the apple dropped by the children in the coach always drops to the same point B, just as if the train were not moving. The woman on the balcony, therefore, can tell by this experiment whether or not the train is moving, but the children inside cannot, since they obtain the same result whether their train is stationary or moving with a uniform velocity v. Of course, we can invite the woman into the train and let her drop an apple from the window to the ground. This experiment will give a result similar to the result of the experiment she performed from the balcony; namely, when the coach is moving, the apple will hit a point on the ground different from the point it would hit if the train were stationary (Figure 1.4). In view of her earlier procedure in determining what is and what is not moving, the woman will have to conclude that the train is standing still (as was the house), but that the ground, with everything on it, is moving in the opposite direction. On the other hand, the people doing the experiments inside the train will never be able to find out whether the train is moving or standing still.

Now, the question arises as to whether there are other kinds of experiments by which one

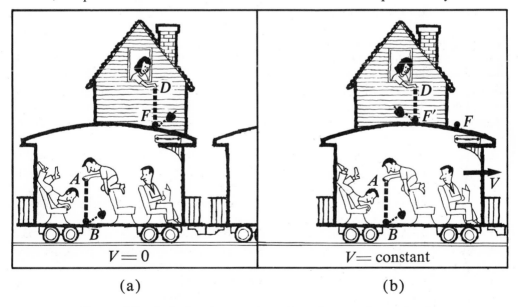

FIGURE 1.2 *Apple-dropping experiment in stationary and moving trains.*

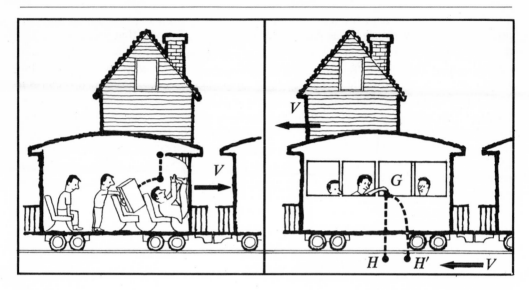

FIGURE 1.3   *An experiment with a heavy suit-*   FIGURE 1.4   *Apple-dropping experiment from*
case.   *the window of a train.*

can definitely tell which is moving—the ground or the train. Furthermore, is it possible, by means of some ingenious experiment performed inside the train, to tell whether it is stationary or in uniform motion? The answer to both these questions is negative. It has been impossible to design an experiment that can determine whether the train is moving and the ground is stationary, or vice versa. Therefore, in the absence of any experimental evidence as to which is moving, we must talk about the motion in a relative sense. For example, we must say that the train is moving with respect to the house with a velocity V in the right-hand direction. This must be equivalent to saying that the house is moving with respect to the train with a velocity V in the left-hand direction. As soon as we define motion in a relative manner, that is, always with respect to another object, we see immediately that the idea of motion loses its meaning if we have only one object. This is exactly what happens to the people inside the train who are trying to determine the motion of the train itself. Their experiment begins and ends in the train. They do not relate it to another object. Therefore, owing to the relative character of motion, they are asking a meaningless question.

Since the experiment gives the same result in both the stationary train and the uniformly moving train, the natural law controlling the motion of the apple must have the same mathematical form whether written for the stationary train or for the uniformly moving train. Indeed, this is the only way we can guarantee, generally, that the same initial conditions will lead to the same numerical answers in both cases.

These considerations form the basis of the *principle of relativity first realized by Galileo*.

(a) Motion is relative; that is, in order to have a meaning, the motion of an object must be referred to some other object (kinematical statement). By definition a reference object like the train is called a *reference frame* or *coordinate system*.

(b) The laws of mechanics have the same mathematical form in all reference frames moving uniformly relative to each other (dynamical statement).

Here we must note at once that, when the motion of the train is not uniform, that is, when the train is accelerated, we immediately feel the difference by experiencing an acceleration in the train. For example, when a bus is accelerating, we accelerate (if we are free) backward, and when it is decelerating, we accelerate forward. If we are not free to move, that is, if we are held somewhere in the train, we experience a force proportional to the acceleration of the train. But nothing different is experienced when the bus is moving with a uniform velocity, no matter how large this uniform velocity is. Thus for relativity considerations to be valid, we should not experience accelerations in the system we are using. If, in a given system, a free object does not experience any acceleration, that system is called an *inertial frame*. In an inertial frame a free object moves uniformly. Furthermore, any frame moving uniformly relative to an inertial frame is also inertial since a free object having uniform velocity relative to the first will have uniform velocity relative to all such frames.

After these preliminaries and definitions, we can now express the content of the principle of mechanical relativity more precisely as follows: *The laws of mechanics have the same mathematical form in all inertial frames.*

1.3. Mathematical Formulation of Galilean Relativity

In order to describe the processes taking place in a reference frame like the train, we use a coordinate system. A coordinate system is composed of three spatial axes attached to the frame to indicate the position of particles in that frame, as well as a clock, attached to the frame, to indicate time (Figure 1.5). In fact, the coordinate system is an idealization of the reference frame and so the words *reference frame* and *coordinate system* are interchangeable.

According to Newtonian mechanics, the motion of massive particles is governed by Newton's equations of motion,

$$f_x = m \frac{d^2x}{dt^2}, \qquad f_y = m \frac{d^2y}{dt^2}, \qquad f_z = m \frac{d^2z}{dt^2}, \tag{1.1}$$

where x, y, and z are the coordinates of the particle along the three spatial axes, and f_x, f_y, f_z are the components of the force along the same axes; t is the time measured by the clock. It is immediately evident that the frame in which these equations are written is inertial, for when the particle is free, that is, $f_x = f_y = f_z = 0$, the accelerations are zero and the particle will move with constant velocity.

Let us denote this inertial frame by S. If we consider another inertial frame S', the principle of relativity tells us that the equations of motion of the same particle [equations (1.1)] in

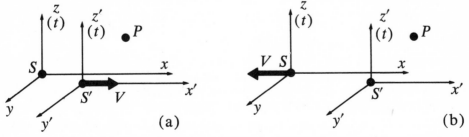

FIGURE 1.5 *Galilean transformations: The basis of classical space and time concepts.*

S' must be written in the same general form, namely,

$$f_{x'} = m' \frac{d^2x'}{dt'^2}, \qquad f_{y'} = m' \frac{d^2y'}{dt'^2}, \qquad f_{z'} = m' \frac{d^2z'}{dt'^2}. \qquad (1.2)$$

It is seen immediately that, as a consequence of these equations, identically prepared experiments will give identical results in both systems by virtue of the sameness of the mathematical form of the equations, so that it will be impossible to distinguish one inertial frame from another by experiments performed in those inertial frames. Experiments performed with more complicated objects such as rigid bodies or collections of particles, fluids, gases, etcetera, will not change this conclusion because the equations of such motions will also have the same form in other inertial frames by virtue of the principle of relativity.

1.4. Transformation Formulas

On the other hand, a given experiment, when observed from one frame and, at the same time, from a different frame, will not in general give the same results, since the primed quantities are *not* the same as the unprimed ones. The question then arises: What are the relations between primed and unprimed quantities? These relations relate to observations of the same quantity in the primed and unprimed reference frames. One thing we can state at this point is that if, in one inertial frame, the force vanishes it must also vanish in the other inertial frame; this suggests that the relation between the force in S and in S' is of the form,

$$
\begin{aligned}
f_{x'} &= \Omega_{11} f_x + \Omega_{12} f_y + \Omega_{13} f_z \\
f_{y'} &= \Omega_{21} f_y + \Omega_{22} f_y + \Omega_{23} f_z \\
f_{z'} &= \Omega_{31} f_z + \Omega_{32} f_z + \Omega_{33} f_z;
\end{aligned}
\qquad (1.3)
$$

further than this we cannot go. We need additional assumptions. In fact, we need three assumptions if we want to determine any one of the quantities in equations (1.2). The assumptions which were made implicitly in Newtonian physics are explicitly enumerated as follows:

(a) Measurement of a force will give the same numerical value whether it is done in S or S'. Thus if the coordinate axes of the two systems are chosen to be parallel, we assume

$$f_{x'} = f_x, \qquad f_{y'} = f_y, \qquad f_{z'} = f_z. \qquad (1.4)$$

(b) The mass of the particle will be observed to have the same numerical value whether it is measured in S or in S':

$$m' = m. \qquad (1.5)$$

(c) The time duration of a given process as measured by the clock in S gives the same numerical value as when measured by the clock in S':

$$t' = t. \qquad (1.6)$$

After these relations are given, the relationship between spatial coordinates can be deduced. In fact we have from equations (1.1) and (1.2)

$$\frac{d^2x'}{dt^2} = \frac{d^2x}{dt^2}, \qquad \frac{d^2y'}{dt^2} = \frac{d^2y}{dt^2}, \qquad \frac{d^2z'}{dt^2} = \frac{d^2z}{dt^2}. \qquad (1.7)$$

By integrating these equations, and assuming that the coordinates coincided at $t = 0$, we have

$$x' = x + \alpha t \qquad y' = y + \beta t \qquad z' = z + \gamma t \qquad (1.8)$$
$$t' = t$$

where α, β, γ are constants. Equations (1.8) are called Galilean transformations. A special case, where the motion of S' is along the x-axis and has the relative velocity $\alpha = -V$, is given by (Figure 1.5)

$$
\begin{aligned}
x' &= x - Vt & \qquad & & x &= x' + Vt' \\
y' &= y & \text{or} & & y &= y' \\
z' &= z & & & z &= z' \\
& & t' = t. & &
\end{aligned}
$$

Under the Galilean transformations, combined with the assumed transformations for force, mass, and time, the laws of motion transform into the same mathematical form from one inertial frame to another, as required by the principle of relativity. In this way we see that Newtonian physics is made consistent with the principle of relativity.

The invariance of Newton's laws of motion under the Galilean transformations and the implications of this invariance for the relativity of motion was known to Newton and his contemporaries. Newton himself did not attach great significance to it. He noticed that his equations of motion do not preserve their form in an accelerated system and he considered this as an objection against the whole idea of relativity. He argued that in the derivation, such quantities as time, mass, and force remain absolute as expressed in equations (1.4), (1.5), and (1.6). The absoluteness of force is especially serious, since this would mean that the acceleration is also absolute and, therefore, that one cannot claim the relativity of motion in general. The great German philosopher and mathematician, Leibniz, on the other hand, advocated that relativity is a general law and even acceleration must be considered relative. Leibniz argued that all appearances are the same whether the motion of a body is referred to one or the other of two arbitrarily moving frames. Newton insisted that this is so only as far as the kinematical appearances are concerned. Dynamically due to the absoluteness of force, the distinction of acceleration is at once possible. For example, we immediately notice whether or not a car is being accelerated by experiencing a force in the car. Newton's views were generally accepted until the present century.

At the beginning of this century it was found that the Galilean transformations and Newton's equations of motion needed revision, but the principle of relativity remained untouched. This revision of the whole of the physics regarding inertial frames later also led to a general theory of relativity in which all motion is relative. In this development of relativistic physics the great physicist and philosopher, Albert Einstein, occupies the most prominent place. His special theory of relativity, that is, the relativity theory of inertial frames, gave modern physics a solid foundation, whereas his general theory of relativity provided us with a consistent theory of gravitation.

Summary: Galilean Relativity

(a) If a law of mechanics is known to hold in one inertial frame, then the principle of relativity states that it holds with the same mathematical form in a second inertial frame.

(b) An observer in the second inertial frame can write down the laws either by analogy with the first system's equations or by transforming the first system's equations by the Galilean transformations:

$$x' = x - Vt \qquad x = x' + Vt'$$
$$y' = y \qquad y = y'$$
$$z' = z \qquad z = z'$$
$$t' = t.$$

(c) The invariance of the form of the equations of mechanics under Galilean transformations is true only in inertial frames. It is lost if we try to transform from an inertial to a noninertial frame.

2

OPTICAL EXPERIMENTS,
CONSTANCY OF THE VELOCITY OF LIGHT

2.1. Michelson-Morley Experiment and the Ether Hypothesis

Galilean relativity, as presented in the first chapter, was consistent with Newtonian mechanics. During the last century a new branch of physics developed: electrodynamics. As is well known, electromagnetic theory explains a great variety of phenomena, including the nature and propagation of light. Contrary to classical mechanics, electromagnetic and light phenomena seemed to present a way of determining the uniform motion of a system by experiments performed on that system alone. If this was so, the principle of relativity explained in the previous chapter could not be maintained as a general principle of nature but would be restricted only to Newtonian mechanics. Let us now see what happened when an attempt was made to determine the motion of the earth by using light phenomena on the earth itself.

The velocity of propagation of light in empty space is a constant equal to

$$c = 3 \times 10^{10} \text{ cm/sec.} \tag{2.1}$$

Maxwell, who first derived this value from his electromagnetic theory of light, accepted the old analogy between light waves and sound waves, and thus the existence of the ether. The ether hypothesis had long existed in optics. Since sound waves cannot be transmitted without a medium to carry them, it was thought that a medium with mechanical properties must exist to transmit light waves. Since light can be transmitted through a vacuum, it was assumed that the medium which carries the light waves, the ether, must fill all of space, including the tiny spaces between the atoms and molecules which constitute matter. By analogy with sound waves, it was assumed that the velocity of propagation, c, must be measured *with respect to the ether*. Actually, the ether hypothesis proved self-contradictory, because it had to be assumed to have contradictory mechanical properties. It had to be the softest and also the hardest substance in the world. It must be assumed softer than anything else known because all material bodies can pass through it without any resistance from the ether. If there were an ether resistance against motion, the earth would have slowed down and fallen into the sun during the billions of years of its existence (the age which geologists read from its crust). On the other hand, it must be harder than any known material because ether vibrations (light) travel with such a high velocity that its elastic constant must be highest of all materials. Such contradictions did not prevent physicists of the nineteenth century from clinging to their belief in the mechanical ether. Since the ether seemed to form a huge sea at rest, within which all other material bodies move, it was thought to form an ideal reference system. The property of absolute rest was attributed to it and it was believed that the laws of optics would take their simplest forms when referred to a coordinate system fixed to the ether.

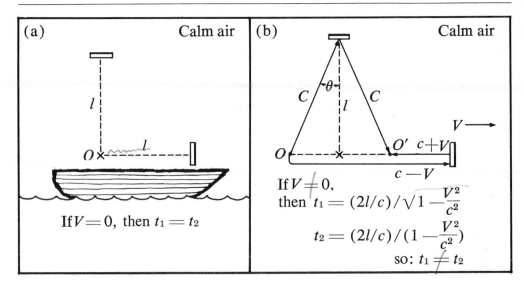

FIGURE 2.1 (a) *A method of navigators to find the velocity of a ship with respect to calm air.* (b) *The negative result of a similar experiment performed with the light rays disproves the mechanical ether hypothesis.*

If we accept the ether hypothesis,† then there must be an ether wind around the earth, since the earth moves around the sun, and thus cannot be permanently at rest relative to the ether. It should be possible to measure the velocity of the earth with respect to the ether by experimenting with light waves, by a method similar to that used by navigators to find the velocity of a ship in *calm* air. Suppose we are on the deck of a ship, and from some point O we send sound waves out in two directions—in the direction of motion of the ship and perpendicular to it (Figure 2.1a). We put two plane reflectors at equal distances from O and reflect the sound waves back to O. Which of these waves will come back to the point O first? Of course, if the ship were stationary in the air, the two waves would come back at exactly the same instant; because, *in the air*, the velocity of the sound waves is constant in all directions. But matters are different if the ship is moving. Suppose the whole setup is moving in the forward direction with respect to the air (Figure 2.1b). Consider the reflector B first. The wave travels the distance OB. Its velocity along OB is c, the velocity of the waves in air. The distance OB can be expressed in terms of l as $OB = (l/\sqrt{1 - v^2/c^2})$. Therefore, the wave reaches B and comes back to the source O (which has now reached the position O') after a time t_1, where

$$t_1 = \frac{2\overline{OB}}{c} = \frac{2}{c} \frac{l}{\sqrt{1 - \dfrac{v^2}{c^2}}}. \tag{2.2}$$

The sound wave which was sent towards A travels in the air at the same rate c. But the reflector A is moving away with a velocity v, so the net velocity with respect to the ship is $c - v$. The wave eventually hits the reflector A, is reflected there, and returns with a velocity

† Actually there existed many versions of the mechanical ether hypothesis. Since they did not differ from each other as far as the concept of relative motion is concerned, we will not discuss each of them separately.

c with respect to the air. But due to the motion of the ship, the point O is moving toward the wave with a velocity v, and the velocity of the wave with respect to the ship is $c + v$, so the time t_2 it takes the wave to come back to the source (now at position O') is

$$t_2 = \frac{l}{c + v} + \frac{l}{c - v} = \frac{2}{c} \frac{l}{1 - \frac{v^2}{c^2}}. \qquad (2.3)$$

Thus, t_1 and t_2 are different, and the difference depends on the velocity v. If we measure the time difference, we can immediately calculate the velocity of the ship. Now, if the analogy between sound waves and light waves is correct, the same reasoning can be applied to light waves and the velocity of the earth with respect to the ether can be found. This is what Albert A. Michelson tried to do in the 1880's. He performed the experiment using light waves, but surprisingly he could detect no difference between t_1 and t_2. They were equal to each other to a high degree of accuracy. The result of the experiment seemed to show that the earth was standing still in the ether. This could not be true, because we know the earth goes around the sun with a speed of about 30 km/sec, and the accuracy of the experiment (using interferometer techniques) was such that a speed of even 5 km/sec could easily be detected. At first Michelson considered the possibility of a motion of the whole solar system in such a direction and of such magnitude as to exactly cancel out the motion of the earth at the time the experiment was done. Of course, if the trouble were such a coincidence, then six months later, when the earth was moving in an opposite direction, the two velocities would add up instead of canceling, and the effect would be observable. However, the experiment was repeated, at a time when the earth was moving in an opposite direction and the same negative result was obtained; t_1 and t_2 were again equal. Since 1881, the same experiment has been repeated many times by various people, at various times and under various conditions, but no one has been able to find any difference between t_1 and t_2. The experiment was also repeated with the reflectors at arbitrary angles θ, rather than perpendicular, and no effect was detected.

Dayton C. Miller was the only one who claimed (1931) the detection of a small velocity, but recently a careful analysis of his experiment revealed that the effect observed by him was due to a systematic error arising from temperature differences within his apparatus.[†] Recently, an experiment similar in content to the Michelson-Morley experiment was performed, again with a negative result by Charles H. Townes and his collaborators, using modern atomic clocks.[‡] Since astronomical evidence makes it untenable that the earth should be in motion with respect to the assumed ether, we are forced to conclude from the experiment that the analogy between sound waves and light waves, or between the air and the ether, is not correct. Thus, the assumption of a mechanical and permanently stationary ether seems to have met with an ultimate contradiction, since motion relative to it is undetectable.

2.2. Elastic Corpuscular Hypothesis and Double Stars

If the ether hypothesis does not work, how then shall we explain Michelson's experiment? If we assume that light acts as a series of elastic mechanical particles when it is emitted by

[†] Shankland, R. S., S. W. McCuskey, F. C. Leone, and G. Kuerti, *Reviews of Modern Physics*, **27** (1955), 167.

[‡] Townes, C. H., J. P. Cederholm, G. F. Bland, and B. L. Havens, *Physical Review Letters*, **1** (1958), 9.

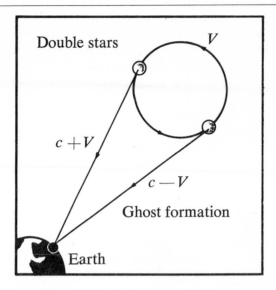

FIGURE 2.2   *The nonexistence of ghost formations proves the corpuscular hypothesis wrong.*

the source, and reflected by the mirrors, then the Michelson experiment could be explained by using the classical relativity principle. This mechanical hypothesis would be equivalent to saying that the velocity of light when emitted is *c with respect to the source*, and that it is reflected according to the laws of reflection of elastic bodies. In that case, light phenomena on board ship would run along the same regardless of the ship's velocity (one can play ping-pong on a uniformly moving ship in just the same way as on the ground). However, in the first place, this would be hard to understand from Maxwell's theory, which describes light as a wave propagation rather than mechanical particle motion; in the second place, the appearance of double stars contradicts this hypothesis. Double stars are pairs of stars which rotate around their center of gravity with comparably large velocities. Their distance from each other is, of course, very small compared to their distance from our solar system. Therefore, the light emitted from them at a time when one of the stars is moving towards us and the other moving away should reach us at very different times. Consequently, the motion around each other and through space would appear very complicated when viewed from our earth. Sometimes we would even see the same component star at two different places simultaneously [ghost stars (Figure 2.2)]: the light emitted when the component star was receding from us and the light emitted later, when the same component star was approaching us, could arrive at the same time to an observer on the earth, just as a fast train will eventually overtake a slow train, the farther they travel. There are many double stars whose distance from the earth and mutual motion are such that these illusions would certainly be observed were the corpuscular hypothesis true. Therefore, we conclude that the experimental evidence is against the corpuscular hypothesis.

2.3. Ether Drag Hypothesis and Aberration

In seeking an explanation for the Michelson-Morley experiment, one may assume that the ether is carried along by moving bodies, just as the air in a train is carried along with

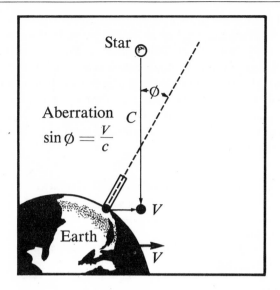

FIGURE 2.3 *Aberration phenomena rule out the transmitting medium hypothesis.*

the motion. The explanation of the Michelson-Morley experiment would then be very easy because on the moving earth the velocity of light would be the same in all directions, just as the velocity of the sound waves in a train is the same in all directions, so that the two light signals would come back at exactly the same time. However, the aberration experiment contradicts this hypothesis, for, if the hypothesis were true, when light enters a telescope, it would be carried along with the medium inside the telescope and a star would be seen with the same angle for a moving and a stationary telescope. But the astronomers have long known that when we observe a fixed star from the earth with a telescope, we do not point it in the exact geometrical direction where the star lies, but a little forward, in the direction of the earth's motion (Figure 2.3). Only then can we see the star. The magnitude of the deflection is given by

$$\sin \phi = -\frac{V}{c}, \tag{2.4}$$

where ϕ is the angle between the light ray and the direction of the earth's motion. The angle ϕ is called the aberration angle. Six months later when the earth is in the opposite side of its orbit, we must direct the telescope backward by the same amount (that is, by $-\phi$) in order to see the same star. Thus, the ether drag hypothesis does not work either.

2.4. Einstein's Postulate

The central problem of this chapter is: *To what coordinate system does the velocity of light, c, refer?* We have tried various alternatives. First, we said it was constant with respect to the ether; in this case, because of the Galilean transformations, the velocity of light in a system moving with respect to the ether would be different in the direction of motion and perpendicular to it. However, the Michelson-Morley experiment shows that this is not the case.

Second, we said that the velocity of light was constant with respect to the emitting body, and that light reflected from mirrors like an elastic body. In this case, the Galilean transformations show that the velocity of light would be different when emitted by moving bodies. But the regular appearance of double stars rules this out.

Finally, we said that the velocity of light is constant with respect to the medium in which it is being propagated; but then the Galilean transformations imply that light is carried by a moving medium exactly as sound waves are carried with the air inside a train. But the aberration experiment contradicts this assertion. We seem to be in an insoluble dilemma. Table 2.1 summarizes this dilemma.

TABLE 2.1. HYPOTHESES VS. EXPERIMENTS

F = Failure, S = Success

Experiment Hypothesis	Michelson-Morley	Double Stars	Aberration
Stationary Ether.	F	S	S
Corpuscular.	S	F	S
Transm. Medium.	S	S	F

As we examine the whole situation carefully, however, we begin to realize the curious fact that we do not get into trouble directly with any of these hypotheses. At the point they meet their failure, an explicit or implicit Galilean transformation is involved. If instead of the Galilean transformations there were a different set of transformations which gave the same velocity c in all systems always, then our difficulties would disappear. For, if the velocity of light were c in the moving system in all directions as well as in the stationary one, we would find exactly the same result in the moving system as in the stationary one. This explains the Michelson-Morley experiment. Also, since the velocity of light is now c in all directions with respect to any given system, say the earth, no matter which component of the double star emits it, the light would have the same velocity c with respect to the earth and the regular appearance of the double stars is explained. In addition, under such an assumption we would be transforming light rays from one frame to another as we transform particles. In other words light rays would not be tied to a medium and not carried by it. This would explain aberration. Effectively, however, the assumption would only amount to saying that the laws of propagation of light waves are the same in all frames. This, in turn, would mean that light waves obey the principle of relativity. The hypothesis that *the velocity of light is c in all directions for all observers moving uniformly with respect to each other* was first introduced by Albert Einstein (1905). In other words, Einstein put forward the hypothesis that the measurement of the velocity of light would give the same numerical value no matter in which reference frame it is measured (Figure 2.4a). He argued simply that the Michelson-Morley experiment failed because of the principle of relativity, and he concluded that the wave-propagation equations must preserve their form, including the numerical value of c, in all reference frames.

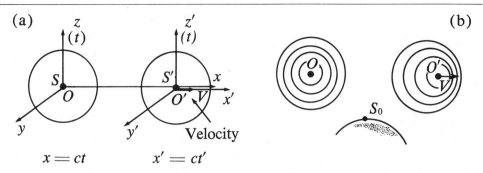

FIGURE 2.4 *The consequences of Einstein's hypothesis:* (a) *For the observer situated at S and S' light waves are always spheres with centers O and O', the sources.* (b) *For an observer situated at S_0 the light rays emitted by O' still form a sphere but the source is no longer the center.*

In order to appreciate the daring quality of Einstein's hypothesis, imagine a stationary train S and a moving train S', as in Figure 2.4a, and that a single spark is produced when they are coincident. The spark will produce a single spherical wave surface expanding with the velocity of light. What is the center of this spherical wave surface? To the observer in S the center is O. The point O' is at the center only at the initial instant. Later it moves away from the center. According to Einstein's hypothesis, however, the reverse is also true. The observer in S' will claim that the center of the spherical wave is O', not O. Thus, although for both observers the velocity of the wave is c and for both of them its surface is a sphere, the first of them will claim the center is at O and the second will claim that the center is at O' (Figure 2.4b); and they are both right! Classically this is a most unintelligible situation as it would imply two different centers for the same spherical surface. Nevertheless, this assumption was made by Einstein under the pressure of the experimental findings.

Einstein's hypothesis, besides its practical usefulness in being able to explain all three of the above optical experiments, has also a profound theoretical implication with regard to the principle of relativity. For it reveals that the principle of relativity is not restricted to classical mechanics only but that electromagnetic and light phenomena as well are subject to it. The great virtue of the Michelson-Morley experiment is that it has shown this by its negative result. Einstein's postulate can be expressed more conveniently by saying that *the law of propagation of light is the same for all inertial frames.* In this form, we see that not only the laws of classical mechanics but also the law of propagation of light and, for that matter, the laws of electromagnetic phenomena, are the same for all systems moving uniformly with respect to each other. Thus, we have come to the conclusion that the principle of relativity is a general principle of nature embracing electromagnetic phenomena as well as particle mechanics.

All these results, however, are gained at the expense of the Galilean transformations. What will take their place? In the next chapter, we shall show that, starting from the hypothesis that "the velocity of light is c in all directions and for all observers moving uniformly with respect to each other," one can derive a new kind of transformation law called Lorentz transformations which take the place of the Galilean transformations. As we know, the Galilean transformations represent the space and time concept of classical physics. Since the transformations are changed, we may conclude that the principle of the constancy of the velocity of light calls for a radical revision of the space and time concept of classical physics.

Summary: Optical Experiments

With respect to what is the velocity of light a constant?

(a) The stationary ether is ruled out by the Michelson-Morley experiment.

(b) The corpuscular hypothesis is ruled out by double stars.

(c) The ether drag hypothesis is ruled out by aberration.

(d) Einstein's hypothesis: the constancy of the velocity of light in all directions and for all inertial frames explains all three of the above experiments.

(e) But then the Galilean transformations must be replaced by some new transformation formulas, because they are inconsistent with Einstein's hypothesis.

(f) Einstein's hypothesis generalizes the classical relativity principle to hold also for electromagnetic and optical phenomena.

3

LORENTZ TRANSFORMATIONS

3.1. The Two Principles of Special Relativity

In the preceding chapter we discussed three optical phenomena, namely, the Michelson-Morley experiment, the aberration experiment, and observations on double stars. We have come to the conclusion that in order to explain all three of these experiments at the same time, we have to give up the idea of understanding the propagation of light in terms of mechanical media or elastic particles. Instead, the following abstract statement must be accepted: In all reference frames which are moving uniformly with respect to each other, light propagates with the constant speed c in all directions. This simply means that the law of propagation of light is the same in all reference frames. In this later form, the Einstein postulate is equivalent to saying that the relativity principle is valid for light propagation as well as mechanical phenomena. The outcome of the Michelson-Morley experiment is then a simple consequence of the fact that the laws of propagation have the same form in all such systems. Thus, on the basis of mechanical and optical experiments, we reach the general conclusion that *relativity is a fundamental principle of nature.*

Since, apparently, relativity is not valid (or it is at least more complicated) for accelerated frames, we may first formulate the principle of relativity only for *inertial frames.* An inertial frame is one in which the Galilean principle of inertia holds. In other words, in an inertial frame, a body left free stays where it was left or moves in a straight line with constant velocity. From this definition it is evident that a reference frame moving uniformly with respect to an inertial frame is also inertial. An equivalent and more intuitive definition is that in an inertial frame objects become weightless. A noninertial frame is one which has acceleration with respect to an inertial frame. In a noninertial frame free objects accelerate and fixed objects acquire weight due to their inertia. We introduce the following two principles:

I. Laws of nature, whether mechanical or optical, are of the same form in all inertial frames.

II. In all inertial frames, the velocity of propagation of light waves is the same in all directions.

These two statements are the basis of *Special Relativity.* The reason it is called special is that it is valid only for inertial frames. Later, Einstein generalized the principle of relativity to include, also, noninertial frames. He has given this extended form the name *General Relativity.* In a later section of this book, we will also discuss General Relativity. Although very important and profound from a philosophical and mathematical point of view, the extended form turned out to be physically significant only for the theory of gravitation. Since gravitational effects are negligibly small compared to electromagnetic and nuclear phenomena, where most of the current research is centered, we will discuss Special Relativity and its various applications in much greater detail.

3.2. Lorentz Transformations

It was explained in the previous chapter that Einstein's postulate is inconsistent with the Galilean transformation (1.2). We must therefore modify the Galilean transformations in such a way that they will incorporate Einstein's postulate while not destroying the essence of relativity in particle mechanics. To this end, let us again consider the two coordinate frames S and S' (Figure 3.1a, b). Let us also look at the Galilean transformations. They are a special case of linear transformations. As our intended transformations, we may consider the more general form of linear transformations.

$$
\begin{array}{ll}
x' = \alpha x + \beta t & x = \alpha' x' + \beta' t' \\
t' = \gamma x + \delta t & t = \gamma' x' + \delta' t' \\
y' = y, \quad z' = z & y = y', \quad z = z'
\end{array}
\tag{3.1}
$$

$$\text{(a)} \qquad\qquad \text{(b)}$$

By considering various special cases and using the two principles stated, we can deduce various conclusions about the nature of the coefficients α, β, γ, and δ. In fact, we will be able to determine them uniquely. Let the point P be chosen to be permanently attached to the origin O' of the frame S'. Then $x' = 0$. But then we must have $V = x/t$ since we know that this point moves uniformly with velocity V with respect to S. Thus we can write $x' = \alpha(x - Vt)$. Similarly, if we choose the point P to be attached to O, that is, at $x = 0$, we must have $-V = x'/t'$ which leads to

$$
\frac{x'}{t'} = \frac{\alpha(0 - Vt)}{\gamma \cdot 0 + \delta t} = -V \qquad \text{that is, } \alpha = \delta.
\tag{3.2}
$$

Furthermore, if we choose the point P in uniform motion in S, that is, if $x/t = v$ is a constant then, since both frames are inertial,

$$
\frac{x'}{t'} = \frac{\alpha(x - Vt)}{\gamma x + \alpha t} = \frac{v - V}{\dfrac{\gamma}{\alpha} v + 1}
\tag{3.3}
$$

must also be a constant. Thus γ/α is a constant. But α itself must be a constant. This is

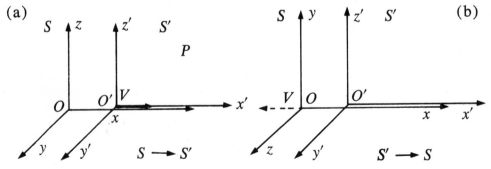

FIGURE 3.1

because in the above situation $x = 0$ gives

$$t' = \alpha t \tag{3.4}$$

as a relation between the rates of the two clocks. Now a clock is by definition a device which measures time at a constant rate. Since this rate should not depend on anything else in each frame, the progress of time in S and S' must be proportional. This means α must be a constant. In this way we see that, in the transformation [3.1(a)], we have

$$x' = \alpha(x - Vt),$$
$$t' = \gamma x + \alpha t, \tag{3.5}$$

all the coefficients being constants.

All these are deduced solely from the considerations of the inertial frames. We have not, as yet, used the second postulate. Consider the equation (3.3) again. If the point in S were moving with the velocity of light in S, then, from the postulate, it must also move with the velocity of light in S'. This gives

$$c = \frac{c - V}{\dfrac{\gamma}{\alpha} c + 1} \qquad \text{that is,} \quad \frac{\gamma}{\alpha} = -\frac{V}{c^2} \tag{3.6}$$

and the transformations reduce to

$$x' = \alpha(x - Vt)$$
$$t' = \alpha\left(t - \frac{V}{c^2} x\right). \tag{3.7}$$

However, this accounts only for propagation in the x direction. The principle states that the velocity of light must give the same numerical value in any direction. Let us consider in S a point moving along the y direction with $c = y/t$. In S' this motion is not necessarily in y' direction. Therefore we may use c^2 to eliminate the complication due to direction. Thus $x = 0$, $y/t = c$ must lead to

$$\frac{x'^2 + y'^2}{t'^2} = c^2. \tag{3.8}$$

Substituting from the transformation formulas, we have

$$(\alpha^2 V^2 t^2 + c^2 t^2)/\alpha^2 t^2 = c^2, \qquad \text{that is,}$$

$$\alpha = \frac{1}{\sqrt{1 - V^2/c^2}}. \tag{3.9}$$

Therefore we have as our transformations

$$x' = \frac{x - Vt}{\sqrt{1 - V^2/c^2}} \qquad\qquad x = \frac{x' + Vt'}{\sqrt{1 - V^2/c^2}}$$

$$y' = y \qquad\qquad\qquad y = y'$$
$$z' = z \qquad\qquad\qquad z = z' \tag{3.10}$$

$$t' = \frac{t - \dfrac{V}{c^2} x}{\sqrt{1 - V^2/c^2}} \qquad\qquad t = \frac{t' + \dfrac{V}{c^2} x'}{\sqrt{1 - V^2/c^2}}.$$

$$\text{(a)} \qquad\qquad\qquad\qquad \text{(b)}$$

The reverse transformations [3.10(b)] are obtained by substituting $-V$ for V or by solving [3.10(a)] for x, y, z, and t, or else going through a similar series of considerations for [3.1(b)]. Here we notice an interesting fact. If the velocity of light were infinite ($c \to \infty$), the Lorentz transformations (3.10) would be identical with the Galilean transformations. This remark makes the relation to the Galilean transformations rather clear. Galilean transformations were conceived when the material velocities considered were small as compared to c.

From a philosophical point of view, it is surprising that the velocity of light enters into such a fundamental structure as space and time transformations (3.10). In order to grasp the meaning of this, we must remember that two observers moving relatively to each other in empty space must use some signals to exchange information and synchronize their clocks. Therefore, the very process of synchronizing time measuring devices and for communication of the quantities to be transformed will involve the "velocity of information" between observers. This realization leads to a general operational interpretation of the Lorentz transformations. These transformations have little to do with the particular subject of electromagnetism. For example, if the observers communicated with a different kind of wave, propagating with a different velocity in empty space, that velocity would have appeared in the Lorentz transformations. For example, if we had a wave that propagated with infinite velocity, we would get exactly the Galilean transformations by synchronizing our clocks with the help of these waves. Is it possible to have a wave with finite velocity and a wave with infinite velocity side by side in nature? Only experiment, of course, can settle such a question. But we can show that if they did, then the principle of relativity could be violated. For we could obtain the Galilean transformations by using the wave with infinite velocity and then, experimenting with the wave with finite velocity, we could detect the motion of the earth by performing a Michelson-Morley experiment. By following this argument, we see that if there were two different waves propagating in empty space with two different invariant velocities c and c', one would be able to detect the motion of the earth and thus violate the principle of relativity. If the principle of relativity is a general principle of nature, *all means of information must propagate in empty space with the velocity c*. In this way we see that the relativistic transformation formulas (3.10) are general and apply to all phenomena of nature. The velocity c is not the particular velocity of electromagnetic waves *but it is the velocity of information in general*.† Since the Lorentz transformations (3.10) apply to all phenomena of nature, they provide a space-time framework whose consequences are general and have universal meaning irrespective of any particular subject.

3.3. A Different Derivation of the Lorentz Transformation

The Lorentz transformations can be derived in a variety of ways. The original derivations of the transformations by Lorentz did not even use Einstein's postulate but only the negative result of the Michelson-Morley experiment and the field (wave) equations of Maxwell. From his derivation to the full relativity theory there was but a small step, but Lorentz failed to see it. Below, we will give a derivation which is based more directly on the relativity principle. The propagation equation for a wave traveling in space with the velocity c is

† Note that information is more than mere physical effect. For example one can carry physical effect in a dispersive medium but for very large distances information would get lost.

of the form

$$\left(\frac{\partial^2}{\partial x^2} + \frac{\partial^2}{\partial y^2} + \frac{\partial^2}{\partial z^2} - \frac{1}{c^2}\frac{\partial^2}{\partial t^2}\right)\Phi(x, y, z, t) = 0. \tag{3.11}$$

The function Φ is called the wave function and the differential operator on the left is the d'Alembert operator. Let us assume that this equation is valid in S. Then, according to the principle of relativity, the equation of propagation of the same wave must be of the same form in S'. Also, due to the second principle, the numerical value of c must be the same:

$$\left(\frac{\partial^2}{\partial x'^2} + \frac{\partial^2}{\partial y'^2} + \frac{\partial^2}{\partial z'^2} - \frac{1}{c^2}\frac{\partial^2}{\partial t'^2}\right)\Phi(x', y', z', t') = 0. \tag{3.12}$$

Since the function $\Phi(x', y', z', t')$ is obtained from $\Phi(x, y, z, t)$ by a substitution of variables we have

$$\Phi(x, y, z, t) = \Phi(x', y', z', t'). \tag{3.13}$$

We first differentiate both sides of this equation according to the rules of partial differentiation. For simplicity, let the wave propagate in the x direction. This means that the wave function will depend only on x and the time t, that is, $\Phi(x, t) = \Phi(x', t')$. Then

$$d\Phi = \frac{\partial \Phi}{\partial x}dx + \frac{\partial \Phi}{\partial t}dt = \frac{\partial \Phi}{\partial x'}dx' + \frac{\partial \Phi}{\partial t'}dt'. \tag{3.14}$$

From (3.5) we have $dx' = \alpha(dx - Vdt)$, $dt' = \gamma dx + \alpha dt$. Substituting these into (3.14) and equating the coefficients, we find

$$\frac{\partial \Phi}{\partial x} = \alpha \frac{\partial \Phi}{\partial x'} + \gamma \frac{\partial \Phi}{\partial t'},$$

$$\frac{\partial \Phi}{\partial t} = -\alpha V \frac{\partial \Phi}{\partial x'} + \alpha \frac{\partial \Phi}{\partial t'}. \tag{3.15}$$

We can apply the same reasoning to the functions $F(x, t) = \partial \Phi/\partial x$ and $G(x, t) = \partial \Phi/\partial t$. Differentiating, say, F in this way

$$\frac{\partial F}{\partial x}dx + \frac{\partial F}{\partial t}dt = \alpha\left(\frac{\partial F}{\partial x'}dx' + \frac{\partial F}{\partial t'}dt'\right) + \gamma\left(\frac{\partial G}{\partial x'}dx' + \frac{\partial G}{\partial t'}dt'\right).$$

Substituting again for dx' and dt' we have

$$\frac{\partial^2 \Phi}{\partial x^2} = \left(\alpha^2 \frac{\partial^2}{\partial x'^2} + 2\alpha\gamma \frac{\partial^2}{\partial x' \partial t'} + \gamma^2 \frac{\partial^2}{\partial t'^2}\right)\Phi, \tag{3.16}$$

and similarly

$$\frac{\partial^2 \Phi}{\partial t^2} = \left(\alpha^2 V^2 \frac{\partial^2}{\partial x'^2} - 2\alpha^2 V \frac{\partial^2}{\partial x' \partial t'} + \alpha^2 \frac{\partial^2}{\partial t'^2}\right)\Phi. \tag{3.17}$$

We can now construct the wave equation (3.11)

$$\left(\frac{\partial^2}{\partial x^2} - \frac{1}{c^2}\frac{\partial^2}{\partial t^2}\right)\Phi = \left[\alpha^2\left(1 - \frac{V^2}{c^2}\right)\frac{\partial^2}{\partial x'^2} + 2\alpha\left(\gamma + \frac{\alpha V}{c^2}\right)\frac{\partial^2}{\partial x' \partial t'} + \left(\gamma^2 - \frac{\alpha^2}{c^2}\right)\frac{\partial^2}{\partial t'^2}\right]\Phi = 0.$$

Since from the relativity principle, the right-hand side of this equation must reduce to the same form as the left-hand side, we have

$$\alpha^2\left(1 - \frac{V^2}{c^2}\right) = 1$$

$$\gamma + \frac{\alpha V}{c^2} = 0 \tag{3.19}$$

$$\alpha^2 - c^2\gamma^2 = 1.$$

These equations are readily solved and give

$$\alpha = \frac{1}{\sqrt{1 - V^2/c^2}}, \qquad \gamma = \frac{-V/c^2}{\sqrt{1 - V^2/c^2}}, \tag{3.20}$$

the same as before.

In passing, we may also point out that instead of equation (3.8) we might have used the aberration formula (2.4) to determine α. This could be considered to be a more direct derivation of Lorentz transformations from experiment. Indeed

$$\tan\theta = \frac{-V/c}{\sqrt{1 - V^2/c^2}} = \frac{x'}{y'} = \frac{-\alpha Vt}{ct}$$

which gives again

$$\alpha = \frac{1}{\sqrt{1 - V^2/c^2}}. \tag{3.21}$$

This shows that the aberration effect is consistent with Einstein's postulate (see Chapter 4 Section 5).

3.4. Transformation of Differential Operators

The previous section reveals an extraordinary symmetry between the differential dx, and the partial differentiation $\partial/\partial x$. For example, (3.15) can be written symbolically as

$$\frac{\partial}{\partial x} = \alpha\frac{\partial}{\partial x'} + \gamma\frac{\partial}{\partial t'}$$

$$\frac{\partial}{\partial t} = -\alpha V\frac{\partial}{\partial x'} + \delta\frac{\partial}{\partial t'} \tag{3.22}$$

which are similar in structure to the linear transfromations (3.1). Substituting the co-efficients we get

$$\frac{\partial}{\partial x} = \frac{\dfrac{\partial}{\partial x'} - \dfrac{V}{c^2}\dfrac{\partial}{\partial t'}}{\sqrt{1 - V^2/c^2}}$$

$$\frac{\partial}{\partial t} = \frac{\dfrac{\partial}{\partial t'} - V\dfrac{\partial}{\partial x'}}{\sqrt{1 - V^2/c^2}} \tag{3.23}$$

which are similar in form to (3.10). Following this approach, we obtain the more general formulas

$$\partial'_x = \frac{\partial_x + \dfrac{V}{c^2}\partial_t}{\sqrt{1 - V^2/c^2}} \qquad\qquad \partial_x = \frac{\partial'_x - \dfrac{V}{c^2}\partial'_t}{\sqrt{1 - V^2/c^2}}$$

$$\partial'_y = \partial_y \qquad\qquad\qquad \partial_y = \partial'_y$$

$$\partial'_z = \partial_z \qquad\qquad\qquad \partial_z = \partial'_z \qquad\qquad (3.24)$$

$$\partial'_t = \frac{\partial_t + V\partial_x}{\sqrt{1 - V^2/c^2}} \qquad\qquad \partial_t = \frac{\partial'_t - V\partial'_x}{\sqrt{1 - V^2/c^2}}$$

where $\partial_x = \partial/\partial x$, $\partial'_x = \partial/\partial x'$, et cetera. These are the transformations of the differentiation operators corresponding to the transformations of variables (3.10). As we will see in the later chapters, when one is dealing with particles, equations (3.10) are more useful. But when we are treating wave propagation or field problems, equations (3.24) are also employed very frequently.

Summary: Lorentz Transformations

(a) Starting from the two principles of Special Relativity one can uniquely derive a set of transformation formulas different from and replacing the Galilean Transformations.

(b) These new transformations, called the Lorentz Transformations, imply a new philosophy of space and time in physics.

(c) If we regard the principle of relativity as a general law of nature, then not only the electromagnetic fields but all types of information must propagate in empty space with the same velocity c in all inertial frames.

(d) The Lorentz transformations cannot be used to transform from an inertial frame to a noninertial frame, or vice versa.

4

THE MEANING OF THE LORENTZ TRANSFORMATIONS

In the previous chapter, starting from the two principles of special relativity, we have derived a new set of kinematical transformation formulas. These replace the classical Galilean transformations and therefore imply a new philosophy of space and time measurements. In this chapter we will try to understand (as much as we can) the nature of this new philosophy of observation and derive various consequences. Let us start with the understanding that if a quantity is measured in S' and a numerical value is obtained, the measurement of the same quantity in a different inertial frame S will not in general yield the same numerical value. Those quantities which have the same value in all reference frames must be very useful and of special interest because they are universally invariant quantities. The velocity of light c is such a quantity, for we have postulated it to be. There are other *invariant* quantities, not necessarily constant, but independent of the coordinate system, as we will see later.

Furthermore, we must bear in mind that a certain statement which is true in a frame S' is not necessarily true in a different frame S. For example, if we say that in S' the energy of a free particle retains its numerical value (that is, is conserved) this statement is true in all inertial frames, since a free particle has a constant velocity in any inertial frame. However, if we say that in S' the energy is 250 ergs this statement is in general not true in other inertial frames because the particle has different velocities in other inertial frames. Those statements which are valid in all inertial frames are called *laws of nature* and, obviously, they are of special interest.

To proceed to an understanding of the space-time relationships implied by the Lorentz transformations we start with the definition of a new term, *an event*. An event is an occurrence which takes place at some instant t and at a point x, y, z. For example, the meeting of a wave front and the needle of a measuring device is an event. Likewise, the arrival of a bullet at a point x, y, z at the instant t is another event. In other words a single point x, y, z, t of the space-time complex is an event. From this definition it follows (because of the Lorentz transformations) that an event has a meaning in any inertial frame but the numerical values describing its position and time are different in every inertial frame we may consider.

Suppose we consider two events, x_1, y_1, z_1, t_1 and x_2, y_2, z_2, t_2 in S. We can consider the differences in coordinates and time

$$\Delta x = x_2 - x_1, \text{ etc.} \qquad \Delta t = t_2 - t_1. \tag{4.1}$$

We define the following special cases: (a) If two events happen at the same time ($\Delta t = t_2 - t_1 = 0$) but not necessarily at the same place they are called *simultaneous*. (b) If two events happen at the same place ($\Delta x = x_2 - x_1 = 0$, et cetera) but not necessarily at the same time, we call them *colocal*. (c) If the two events happen at the same place, and at the same time ($\Delta x = 0$, $\Delta y = 0$, $\Delta z = 0$ and $\Delta t = 0$) we call them *coincident*.

If two events are coincident in one inertial frame, then they are coincident in all inertial frames. This is because from the Lorentz transformations (3.10) we obtain by differentiation

$$\Delta x' = \frac{\Delta x - V\Delta t}{\sqrt{1 - V^2/c^2}}$$

$$\Delta y' = \Delta y,$$

$$\Delta z' = \Delta z, \tag{4.2}$$

$$\Delta t' = \frac{\Delta t - \dfrac{V}{c^2}\Delta x}{\sqrt{1 - V^2/c^2}}.$$

This, in the general case, leads to $\Delta x' = \Delta y' = \Delta z' = 0$, $\Delta t' = 0$ if $\Delta x = \Delta y = \Delta z = 0$, $\Delta t = 0$. Thus the statement of two events being coincident has a universal meaning, being true in all inertial frames. Colocality and simultaneity on the other hand have no universal meaning, as we will demonstrate below.

4.1. Relativity of Colocality; Time Dilatation

Let us consider for convenience that we are in S so that S' is moving (Figure 3.1). We are interested in knowing how certain things first considered in S' by its observer would appear to us from our own frame S. Let us consider two events in S' which take place at the same point x'_0, that is, ($\Delta x' = 0$). For the sake of simplicity consider this to be on the x' axis so that $y' = z' = 0$. From the general transformations (4.2) we have,

$$\Delta x = \frac{V\Delta t'}{\sqrt{1 - V^2/c^2}} \qquad \text{(a)},$$

$$\Delta t = \frac{\Delta t'}{\sqrt{1 - V^2/c^2}} \qquad \text{(b)}. \tag{4.3}$$

We will interpret this special case as follows:

(a) The two events which happened at the same point in S' do not happen at the same point in S. They happen a distance $\Delta x = V\Delta t'/\sqrt{1 - V^2/c^2}$ apart. If, for the moment, we disregard the denominator this is easy to visualize, classically, by considering two successive firings of a fixed gun in a train. The two firings, which happened at the same point in the train, happen at a distance $d = V\Delta t$ away with respect to earth. The denominator $\sqrt{1 - V^2/c^2}$, is the relativistic correction to the classical formula.

(b) In S the time it takes between the two events is longer than in the moving frame S'. For example, consider a clock fixed at a point ($x' = x'_0$, $\Delta x' = 0$) in S'. Let the two events be two sparks produced in S' exactly one hour apart. In the system S the two sparks will be observed to happen at two different places and it will take more than 60 minutes, for a clock fixed in S, if we measure the time between these two sparks. Thus, a *stationary* process in S' would take more time when observed from a system moving with respect to S'. Since a clock is by definition, a time-keeping instrument, fixed to the reference frame, we can express the result just reached by saying that the clock of a moving system appears slowed down when observed from a stationary frame.

These considerations are not pure fantasy. They are facts already confirmed in the laboratory. Certain elementary particles have a lifetime T_0 (for π-mesons $T_0 = 2.2 \times 10^{-6}$ sec.). When one observes them in fast motion, namely, in a synchrotron, their lifetimes become larger according to $T = T_0/\sqrt{1 - V^2/c^2}$.

It is important to bear in mind that owing to the symmetry of the two systems S and S' these results are completely reciprocal, namely, the clock S also is seen to be slow when observed from the system S'. Thus, the effect here discussed is relative; either clock is found slowed down when observed from the other reference frame.

4.2. Relativity of Simultaneity; Lorentz Contraction

Since the formulas (4.2) are symmetric in $\Delta x'$ and $\Delta t'$ we can deduce similar results for distances. Take a distance $\Delta x'$ in S'. With this we mean that the two end points of $\Delta x'$ are considered simultaneously in S' so that $\Delta t' = 0$. We then have

$$\Delta x = \frac{\Delta x'}{\sqrt{1 - V^2/c^2}} \qquad \text{(a)},$$

$$\Delta t = \frac{(V/c^2)\,\Delta x'}{\sqrt{1 - V^2/c^2}} \qquad \text{(b)}. \qquad (4.4)$$

We may interpret these as follows:

(a) The distance $\Delta x'$ as observed from the stationary frame, S', appears larger, compared to what is observed in S. Fitzgerald and Lorentz tried to explain the negative outcome of the Michelson-Morley experiment by assuming a contraction of the moving bodies in the direction of motion as measured in their rest frames. We see here that no contraction of this kind exists. Relatively speaking, however, if the length at rest is compared to its value in motion the rest length can be said shorter as $\Delta x' = \Delta x\sqrt{1 - V^2/c^2}$ (see also next section).

(b) Two events which are simultaneous in S' happen at two different times as observed from S, the time difference being given by $\Delta t = V\Delta x/c^2$. This is the analogue of the two events happening at two different points in S that happened at the same point in S'; but intuitively we cannot grasp it as easily. In the next section we will try to show in a simple manner how it comes about.

4.3. Distribution and Synchronization of Clocks

In this section the meaning of the Lorentz transformations will be further clarified. These transformations are intimately connected with the process of setting up a consistent way of measuring time and of synchronizing clocks. A clock is a periodic phenomenon, whose periods are equally spaced and independent of the physical processes taking place in a given inertial frame. Taking advantage of the universal constancy of the velocity of light we may construct in S' a clock, by reflecting light signals back and forth between two mirrors [Figure 4.1(a)]. For later convenience we do this as follows: From the middle point M' we send two light pulses in opposite directions and we measure the time by counting the number of times the light pulses come back to M' in coincidence. The period of such a clock is $\Delta t' = a/c$. If the mirrors are mounted on a rigid body, this serves as good a clock as any we can devise. Furthermore, since c is the same in all directions, the clock may be oriented in any direction we like and, from the sameness of c in all inertial frames, we can

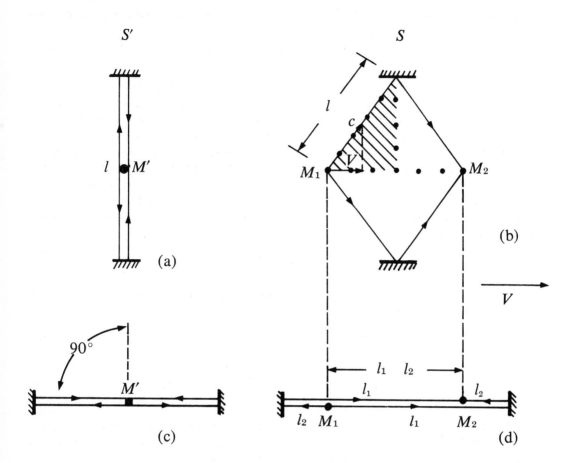

FIGURE 4.1 *Motion of one light clock relative to another:* (a) *stationary clock;* (b) *moving clock;* (c) *rotated stationary clock;* (d) *rotated moving clock. The figure is drawn such that the length of the clock is 8 feet and the velocity of the moving clocks is* $V = (\tfrac{3}{5})c$. *The time dilatation and the length variation are clearly seen from the figure.*

indeed set it up in any inertial frame we choose. Now let us construct such an identical clock and set it to work in S. If the motion of S' is perpendicular to the line connecting the two mirrors, we see that the path of the reflected pulses of the previous case appear as in [Figure 4.1(b)]. Now since c is the same in S as in S' and, due to axial symmetry $a = a'$, (if a' was smaller or larger than a we could tell that the system was moving, which is impossible according to the principle of relativity) the wave appears to require, for a second coincidence, the time

$$\Delta t = \frac{1}{c} \frac{a}{\cos \theta} = \frac{\Delta t'}{\sqrt{1 - V^2/c^2}}. \tag{4.5}$$

This reasoning is of course applicable just as well to the clock when viewed from the other system and, therefore, as observed from S', the clock of S would appear to operate in a similar way, namely, $\Delta t' = \Delta t/\sqrt{1 - V^2/c^2}$. Furthermore, in S the two successive meetings of the signals are not colocal, that is, they do not take place at the same place. The distance between the two coincidences is

$$\Delta x = V \Delta t = \frac{V \Delta t'}{\sqrt{1 - V^2/c^2}}. \tag{4.6}$$

These two effects stem from the colocality in S' and may be denoted as Δt_c and Δx_c.

Now let us orient the clocks in the direction of relative motion (Figure 4.1 c,d). This is possible in each frame since c is the same in all directions in every frame. This time we turn our attention to the collision of each signal with the mirrors of S'. In S' these are simultaneous. From S they do not appear simultaneous since the middle point M' is moving relative to the wave fronts, and since we know that they coincide at M'. One of them will reach the mirror earlier as observed from S. Let l_1 and l_2 be the distances traveled by each wave until it collides with a mirror. Since the clock under consideration is equivalent to that of the previous case, the total length covered by light between two coincidences is again equal to $a/\cos \theta$

$$\Delta x = l_1 + l_2 = \frac{\Delta x'}{\sqrt{1 - V^2/c^2}}. \tag{4.7}$$

On the other hand, since the two pulses coincide at the middle point M', they will reach the mirrors with a time difference

$$\delta t = \frac{l_1 - l_2}{c} \quad \text{where} \quad \frac{l_1}{l_2} = \frac{c + V}{c - V} \tag{4.8}$$

from which we obtain

$$\delta t = \left(\frac{l_1 - l_2}{l_1 + l_2}\right) \frac{l_1 + l_2}{c} = \frac{V \Delta x}{c^2} = \frac{(V/c^2)\, \Delta x'}{\sqrt{1 - V^2/c^2}}. \tag{4.9}$$

The effects (4.7) and (4.9) are the results of the simultaneity of the signals in S' and they may be denoted as Δx_s and Δt_s. Collecting together, we find, in the general case the Lorentz transformations (4.2). It is then evident that we can write

$$\Delta x = \Delta x_s + \Delta x_c = \frac{\partial x}{\partial x'} \Delta x' + \frac{\partial x}{\partial t} \Delta t',$$

$$\Delta t = \Delta t_s + \Delta t_c = \frac{\partial t}{\partial x'} \Delta x' + \frac{\partial t}{\partial t'} \Delta t'. \tag{4.10}$$

From the considerations of this section it becomes clear that we can define time through a stationary light clock or any other process which keeps time in a fashion equivalent to such a light clock. Distant clocks can be synchronized in any given frame by sending out light rays from the middle point of the line connecting them. In this way we will imagine a clock at *each point* of a reference frame (a rigid body); all these identical clocks will be arranged to indicate the same time whenever they are observed from the middle point of a line connecting them (for example, imagine two small clocks at the mirrors in Figure 4.1, synchronized with our M'). But these clocks will not appear so synchronized as observed from a moving reference frame, whose clocks are synchronized everywhere by the same method as above. Any two clocks separated by $\Delta x'$ and synchronized in S' will appear to be out of synchronism from S by the amount

$$\Delta t = \frac{(V/c^2)\, \Delta x'}{\sqrt{1 - V^2 c^2}}. \tag{4.11}$$

Thus, it is clear from what has been said up to now that the Lorentz transformations introduce a completely new philosophy of space and time, fundamentally different from the classical concepts.

Before we conclude this section we may ask: Would the photograph of a moving frame show a contraction? If the only light signals coming to the camera originated from our coincidences, the answer is evidently yes. On the other hand, if the frame is continuously illuminated, it can be shown that no contraction will be photographed. J. L. Terrel and R. Weinstein recently discussed this interesting point.†

4.4. Transformations of Velocities

We would now like to see how velocities in the system S will appear from S' and vice versa. For this, let us differentiate the Lorentz transformations (3.10) and divide by dt and dt', respectively. We also put $u_x = dx/dt$, $u_y = dy/dt$, et cetera.

$$u_x' = \frac{u_x - V}{1 - \dfrac{u_x V}{c^2}} \qquad\qquad u_x = \frac{u_x' + V}{1 + \dfrac{u_x' V}{c^2}}$$

$$u_y' = \frac{u_y \sqrt{1 - \dfrac{V^2}{c^2}}}{1 - \dfrac{u_x V}{c^2}} \qquad\qquad u_y = \frac{u_y' \sqrt{1 - \dfrac{V^2}{c^2}}}{1 + \dfrac{u_x' V}{c^2}} \qquad (4.12)$$

$$u_z' = \frac{u_z \sqrt{1 - \dfrac{V^2}{c^2}}}{1 - \dfrac{u_x V}{c^2}} \qquad\qquad u_z = \frac{u_z' \sqrt{1 - \dfrac{V^2}{c^2}}}{1 + \dfrac{u_x' V}{c^2}} \cdot$$

(a)   (b)

These formulas, which describe the combination of velocities, are very different from the Galilean case, in which the results would simply be

$$\begin{aligned} u_x' &= u_x - V & u_x &= u_x' + V \\ u_y' &= u_y & u_y &= u_y' \\ u_z' &= u_z & u_z &= u_z'. \end{aligned} \qquad (4.13)$$

In order to illustrate this, we consider a train moving with respect to the earth with a velocity V, and a man on the train firing a bullet in the forward direction with the velocity u with respect to the train. What is the velocity of the bullet with respect to the earth? According to the formulas (4.12), we have

$$w = \frac{u + V}{1 + \dfrac{uV}{c^2}}, \qquad (4.14)$$

whereas, classically, we would have $w = u + V$. When u and V are small compared to c, the classical and the new results do not differ significantly, but when one of the velocities

† *Phys. Rev.* **116** (1959), 1041; *Am. J. Phys.* **28** (1960) 607.

approaches c, the situation is very different. For example, let the man in the train send out light waves instead of firing a bullet:

$$w = \frac{c + V}{1 + \dfrac{cV}{c^2}} = c.$$

Nevertheless, these results are very strange when looked at from the classical point of view.

At this point, we may also point out that no *relative velocity* can exceed c, for then the Lorentz transformations would become imaginary. But this does not mean that no *velocity* higher than c can be considered. For example, take two trains approaching a station from opposite directions, both with the velocity of light. According to an observer at the station, the two trains are approaching each other with a velocity $2c$ (here two objects are in question). But with respect to a man on one of the trains, the other train is approaching with a velocity $w = (c + c)/(1 + c^2/c^2) = c$. In other words, to the man on the train, the velocity of the station and the velocity of the other train are the same! This strange result can be made understandable by the following example: Consider a train moving with respect to the station with the velocity of light. Now, let a man fire a bullet with the velocity u with respect to the train. From the station, both the train and the bullet will appear to have the same velocity c. How can this be? Only because, due to the Lorentz contraction, the length of the train will appear $\Delta x' = \Delta x \sqrt{1 - V^2/c^2} = 0$; thus, both the train and the bullet in it will appear continuously to be on a very thin ($\Delta x = 0$) sheet advancing with the velocity of light.

The fact that c must be the upper limit of all *relative velocities* is one of the major conclusions of the theory of relativity. We will see later that it is impossible to accelerate a material body to the velocity of light in a system with respect to which it was originally at rest. Also, if it were feasible to consider relative velocities higher than c, it would be possible to find systems in which the effect of a phenomenon would precede its cause. However, relativity does not prevent us from considering purely *geometrical velocities* exceeding c, but only from measuring physical *relative velocities* exceeding c. Consider, for example, a plane wave of light falling on a plane surface such that the wave front and the surface make a small angle, θ. It can easily be seen that the intersection of these two planes will move with the velocity $V = c/\tan \theta > c$. However, this is a purely geometrical velocity. It does not carry energy or information. For this reason, such a wave velocity is called a *phase velocity*. In wave mechanics, one encounters a similar unphysical velocity, namely, the phase velocity of the de Broglie waves. Later, we will consider these more extensively.

In order to appreciate fully the formula (4.14), we consider three coordinate systems, S, S', and S''. S' moves with respect to S with a velocity V and S'' moves with respect to S' with a velocity u. Of course, the Lorentz transformations between these systems will hold, using V and u, respectively, in each case. If we want to effect a Lorentz transformation between S and S'', we must use the velocity w calculated from formula (4.14). This property of the Lorentz transformations is called *transitivity*. It arises from the fact that the Lorentz transformations have the properties of what the mathematicians call a *continuous group*.

Before we close this section, we must mention the Fizeau's experiment, which was performed a long time ago but was not explained satisfactorily until the theory of relativity was discovered. Fizeau pumped water through a glass tube (Figure 4.2) with a constant velocity and measured the velocity of light waves in that tube. The result was

$$w = c' + V - n^2 V \tag{4.15}$$

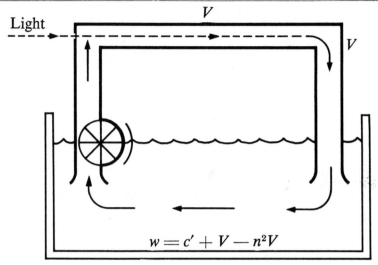

$$w = c' + V - n^2V$$

FIGURE 4.2 *Fizeau's experiment.*

where c' is the velocity of light in stationary water and $n = (c'/c)$ is the index of refraction. Note that if the light rays were carried by the transmitting medium, the result would be $c' + V$. However, the result (4.15) can be obtained easily from (4.14) as

$$w = \frac{c' + V}{1 + \dfrac{c'V}{c^2}} = (c' + V)\left(1 - n\,\frac{V}{c}\right) = c' + V - n^2V,$$

neglecting higher order terms in V.

4.5. Transformation of Angles and Frequencies

Consider a particle in a system S moving in the xy plane with the velocity u. The angle θ that this direction makes with the x axis is given by

$$\tan \theta = \frac{u_y}{u_x}\,;\qquad u_x = u \cos \theta,\qquad u_y = u \sin \theta. \tag{4.16}$$

In a coordinate system S', moving uniformly with respect to S, we get from (4.12)

$$\tan \theta' = \frac{u_y'}{u_x'} = \frac{u_y\sqrt{1 - V^2/c^2}}{u_x - V} = \frac{u \sin \theta\sqrt{1 - V^2/c^2}}{u \cos \theta - V}. \tag{4.17}$$

As an application of this interesting formula, consider the case of light, that is, $u = c$.

$$\tan \theta' = \frac{\sin \theta\sqrt{1 - V^2/c^2}}{\cos \theta - V/c} \tag{4.18}$$

Let $\theta = \pi/2$, $\theta' = \pi/2 + \phi$ then we see that (Figure 4.3)

$$\tan \phi = \frac{-V/c}{\sqrt{1 - V^2/c^2}}\,,\qquad \sin \phi = -\frac{V}{c} \tag{4.19}$$

which is the aberration formula (2.4) that we have previously discussed.

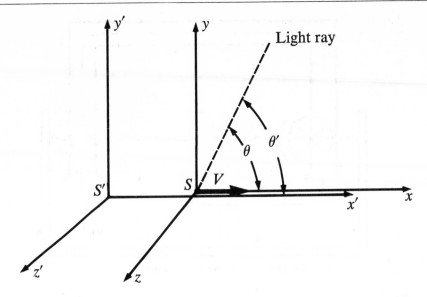

FIGURE 4.3   *Aberration. The angles of a light ray with x-axis and x'-axis are different.*

The derivation of the aberration formula could also be accomplished by using equations (3.24). Since it will give us some extra insight, we will also present this derivation. Let us consider, in the system S, a plane wave propagating in the direction given by the direction cosines α, β, and γ. Such a wave may be described in S by the wave function:

$$\Phi = A \exp\left[2\pi i\nu\left(t - \frac{\alpha x + \beta y + \gamma z}{c}\right)\right] \tag{4.20}$$

where $\alpha^2 + \beta^2 + \gamma^2 = 1$. This function is a solution of the wave equation (3.11). Now, the same plane wave is described in S' by the function

$$\Phi = A \exp\left[2\pi i\nu'\left(t' - \frac{\alpha'x' + \beta'y' + \gamma'z'}{c}\right)\right]. \tag{4.21}$$

By partial differentiation, we see that, symbolically, $\partial_x = \partial/\partial x = -i2\pi\nu\alpha/c$, $\partial_y = -i2\pi\nu\beta/c$, $\partial_z = -i2\pi\nu\gamma/c$, $\partial_t = i2\pi\nu$. Similar expressions also hold for ∂'_x, ∂'_y et cetera. Putting these into the formulas (3.24) we obtain

$$\nu' = \nu\,\frac{1 - \dfrac{V}{c}\alpha}{\sqrt{1 - V^2/c^2}}, \qquad \alpha' = \frac{\alpha - \dfrac{V}{c}}{\sqrt{1 - V^2/c^2}}, \tag{4.22}$$

$$\beta' = \beta\,\frac{\sqrt{1 - V^2/c^2}}{1 - \dfrac{V}{c}\alpha}, \qquad \gamma' = \gamma\,\frac{\sqrt{1 - V^2/c^2}}{1 - \dfrac{V}{c}\alpha}.$$

The first of these expressions is the relativistic form of the Doppler shift of frequencies.

Its Newtonian form is obtained by neglecting V^2/c^2 as compared to 1.

$$\nu' \simeq \nu\left(1 - \frac{V}{c}\alpha\right). \tag{4.23}$$

The other formulas yield the expressions for the aberration. Indeed, let us consider the case which we considered previously, namely, propagation perpendicular to the z-axis (that is, in the xy plane). Putting

$$\cos\theta' = \frac{\cos\theta - V/c}{1 - \dfrac{V}{c}\sin\theta}, \qquad \sin\theta' = \frac{\sin\theta\sqrt{1 - V^2/c^2}}{1 - \dfrac{V}{c}\cos\theta}, \tag{4.24}$$

we see that

$$\tan\theta' = \frac{\sin\theta\sqrt{1 - V^2/c^2}}{\cos\theta - V/c}, \tag{4.25}$$

which is identical to (4.18).

Note, however, that in this derivation the aberration of light as well as the second order term V^2/c^2 in the Doppler effect would disappear in the limit of Galilean transformations. This is because in this limit we have $\partial'_x = \delta_x$, $\delta'_t = \delta_t + V_x$, leading to $\nu' = \nu(1 - \dfrac{V}{c}\alpha)$ and $\alpha' = \alpha$. Thus aberration cannot exist in a wave theory of light invariant under Galilean transformations, whereas a corpuscular theory invariant under the same transformations will exhibit this property. Here we witness the important fact that special relativity attributes both wave and corpuscular properties to the propagation of light.

Summary: Consequences of the Lorentz Transformations

(a) Lorentz transformations have profound kinematical consequences. Moving clocks appear to be slowed down; moving lengths appear to be shortened.

(b) Simultaneity becomes relative. Two events which happen at two different points, and are simultaneous in a given inertial frame, are not simultaneous in any other inertial frame moving relative to the first.

(c) The classical composition of velocities does not hold.

(d) The aberration and Doppler formulas are modified by the Lorentz transformations.

(e) The Lorentz transformations imply a new and consistent process of space-time measurements based on the universal constancy of the velocity of light.

5

MINKOWSKI SPACE

5.1. Time As a Fourth Dimension

A very interesting form of the Lorentz transformations is obtained from the similarity of the combination of velocities (4.14) to the combination of tangents. In particular, notice the similarity of equation (4.14) to Figure 5.1,

$$\tan i(\beta + \alpha) = \frac{\tan i\beta + \tan i\alpha}{1 - \tan i\beta \tan i\alpha} \tag{5.1}$$

which suggests the identification

$$\frac{V}{c} = i \tan i\alpha. \tag{5.2}$$

When we put this into the Lorentz transformations, we obtain

$$x = x \cos i\alpha + ict \sin i\alpha \qquad x = x' \cos i\alpha - ict' \sin i\alpha$$
$$ict' = -x \sin i\alpha + ict \cos i\alpha \qquad ict = x' \sin i\alpha + ict' \cos i\alpha \tag{5.3}$$

These formulas are similar to the expressions describing a rotation of coordinate axes in plane geometry

$$x' = x \cos \theta + y \sin \theta$$
$$y' = -x \sin \theta + y \cos \theta. \tag{5.4}$$

From this analogy, the simple geometric nature of the Lorentz transformations becomes apparent (Figure 5.2):

(a) Time, or more conveniently ict, may be considered as a fourth dimension.

(b) Lorentz transformations are imaginary rotations in the x, ict plane through an angle, $i\alpha$.

(c) What we call velocity is the tangent of the angle $i\alpha$.

(d) Time dilation and the Lorentz contraction formulas are the simple results of projecting the time and length units on the axes of the new system.

(e) The result of two successive Lorentz transformations by $i\alpha$ and $i\beta$ is equivalent to a single Lorentz transformation by $i(\alpha + \beta)$, that is, they satisfy transitivity.

(f) Two objects which can be obtained from each other by a Lorentz transformation are physically the same.

This purely geometrical interpretation of the Lorentz transformations is of great importance in the theory of relativity. Its importance comes from the fact that it replaces the classical space-time framework. The new framework can now be regarded as a geometry whose properties can be studied independently of any particular subject, such as electromagnetism. The consequences of the geometry are general and apply to all natural phenomena. The

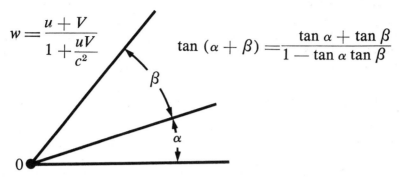

FIGURE 5.1 *Analogy of* (4.14) *to the combination of tangents.*

four-dimensional space-time geometry implied by the Lorentz transformations is called Minkowski space.

5.2. Space-Time Continuum; ds^2 As an Invariant

It is clear from the above considerations that space and time cannot be considered as entities separate from each other. As in the case of the x, y plane, the important reality is the x, ict plane. The axes may be chosen in any desired manner. To describe the objects on a plane, we may set up other types of coordinate systems, namely, polar, elliptical, curvilinear, et cetera. All these descriptions would be equivalent, even though the parameters used to describe the plane are different. Likewise, space and time must be understood in terms of a space-time reality or *Space-Time Continuum*, but the way of describing this, that is, the coordinate system employed, should not matter.

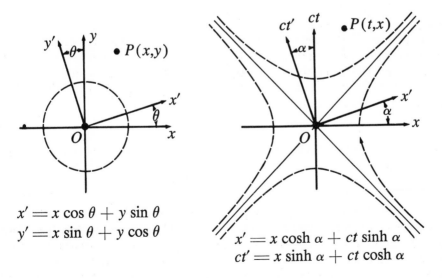

FIGURE 5.2 *Time is a fourth coordinate: A Lorentz transformation is a rotation in space-time.*

To express this idea we look for a quantity that is unaffected by different choices of coordinate systems. In other words, we ask for an *invariant* of the continuum. The analogy to a plane provides this invariant. In fact on the x, y plane $dx^2 + dy^2$, the square of the distance between two points is an invariant. Similarly $dx^2 - c^2 dt^2$, the square of the distance between two events, is an invariant in the x, ict plane. Thus, we arrive at the general invariant

$$ds^2 = dx^2 + dy^2 + dz^2 - c^2 dt^2 = dx'^2 + dy'^2 + dz'^2 - c^2 dt'^2 \qquad (5.5)$$

expressing the unity of the space-time continuum. This expression is the generalization of the Pythagorean Line element $dx^2 + dy^2 + dz^2$ into the four dimensional space-time geometry.

Some insight into the nature of the line element is gained by considering some special cases. For example, $ds^2 = 0$ describes an event traveling with the velocity of light,

$$dx^2 + dy^2 + dz^2 - c^2 dt^2 = 0. \qquad (5.6)$$

Since ds^2 is invariant, this equation is valid in all reference frames, so that an event moving with the velocity of light will appear so from all inertial frames. Another interesting case is an object at rest in a reference frame S_0. Since the object is at rest its displacements vanish, $dx = dy = dz = 0$. Let us denote time by $dt = d\tau$ in this case

$$ds^2 = -c^2 d\tau^2. \qquad (5.7)$$

Now as observed from a moving system, S, the object will appear moving, but since ds^2 is invariant

$$ds^2 = -c^2 d\tau^2 = dx^2 + dy^2 + dz^2 - c^2 dt^2. \qquad (5.8)$$

Note that along with ds, we have $d\tau = ds/ic$ as an invariant. The time as measured in the rest frame, $d\tau$, is called the *proper time*.

$$d\tau = \sqrt{1 - v^2/c^2} \, dt \qquad (5.9)$$

This formula is again none other than the expression of the time dilation. It indicates that a moving clock will appear slowed down.

The invariance of ds^2 is a major concept of relativity. It is also a powerful tool in many of its applications. The skillful use of this invariance often avoids an explicit Lorentz transformation. The formula (5.9) is an example. As another example, consider the derivation of the Lorentz contraction. In S_0, let a distance dx_0 be considered ($dt_0 = 0$); $dS^2 = dx_0^2$. Then from the moving system

$$ds^2 = dx^2 - c^2 dt^2 = dx_0^2.$$

But from the examination of (Figure 5.2) we see that the angle $i\alpha$ gives $i \tan i\alpha = c \, \partial t/\partial x = V/c$. We obtain

$$dx_0 = \sqrt{1 - v^2/c^2} \, dx.$$

These show that dx and $ic \, dt$ are essentially the components of the space-time distance ds. If ds is oriented in the time direction, it manifests itself as the *proper time*. If it is oriented in space direction it manifests itself as the *proper distance*. If it is arbitrarily oriented, it involves both time and space components, thus describing various motions and propagations. If $ds^2 = 0$ (null case), the motion is that of a propagation with the velocity of light. In all cases the ds^2 relating any two events is *invariant*. Note that if ds is imaginary it can always be transformed to a proper time (the coordinate system in which the two events are colocal). Such distances are called *timelike*. On the other hand, if *ds* is real there is a coordinate system in which the two events are simultaneous and *ds* appears as the spacial, *proper distance* between the two events. Such space-time distances are called *spacelike*. No proper Lorentz transformation will transform a timelike distance into a spacelike one or vice versa.

5.3. The Clock Paradox of Minkowski Space

An interesting result is that if the system S' moves on a closed path and comes back to its original place, the clock of S' will be found delayed compared to a clock in S. One may think that with respect to S' the system S has also performed such a closed loop motion that upon arrival there will be a confusion as to which is retarded. However, since S is an inertial system, S' cannot be one. Therefore, we must believe in S but not S', because it did not stay inertial (it is accelerated at least somewhere with respect to S which is inertial). This problem is called the "clock paradox" of special relativity. Incidentally, there is no paradox here. The laws so far considered are not valid for a noninertial frame and that is the end of it. The actual question is how to generalize the theory so as to enable the observer in S' to make predictions which agree with S. The solution of this problem belongs to general relativity. Within the framework of Minkowski space alone, there is an inadequacy in the definition of time for observers moving nonuniformly with respect to each other. This of course means that the space represented by the Minkowskian form (5.5) is not general enough, but applicable only to inertial systems.

The breakdown of Minkowskian space-time for a noninertial observer can be clearly illustrated by the following example. Let an observer O be situated at the origin of an inertial system S. Let another observer O' perform a uniform rotation along a circle C defined in S. The observer O' is evidently not an inertial observer. Nevertheless, applying the special relativistic concepts, we see that (Figure 5.3)

(a) The clock of O' runs at a slower rate than the clock of O, the ratio being $\sqrt{1 - v^2/c^2}$.

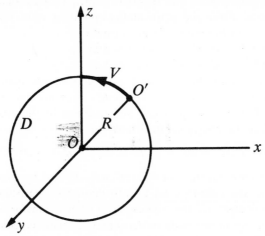

FIGURE 5.3   *Space-time of a noninertial observer. Here, $t' < t$; $D/2R = \pi$ for O, but $D'/2R' < \pi$ for O'.*

(b) The length of the circumference of the circle will be shorter with respect to O' by the ratio $\sqrt{1 - v^2/c^2}$.

(c) The radius R of the circle will be the same for both observers.

Thus, in addition to the difficulty in the rates of clocks, one is led to the strange conclusion that, with respect to O', the ratio between the circumference and the diameter of the circle under consideration will be less than π. These considerations show definitely that Lorentz transformations cannot be used to transform natural laws from an inertial system to a noninertial one. In other words, *special relativity is not valid in a noninertial frame of reference.*

5.4. The Complete Lorentz Transformations, Lorentz Group.

If we let $x^1 = x$, $x^2 = y$, $x^3 = z$, $x^4 = ict$, the most general transformations under which the line element (5.5) remains invariant may be written as

$$x'^{\nu} = \sum_{\mu} a_{\mu}^{\nu} x^{\mu} + b^{\nu} \tag{5.10}$$

where a_{μ}^{ν} and b^{ν} are constants, and a_{μ}^{ν} satisfies (orthonormality)

$$\sum_{\sigma} a_{\mu}^{\sigma} a_{\sigma}^{\nu} = \delta_{\mu}^{\nu}; \qquad \delta_{\mu}^{\nu} = \begin{cases} 1 \text{ if } \mu = \nu \\ 0 \text{ if } \mu \neq \nu. \end{cases} \tag{5.11}$$

(Here the superscripts should not be considered as exponents; they are indices.) Indeed if we differentiate (5.10) and put it into (5.5) we see that ds^2 remains invariant due to (5.11). The general form (5.10) contains as special cases

(a) Ordinary space rotations in the xy, yz, and zx planes,

(b) Space-time (Lorentz) rotations in the xt, yt, and zt planes.

(c) Translation of the axes by constant amounts, b^{ν}.

These three types of transformations can be carried out in a continuous manner and are therefore called *continuous* or *proper* transformations. They are also referred to as continuous or proper *Lorentz groups*. The relativity principle of Einstein refers to these continuous transformations. From the mathematical point of view, however, the equations (5.8) also contain the following types of transformations:

(d) Space-inversion $x'^4 = x^4$, $x'^i = -x'^i$; $i = 1, 2, 3$.

(e) Time-reversal $x'^4 = -x^4$, $x'^i = x^i$; $i = 1, 2, 3$.

These transformations cannot be produced in a continuous manner. They are called *discontinuous* or *improper* Lorentz transformations. They are also referred to as discontinuous or improper Lorentz group. These are members of the group of Lorentz transformations because they, too, leave ds^2 invariant; that is,

$$ds^2 = dx^2 + dy^2 + dz^2 - c^2 \, dt^2 = dx'^2 + dy'^2 + dz'^2 - c^2 \, dt'^2.$$

The discontinuous Lorentz transformations are characterized by some of the a_{μ}^{μ} becoming negative. For example, the time-reversal transformation is characterized by a_4^4 becoming negative. The relative changes in a body caused by a proper transformation can be canceled by a corresponding change in our body or coordinate system. To cancel the change caused by an improper transformation we would have to tear our body apart and rearrange all its atoms. The improper transformations are thus very drastic and must be treated with caution.

Space-inversion essentially means going from a right-handed Cartesian system to a left-handed one, or vice versa. According to this, the reflection of one single space axis, say, $x \rightarrow -x$ (mirroring with respect to the yz plane) must be equivalent to reflecting all three space axes, while the reflection of two space axes must be equivalent to no inversion at all. This must indeed be so, because the final effect of reflecting two space axes can also be effected by a rotation, that is, a continuous transformation. For example, the reflection of the x and y axes is equivalent to a $180°$ rotation around the z axis. Thus, if we want to exclude the space reflection transformations we must require det $|a_k^u| > 0$; $i, k = 1, 2, 3$; while to exclude time reversal, we simply need $a_4^4 > 0$.

The continuous and the discontinuous transformations together are called the *complete* Lorentz transformations or complete Lorentz group. They are the complete set of transformations allowable under the mathematical form of (5.10). If we exclude time reversal, that is, if $a_4^4 > 0$, the remaining set of transformations is called *orthochroneous*.

5.5. The Cobalt Experiment

A question arises: Are the equations governing natural laws invariant under the complete set of Lorentz transformations, or are they invariant only under the proper Lorentz transformations as originally formulated by Einstein? Until recently it was believed that the laws of nature were invariant under all of the transformations. However, a very interesting experiment, first suggested by C. N. Yang and T. D. Lee† has shown that space inversion is not a valid operation for all phenomena of nature. There are certain processes associated with the β-decay which violate space inversion invariance. In order to understand clearly this important result we will discuss the experiment which led to it.

A piece of radioactive cobalt, Co^{60}, is placed in a magnetic field and cooled to a very low temperature. Since at low temperature the thermal agitation is very small, the magnetic moments and consequently the spins of the cobalt nuclei are aligned along the magnetic field. Observation shows that in this arrangement practically all the electrons emitted from the cobalt nucleus come out in a direction opposite to the magnetic field [Figure 5.4(a)]. Now this result is not consistent with the inversion postulate, because if we consider the mirror image of the arrangement [Figure 5.4(b)], the electrons would appear to be coming out in the same direction as the magnetic field which, experiment tells us, is wrong. Therefore, the mirror-image process does not take place in nature. We conclude from this that the β-decay process is not invariant under space-inversion. If space-inversion were valid, equal numbers of electrons would have come out both in the direction of the magnetic field and opposite to it. In this case, both the original experiment and its mirror image would be possible processes. It has been found (since 1957) that there are phenomena called *weak interactions* which are, in general, not invariant under space inversion. This state of affairs has also cast some doubt on the time-reversal transformations.

We recall that a space inversion is equivalent to a transformation from a right-handed coordinate system to a left-handed one, or vice versa. The above results can then be described by saying that the weak interaction processes do not show right-left symmetry. Something in these processes must be either right-handed or left-handed, or at least not quite symmetric.

We asserted earlier in this chapter that the Minkowski space, given by the invariance of

† *Phys. Rev.*, **111** (1956), 254.

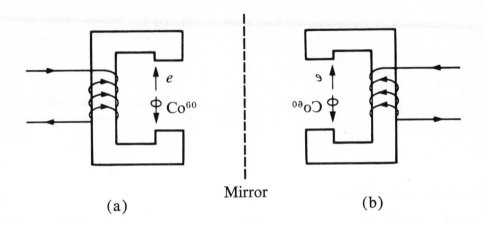

FIGURE 5.4   *The cobalt experiment: (a) The actual experiment; (b) The mirror image which does not materialize.*

the line element (5.5), is a geometry and thus applies to all phenomena. The space-inversion and time-reversal transformations are part of this philosophy of geometry. But we see that there are phenomena which deny the conclusion reached by the invariance of ds^2. Does this mean that Minkowski space is not a general framework but applies only to a certain class of phenomena? This point is the subject of current discussions in physics. However, it has already been agreed by the majority of theoreticians that the Lorentz transformations and the Minkowski space are valid but that some of the particles (say, electrons and neutrinos) have more structure than we previously thought them to have. For example, the neutrino has a definite property with respect to space inversion. It is left-handed! There do not exist right-handed neutrinos in a right-handed coordinate system. Similarly, the electron is predominantly left-handed (when emitted in weak interactions) but its antiparticle, the positron, comes out predominantly right-handed. It is found that when a particle emitted in the weak interactions is left-handed, its antiparticle is emitted as right-handed, and vice versa. If we apply a space inversion transformation, all right-handed particles become left-handed and all left-handed particles become right-handed. Therefore, if one performs *a space inversion transformation, and at the same time changes all particles into their antiparticles*, the symmetry is restored, that is, the resulting situation is then a possible physical situation. For example, if the mirror image arrangement were made of antimatter, that is, if anti-Co^{60} were used and positrons were observed instead of electrons, then the mirror-image process shown would be a possible one. In any case, the fact that these questions are being investigated both theoretically and experimentally shows that the theory of relativity is a living subject and is under current investigation.

A certain amount of myth has developed around the space-inversion and time-reversal transformations. Some people have the impression that time-reversal makes time run backwards while space-inversion turns space inside out. These erroneous impressions are usually created if one insists on understanding the meaning of these transformations purely in geometrical terms. One must always discuss the effects of any transformation in relation to the physical objects contained in the geometry. If one does so, it becomes clear that the requirements of invariance under these transformations refer to some symmetries of physical objects or situations. For example if, in a certain situation, space inversion is valid, that situation and its mirror image are equally possible; therefore, they should occur with equal frequency in nature. However, if space-inversion is completely violated, the situation corresponding to the mirror image of an observed process is not possible and does not occur in nature. Between these two extreme limits lie various degrees of violation implying various ratios of the frequency of occurrences of a phenomenon and its mirror image. In a similar manner, the validity of the time-reversal transformation, say, for the motion of an object, means that for this object it is equally permissible to carry out the motion in reverse order (like a moving picture played backward). If time-reversal is violated, the object should not be able to perform an observed motion in reverse. We must bear in mind that the geometry of Minkowski which we have so far developed is only a kinematics. To draw actual physical conclusions, we must first introduce material elements into this empty framework. Only then will we be able to draw conclusions from it pertaining to the physical world.

Summary: Minkowski Space

(a) The kinematics of special relativity can be presented purely as a four-dimensional geometry, time being the fourth coordinate.

(b) This geometry, called the Minkowski geometry, generalizes the invariance of length of the Euclidean geometry (Pythagorean theorem) to a four-dimensional space-time continuum.

(c) Lorentz transformations cannot be used to transform the laws of nature from an inertial frame to a noninertial frame. Therefore, the Minkowski space cannot be used in a noninertial system as the space-time framework for describing natural phenomena.

(d) Mathematically, Lorentz transformations include *proper* and *improper* Lorentz transformations plus *translations*. Recent discoveries (1957) in physics have shown that dynamically the laws of nature are not always invariant under space-inversion.

(e) The Cobalt experiment implies that if we take the mirror image (space inversion) of a physical situation and change all the particles in the image into their antiparticles, the resulting situation is a physically possible situation. The mirroring alone is not always sufficient.

6

MATHEMATICAL AIDS AND NOTATION

The Lorentz space given by the Cartesian coordinates $x^1 = x$, $x^2 = y$, $x^3 = z$, $x^4 = ict$ may be associated with the invariant line element

$$ds^2 = dx^2 + dy^2 + dz^2 - c^2 dt^2 = \sum_{\mu,\nu} g_{\mu\nu} dx^\mu dx^\nu, \qquad (6.1)$$

where the $g_{\mu\nu}$ are given as

$$g_{\mu\nu} = \delta_{\mu\nu} = \begin{cases} 1 \text{ if } \mu = \nu \\ 0 \text{ if } \mu \neq \nu. \end{cases} \qquad (6.2)$$

We will also use lower indices $x_1 = x$, $x_2 = y$, $x_3 = z$, $x_4 = ict$ defined by $x_\mu = \sum_\nu g_{\mu\nu} x^\nu$, and we will write the above line element as

$$ds^2 = g_{\mu\nu} dx^\mu dx^\nu = dx_\nu dx^\nu, \qquad (6.3)$$

where the repeated indices appearing once in the lower and once in the upper position are automatically summed over. This is called the *summation convention* which eliminates the summation sign, Σ. It is understood that the indices repeated in the lower part or upper part alone are not summed over. For example, $g_{\mu\mu} = 1$, $x_i x_i = x_i^2$, but $x_\mu x^\mu = x^2 + y^2 + z^2 - c^2 t^2$. The $g_{\mu\nu}$ is a device to lower the indices. Likewise, we can define a $g^{\mu\nu}$ to raise indices. In the Cartesian space used above $g^{\mu\nu} = g_{\mu\nu}$, $g_{\mu\nu} g^{\mu\sigma} = g_\nu^\sigma = \delta_\nu^\sigma$. The real usefulness of all this notation becomes clear if we consider the line element in another, say, spherical, coordinate system (Figure 6.1):

$$ds^2 = dr^2 + r^2 d\theta^2 + r^2 \sin^2 \theta \, d\phi^2 - c^2 dt^2 = g_{\mu\nu} dx^\mu dx^\nu \qquad (6.4)$$

where

$$x^1 = r, \ x^2 = \theta, \ x^3 = \phi, \ x^4 = t, \ g_{11} = 1, \ g_{22} = r^2, \ g_{33} = r^2 \sin^2 \theta, \ g_{44} = -c^2. \quad (6.5)$$

The lowering and the raising of indices are accomplished by

$$dx_\mu = g_{\mu\nu} dx^\nu, \qquad dx^\mu = g^{\mu\nu} dx_\nu \qquad (6.6)$$

where again

$$g_{\mu\nu} g^{\mu\sigma} = \delta_\nu^\sigma. \qquad (6.7)$$

Thus the notation we have developed works uniformly for any coordinate system, although for the Cartesian system it reduces to one of the utmost simplicity. In the part of this book on special relativity, we will work mostly with the Cartesian coordinate system. For this reason, in this chapter the mathematical aids will be developed in terms of Cartesian coordinates. The reader is referred to Chapter XIV for a more comprehensive treatment of the material of this chapter.

In the Lorentz space given in terms of Cartesian coordinates the variables x^μ form the components of a vector called the *position vector*. The position vector transforms from one

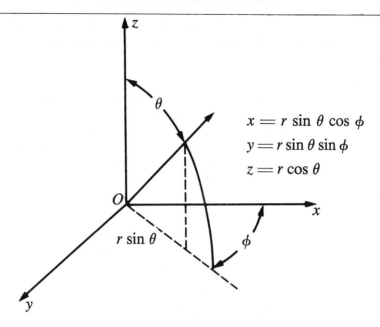

FIGURE 6.1 *Polar coordinates.*

Cartesian coordinate system to another, according to

$$\Delta x'^{\mu} = \frac{\partial x'^{\mu}}{\partial x^{\nu}} \Delta x^{\nu}. \tag{6.8}$$

Any aggregate of four quantities U^{ν} which transforms like the position vector is called a *vector*.

$$U'^{\mu} = \frac{\partial x'^{\mu}}{\partial x^{\nu}} U^{\nu}. \tag{6.9}$$

The square of a vector is defined as

$$U^2 = g_{\mu\nu} U^{\mu} U^{\nu} = U_{\nu} U^{\nu}. \tag{6.10}$$

We can define quantities $U^{\mu\nu}$ or $U_{\mu\nu}$ which, for each index, behave like a vector. Evidently such a quantity must transform like

$$U'^{\mu\nu} = \frac{\partial x'^{\mu}}{\partial x^{\alpha}} \frac{\partial x'^{\nu}}{\partial x^{\beta}} U^{\alpha\beta}. \tag{6.11}$$

$U^{\mu\nu}$ is called a *tensor of second rank* or a *second order tensor*. A second order tensor is said to be symmetric if $U^{\mu\nu} = U^{\nu\mu}$, and it is called *antisymmetric* if $U^{\mu\nu} = -U^{\nu\mu}$. The quantity

$$U_{\mu}^{\mu} = g_{\mu\nu} U^{\mu\nu} = U_1^1 + U_2^2 + U_3^3 + U_4^4 \tag{6.12}$$

is called the *trace*. The trace of an antisymmetric tensor vanishes. Tensors of higher rank are similarly defined

$$U'^{\mu\nu\cdots\sigma} = \frac{\partial x'^{\mu}}{\partial x^{\alpha}} \frac{\partial x'^{\nu}}{\partial x^{\beta}} \cdots \frac{\partial x'^{\sigma}}{\partial x^{\lambda}} U^{\alpha\beta\cdots\lambda} \tag{6.13}$$

An index, say β, of $U_\gamma^{\alpha\beta\ldots\lambda}$ may be lowered, namely, $U_\gamma^{\alpha\ldots\lambda} = g_{\gamma\beta}\,U^{\alpha\beta\ldots\lambda}$. A vector U^μ is called a tensor of *first rank*. A quantity Φ which transforms under a proper Lorentz transformation as

$$\Phi' = \Phi \tag{6.14}$$

is called a *scalar*. This can also be called a tensor of *zero rank*. Thus we can construct quantities which transform under a Lorentz transformation in such a way as to retain their original tensorial identities. Since such quantities preserve their meaning in any coordinate system, they are very useful in constructing physical theories. They are called *representations* of the *Lorentz group*. Scalars, vectors, and tensors are representations of the Lorentz group. If, under a space inversion, a tensor changes its sign, it is called a pseudo-tensor. Thus if under $x^i \to -x^i$, $x^4 \to x^4$,

$$\Phi' = -\Phi \qquad \text{pseudo-scalar,}$$
$$U'^\mu = -U^\mu \qquad \text{pseudo-vector, etc.} \tag{6.15}$$

Under a proper Lorentz transformation the need for this distinction does not arise.

It is interesting and also very important to realize that scalars, vectors, and tensors are *not* the only representations of the Lorentz group. Some quantities called *spinors* are also representations. One of the most familiar and useful spinors is the *four-component spinor*. A four-component spinor is defined as a column matrix (see Appendix B),

$$\psi = \begin{pmatrix} \psi_1 \\ \psi_2 \\ \psi_3 \\ \psi_4 \end{pmatrix} \tag{6.16}$$

such that if we consider its so-called *Pauli adjoint* $\bar\psi = (\psi_1^*,\ \psi_2^*,\ -\psi_3^*,\ -\psi_4^*)$, then

$$\Lambda = \bar\psi\psi \qquad \text{is a scalar;}$$
$$U_\mu = \bar\psi\gamma_\mu\psi \qquad \text{is a vector.} \tag{6.17}$$

Here γ_μ are given by the matrices (see Chapter 11, equation 11.7)

$$\gamma_1 = \begin{pmatrix} \mathbf{O} & \begin{matrix} 0 & -i \\ -i & 0 \end{matrix} \\ \begin{matrix} 0 & i \\ i & 0 \end{matrix} & \mathbf{O} \end{pmatrix} \qquad\qquad \gamma_2 = \begin{pmatrix} \mathbf{O} & \begin{matrix} 0 & 1 \\ -1 & 0 \end{matrix} \\ \begin{matrix} 0 & -1 \\ 1 & 0 \end{matrix} & \mathbf{O} \end{pmatrix}$$

$$\gamma_3 = \begin{pmatrix} \mathbf{O} & \begin{matrix} -i & 0 \\ 0 & i \end{matrix} \\ \begin{matrix} i & 0 \\ 0 & -i \end{matrix} & \mathbf{O} \end{pmatrix} \qquad\qquad \gamma_4 = \begin{pmatrix} \begin{matrix} 1 & 0 \\ 0 & 1 \end{matrix} & \mathbf{O} \\ \mathbf{O} & \begin{matrix} -1 & 0 \\ 0 & -1 \end{matrix} \end{pmatrix}. \tag{6.18}$$

Note that these matrices satisfy the relations (the reason for this is given in Chapter 11)

$$\gamma_\mu\gamma_\nu + \gamma_\nu\gamma_\mu = 2g_{\mu\nu}. \tag{6.19}$$

Let the Lorentz transformation of ψ be

$$\psi' = S\psi, \qquad \text{then} \qquad \bar{\psi}' = \bar{\psi}S^\dagger \tag{6.20}$$

where $S^\dagger$ is the hermitian conjugate of the matrix S. In the new frame

$$\Lambda = \bar{\psi}'\psi' = \bar{\psi}S^\dagger S\psi, \tag{6.21}$$

$$U'_\mu = \bar{\psi}'\gamma_\mu\psi' = \bar{\psi}S^\dagger\gamma_\mu S\psi = \frac{\partial x'^\sigma}{\partial x^\mu}\,\bar{\psi}\gamma_\sigma\psi. \tag{6.22}$$

Equation (6.21) requires that the transformation matrix S be unitary

$$S^{-1} = S^\dagger \tag{6.23}$$

and equation (6.22) requires

$$S^{-1}\gamma_\mu S = \frac{\partial x'^\sigma}{\partial x^\mu}\,\gamma_\sigma. \tag{6.24}$$

From these conditions, the nature of the transformation matrix may be determined. It can be shown by using (6.19), (6.23), and (6.24) that (see problem 12.1)

$$S = \exp\left(\tfrac{1}{4}\gamma^\mu\gamma^\nu\phi_{\mu\nu}\right) \tag{6.25}$$

where $\phi_{\mu\nu} = -\phi_{\nu\mu}$ is the amount of rotation in the (x^ν, x^μ) plane (see the examples in Chapter 11). Using this transformation, one can also prove directly that

$$
\begin{array}{ll}
\bar{\psi}\psi & \text{is a scalar} \\
\bar{\psi}\gamma_\mu\psi & \text{is a vector} \\
\bar{\psi}(\gamma_\mu\gamma_\nu - \gamma_\nu\gamma_\mu)\psi & \text{is an antisymmetric tensor} \\
\bar{\psi}\gamma_5\gamma_\mu\psi & \text{is a pseudo-vector} \\
\bar{\psi}\gamma_5\psi & \text{is a pseudo-scalar}
\end{array}
\tag{6.26}
$$

where $\gamma_5 = \gamma_1\gamma_2\gamma_3\gamma_4$. Formally, we summarize these by saying that 1, γ_μ, $\gamma_\mu\gamma_\nu - \gamma_\nu\gamma_\mu$, $\gamma_5\gamma_\mu$, γ_5 are, respectively, scalar, vector, antisymmetric tensor, pseudo-vector, and pseudo-scalar. They are the only tensorial quantities that can be formed from γ-matrices. The reason is simple: γ-matrices are 4×4 matrices. They can represent at most $4 \times 4 = 16$ linearly independent components. The above quantities have, respectively, 1, 4, 6, 4, 1 components, adding up to 16.

By explicitly evaluating (6.25), say, for a rotation in the y, z plane (around the x-axis) by an angle $\phi_{32} = -\phi_{23} = \phi$

$$S_{23} = e^{\frac{1}{2}\gamma_2\gamma_3\phi} = 1 - \gamma_2\gamma_3\left(\frac{\phi}{2}\right) + \frac{1}{2}\left(\frac{\phi}{2}\right)^2 + \gamma_2\gamma_3\frac{1}{6}\left(\frac{\phi}{2}\right)^3 \cdots,$$

and collecting terms, we obtain the matrix

$$S_{23} = \cos\frac{\phi}{2} - \gamma_2\gamma_3\sin\frac{\phi}{2} = \begin{pmatrix} \cos\dfrac{\phi}{2} & i\sin\dfrac{\phi}{2} & 0 & 0 \\[2mm] i\sin\dfrac{\phi}{2} & \cos\dfrac{\phi}{2} & 0 & 0 \\[2mm] 0 & 0 & \cos\dfrac{\phi}{2} & i\sin\dfrac{\phi}{2} \\[2mm] 0 & 0 & i\sin\dfrac{\phi}{2} & \cos\dfrac{\phi}{2} \end{pmatrix}. \tag{6.27}$$

This shows that under this rotation

$$\psi'_1 = \psi_1 \cos\frac{\phi}{2} + \psi_2 i \sin\frac{\phi}{2}, \qquad \psi'_3 = \psi_3 \cos\frac{\phi}{2} + \psi_4 i \sin\frac{\phi}{2},$$

$$\psi'_2 = \psi_1 i \sin\frac{\phi}{2} + \psi_2 \cos\frac{\phi}{2}, \qquad \psi'_4 = \psi_3 i \sin\frac{\phi}{2} + \psi_4 \cos\frac{\phi}{2}. \tag{6.28}$$

The transformation properties of the spinor are thus formally similar to those of a vector, except that for a Lorentz rotation of angle ϕ, the spinor rotates by only $\phi/2$. Due to this property, the spinor is sometimes called a *half vector*. If a vector transformation

$$U'^\mu = \frac{\partial x'^\mu}{\partial x^\nu} U^\nu$$

is represented by $U' = \mathscr{L}U$, then formally,

$$\mathscr{L}^0, \mathscr{L}^{\frac{1}{2}}, \mathscr{L}^1, \mathscr{L}^{\frac{3}{2}}, \mathscr{L}^2 \ldots \tag{6.29}$$

represent the transformations of a scalar, spinor, vector, $\frac{3}{2}$ order spinor, second order tensor, et cetera. According to this, spinors are in general half-integer rank tensors. It has been shown by mathematicians that integer rank and half-integer rank tensors, that is, tensors and spinors, are the only finite representations of the Lorentz group.

Since the differentiation ∂_μ behaves as a vector (see 3.23), we can obtain new tensors by differentiating tensors; for example

$$V_\mu = \partial_\mu \Phi, \qquad\qquad T_{\mu\nu} = \partial_\mu U_\nu$$

$$f_{\mu\nu} = \partial_\mu A_\nu - \partial_\nu A_\mu, \qquad h_{\mu\nu} = \partial_\mu A_\nu + \partial_\nu A_\mu \tag{6.30}$$

$$\zeta = \partial_\mu U^\mu, \qquad\qquad \lambda_{\mu\nu} = \partial_\mu \partial_\nu \Phi$$

$$\lambda = \partial_\mu \partial^\mu \Phi \text{ etc.}$$

Among these, the following are most important in physical theories:

$$\text{gradient: } \partial_\mu \Phi, \qquad\qquad \text{curl: } \partial_\mu A_\nu - \partial_\nu A_\mu,$$

$$\text{divergence: } \partial_\mu A^\mu, \qquad \text{d'Alembertian: } \partial_\mu \partial^\mu \Phi. \tag{6.31}$$

The gradient and the d'Alembertian operators ∂_μ and $\partial_\mu \partial^\mu$ are applicable to any tensor or spinor, whereas the divergence and curl can apply only to vectors and higher order integer tensors.

The ordinary derivative of a quantity with respect to a parameter η is given by

$$\frac{d\Phi}{d\eta} = \frac{\partial \Phi}{\partial x^\mu} \frac{dx^\mu}{d\eta}, \qquad \frac{d}{d\eta} = \frac{dx^\mu}{d\eta} \frac{\partial}{\partial x^\mu}. \tag{6.32}$$

For example, the ordinary time derivative d/dt is given as

$$\frac{d}{dt} = \frac{\partial}{\partial t} - \left(v_x \frac{\partial}{\partial x} + v_y \frac{\partial}{\partial y} + v_3 \frac{\partial}{\partial z} \right). \tag{6.33}$$

which is usually called a comoving time derivative.

Under certain conditions, new tensors can also be formed by integration. In this respect, we first consider the differentials

$$d\Omega = dx\, dy\, dz\, ic\, dt,$$
$$dx^\mu = (dx,\, dy,\, dz,\, ic\, dt),$$
$$dS_\mu = (dy\, dzic\, dt,\, dx\, dzic\, dt,\, dx\, dyic\, dt,\, dx\, dy\, dz),$$
$$dS^{\mu\nu} = dx^\mu\, dx^\nu.$$

(6.34)

We can construct the integrated quantities

$$\Lambda = \int \Phi\, d\Omega \quad \text{scalar,} \qquad \Lambda = \int A_\mu\, dx^\mu \quad \text{scalar,}$$
$$\Lambda^\mu = \int T^{\mu\nu}\, dS_\nu \quad \text{vector,} \qquad \Lambda = \int U^\mu\, dS_\mu \quad \text{scalar, etc.}$$

(6.35)

Among such expressions, the following are important:

$$\oint A_\mu\, dx^\mu \quad \text{line integration,} \qquad \int dx^\mu\, dx^\nu\, B_{\mu\nu} \quad \text{2-surface integration,}$$
$$\int A^\mu\, dS_\mu \quad \text{3-surface integration,} \qquad \int_\Omega \Phi\, d\Omega \qquad \text{space-time integration.}$$

(6.36)

The ordinary theorems for these integrations, namely, Gauss' and Stokes' theorems, can be generalized in Lorentz space. The generalized Gauss' theorem,

$$\int_S A^\mu\, dS_\mu - \int_{S'} A^\mu\, dS_\mu = \int_\Omega \partial_\mu A^\mu\, d\Omega,$$

(6.37)

will be useful later. If $\partial_\mu A^\mu = 0$, we have

$$\Lambda = \int_S A^\mu\, dS_\mu = \int_{S'} A^\mu\, dS_\mu \qquad \text{invariant.}$$

(6.38)

Thus, when $\partial_\mu A^\mu = 0$, the result of the integration is a true scalar and is independent of the choice of the 3-surface, S. Similarly, if $\partial_\nu T^{\mu\nu} = 0$, then

$$P^\mu = \int_S T^{\mu\nu}\, dS_\nu$$

(6.39)

is a vector independent of the surface of integration. These statements will be useful later in formulating conservation laws.

Let ρ be a density function representing a physical quantity at rest, such as the rest density of charge. Then

$$Q = \int \rho\, dx\, dy\, dz = \int \rho\, dS_4$$

(6.40)

represents the total charge. If the charge in question is concentrated at a point r', then the density becomes singular and infinite at r'. Let $\rho = Q\delta(r - r')$ where $\delta(r - r')$ is a singular function becoming infinite at $r - r'$, but vanishing otherwise. Then from (6.40)

$$\int \delta(r - r')\, dx\, dy\, dz = 1.$$

(6.41)

Let

$$\delta(r - r') = \delta(x - x')\, \delta(y - y')\, \delta(z - z')$$

(6.42)

$$\int_{-\epsilon}^{+\epsilon} \delta(x - x')\, dx = 1.$$

(6.43)

These functions are called Dirac δ-functions. It may now be proved that

$$f(x') = \int f(x)\,\delta(x - x')\,dx \tag{6.44}$$

$$\delta(x) = \delta(-x), \qquad \delta(ax) = \frac{1}{a}\,\delta(x), \tag{6.45}$$

and, more generally, if the equation $f(x) = 0$ has the roots $x_1, x_2, \ldots x_n$,

$$\delta(f(x)) = \sum_{j=1}^{n} \frac{1}{|f'(x_j)|}\,\delta(x - x_j). \tag{6.46}$$

This can be proven by differentiating $\delta(f(x))$. As an example, if $f = x^2 - x'^2$, we have

$$\delta(x^2 - x'^2) = \frac{1}{|2x'|}\,[\delta(x - x') + \delta(x + x')]. \tag{6.47}$$

The proper Lorentz transformations can be built up from the infinitesimal Lorentz transformations

$$x'^\mu = (g^{\mu\nu} + \alpha^{\mu\nu})x_\nu + \epsilon^\mu, \qquad \alpha^{\mu\nu} = -\alpha^{\nu\mu} \tag{6.48}$$

where ϵ^μ is an infinitesimal translation and $\alpha^{\mu\nu}$ is an infinitesimal rotation. For space rotations, $\alpha^{12} \to d\phi$, et cetera, the infinitesimal angle variables are real. For space-time rotations (moving frame) they are $\alpha^{14} \to id\beta$, et cetera, that is, pure imaginary. The variation of a coordinate under an infinitesimal Lorentz transformation

$$\delta x^\mu = x'^\mu - x^\mu = \alpha^{\mu\nu}x_\nu + \epsilon^\mu \tag{6.49}$$

is an important quantity in the variational formulation of physical laws. To build up finite proper transformations, we carry out an infinite number of successive infinitesimal transformations. The discontinuous transformations, that is, reflections, cannot be obtained from infinitesimal transformations.

The essence of the variational treatment of dynamical laws is as follows: One first ignores the dynamical laws and considers all variations possible in their absence, while obeying the kinematical conditions such as Lorentz transformations. Later these variations are again restricted so as to give the motions which are actually realized in nature. Such a restricting statement is called a variational principle. In this process the symmetry conditions, such as Lorentz transformations, lead to conservation laws; whereas the variational principle provides the equations of motion. In Chapter 12, a single constraining statement, namely, the *principle of stationary action*, is assumed to contain all the dynamics associated with physical systems.

Thus we will need the variation of field functions $\psi(x)$ and of a function of the field functions and their derivatives, $\mathscr{L}(\psi, \partial_\mu\psi \ldots)$, et cetera, in a variational treatment of fields. The variation of a field function $\psi(x)$ arises from three sources: (a) the independent variation at the point x, $\delta_0\psi$; (b) variation through the dependence on x,

$$\frac{\partial\psi}{\partial x^\mu}\,\delta x^\mu;$$

and (c) variation through its transformation property as scalar, vector, or tensor $\psi' - \psi = \frac{1}{2}S_{\mu\nu}\psi\alpha^{\mu\nu}$. Thus, using (6.49),

$$\delta\psi = \delta_0\psi + \frac{\partial\psi}{\partial x^\mu}(\alpha^{\mu\nu}x_\nu + \epsilon^\mu) + \tfrac{1}{2}S_{\mu\nu}\psi\alpha^{\mu\nu}. \tag{6.50}$$

The tensor $S_{\mu\nu}$ is zero if ψ is a scalar. For vector and spinor ψ see problem 12.1. The variation of a function $\mathscr{L}(\psi, \partial_\mu\psi)$, arises from two sources: (a) the independent variation of $\mathscr{L}$ at x, $\delta_0\mathscr{L}$; and (b) the variation through its dependence on ψ and $\partial_\mu\psi$.

$$\delta\mathscr{L} = \delta_0\mathscr{L} + \frac{\partial\mathscr{L}}{\partial\psi}\,\delta\psi + \frac{\partial\mathscr{L}}{\partial(\partial_\mu\psi)}\,\delta(\partial_\mu\psi). \tag{6.51}$$

The operation of variation, δ, commutes with the operations of differentiation and of integration

$$d\delta = \delta d, \qquad \partial\delta = \delta\partial, \qquad \int\delta = \delta\int. \tag{6.52}$$

From these and equation (6.50) the variation of any quantity of interest such as $\delta\mathscr{L}$ may be evaluated.

7

PARTICLE DYNAMICS IN MINKOWSKI SPACE

7.1. Conservation Principles

In the previous chapters we have constructed a new kinematics on the basis of the principle of relativity. This new kinematics turned out to be equivalent to a four-dimensional space-time geometry which takes the place of the three-dimensional absolute space plus the one-dimensional absolute time of Newtonian physics. A geometry, however, is an empty frame in which the picture of the material world has still to be painted. In this part of the book we will introduce material elements into the Minkowski space and try to formulate the laws governing them. To do justice to the principle of relativity, these laws must be form-invariant under a Lorentz transformation.

In order to construct a dynamics, kinematical statements alone are not sufficient. One must postulate new principles along with the material elements introduced. These new principles, of course, must also be extracted from the realm of experience, as were the two principles of special relativity. The basic material element to be added to the kinematics turns out to be the mass or energy. Any entity which has the property of mass or energy is, by definition, a material object. Ordinary bodies, particles with mass, electric or magnetic fields, and light and other kinds of radiation are examples of material objects. A system composed of one or more material objects is called a material system. The reader is assumed to be familiar with these concepts from Newtonian physics. The new principles which we will postulate are the principles of conservation, of energy, momentum, and angular momentum. The experimental basis for these conservation principles will not be discussed in detail. Suffice it to say that they are the results of the most exhaustive scientific observations performed since the time of Archimedes. Here we simply state them as: *The energy, momentum, and angular momentum of an isolated material system remain constant.* A second statement concerning the nature of energy will be added to this, namely, *the energy of an isolated system can never be negative.* We will call this the *principle of positive definiteness of energy*. In Chapter 12 conservation laws will be found to be related to the homogeneity and isotropy of space-time geometry.

7.2. Fields and Particles

The types of material objects that we can construct, on the basis of the principle of relativity plus the conservation laws, are severely restricted. For example, the familiar concept of a rigid body is not allowed. In order to see why this is so, let us suppose that some extended body is set in motion by an external force acting at one of its points. If the body is assumed to be rigid, all of its points should be set in motion at the same time; otherwise, the body will be deformed. Since the force can be propagated at most with the velocity c, we see that all the points of a body cannot start moving simultaneously. The body cannot be rigid. Thus, extended physical objects must be described like deformable bodies, that is, by functions of x, y, z, t. Such functions are called "Fields." However, not every function of the coordinates is acceptable as a physical quantity. This is because these functions must enter into the expressions of natural laws in the same way in all reference frames. In other words, only those functions are allowable which retain their identity under a Lorentz transformation. In Chapter 6 we have seen that scalars, vectors, tensors, and spinors are such quantities.

This discussion also carries an important conclusion for the so-called elementary particles. An elementary particle is, by definition, a material object which takes part in physical phenomena only as a unit. In other words, from the physical point of view it should not be useful to think of any component part to an elementary particle or to analyze it further. In order to describe the state of the motion of an elementary particle, it is sufficient to know only its position, velocity, and rotation as a whole. It is clear that this would imply a rigid structure if the particle had any classically meaningful extension at all. Thus, elementary particles must be pictured as point particles in the theory of relativity. In other words, *only fields and point particles are acceptable*. A classically acceptable point particle, on the other hand, cannot have an angular momentum of its own. Since, in nature, particles such as the electron or proton have what we call spin or intrinsic angular momentum, the above picture of a concentrated mass point is not a realistic one. Our intuitive concept of a point particle has to undergo a great deal of modification. There is a school of thought, the so-called *quantized field theory approach*, in which these problems are considered as follows: The physical world is described in terms of fields. These fields, however, are quantized according to the precepts of quantum theory giving rise to discrete, particle-like properties when we measure them. These discrete units are called particles or quanta associated with the field. The image of a particle used here is essentially different from the classical one, and it turns out that spin properties as well as other attributes of particles may be correctly inferred. Thus, if the quantized field theory approach is valid, particles and fields find a uniform description. However, the validity of this approach has been questioned, due to some apparently insurmountable theoretical and experimental difficulties, and a new direction, called the *dispersion relations approach* in which the field concept does not appear as a central physical model is being studied. In the present chapter, we will adhere to our intuitive picture of a material particle; that is, an extremely small mass concentration which may possess energy and momentum but not intrinsic angular momentum. This will give us the means to study mass, energy, and momentum relationships in a simple manner.

Another implication of the impossibility of rigid bodies goes much deeper. As we remember, a reference frame itself is supposed to be a rigid body. If a rigid body is to be rejected, how can we preserve the very basis of our theory, namely, the reference frame? The answer to this dilemma is that if we do not apply forces on our reference frame, that is, if we do not accelerate it, the above objection does not arise. This indeed is what we mean by an inertial frame. But if we want to be completely free from the objection, we must also assume that the reference frame does not interact with the material system under observation. Obviously, this condition is never satisfied since the very act of observation involves receiving light or other kinds of energy by the observer, which essentially involves an interaction. The discussion may be carried even further. In any realistic theory we must assume the existence of some sort of communication between observers. Otherwise, it would be impossible to receive the information relating to the quantities to be transformed. But the transmission of information necessarily means an interaction between the reference frames. This, again, conflicts with the idea of an inertial frame. In order to overcome these objections, we assume that the effects arising from the acts of observation and of communication are negligible, that is, the system under observation and the reference frames we use are much heavier than the objects carrying the information.

These considerations show how idealized the foundations of our theory are. In spite of this, we will go ahead and build a world picture on these concepts. For, in the first place, we do not know of any better framework in which to work; and, in the second place, within its limitations this framework leads to results which are confirmed by experiment to a very high degree of accuracy.

7.3. Introduction of Mass and Momentum

In constructing a dynamics, one must first introduce mass and momentum into the kinematics. It is well known how this is done in Newtonian mechanics. In order to do it in the Minkowski space it is advisable to keep the concepts and definitions as close as possible to the Newtonian case, because one of our aims is eventually to satisfy the conservation laws which are valid also in Newtonian mechanics. As a definition, we take the momentum of a particle of mass m to be the four vector

$$p_\mu = mv_\mu \qquad (\mu = 1, 2, 3, 4) \tag{7.1}$$

where $v_\mu = dx_\mu/dt$ is the velocity of the particle and m its mass. The space components of this four vector are mv_x, mv_y, and mv_z. It has also a time component $p_4 = imc$. The nature and implications of this definition will now be investigated by making use of the concept of relativity. Let us consider the inertial frame, S_0, in which the particle is at rest. In this frame there is only the fourth component, $p_4^0 = im_0c$, where m_0 is the rest mass of the particle. To obtain the momentum of a moving particle we observe the particle from a new reference frame. Let the direction of motion be along the x-axis. Now, Lorentz transformations are

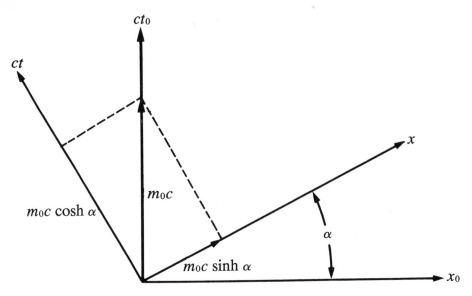

FIGURE 7.1 *The momentum of a particle at rest is directed into time direction (energy).*

equivalent to imaginary rotations, and thus we write (Figure 7.1)

$$p_1 = im_0c \sin i\alpha = \frac{m_0 v}{\sqrt{1 - v^2/c^2}}$$

$$p_2 = 0, \qquad p_3 = 0 \tag{7.2}$$

$$p_4 = im_0c \cos i\alpha = \frac{im_0c}{\sqrt{1 - v^2/c^2}}.$$

By comparing with (7.1) we see that the mass at rest, m_0, and the mass in motion, m, are related by

$$m = \frac{m_0}{\sqrt{1 - v^2/c^2}}. \tag{7.3}$$

This result is called the relativistic variation of mass. The geometrical significance of this result may be clearly seen by pointing out that the length or the magnitude of a four-vector must be the same in both frames. Thus we have

$$p^2 + (imc)^2 = (im_0c)^2 \quad \text{or} \quad p^2 + m_0^2c^2 = m^2c^2 \tag{7.4}$$

This is a more convenient formula than (7.3), of which we will make frequent use later. The definition of momentum may be simplified if we write it in terms of m_0 and the proper time τ.

$$p_\mu = m_0 \frac{dx_\mu}{d\tau} = m_0 u_\mu. \tag{7.5}$$

In this form its four-vector character is self evident. The definition of angular momentum can then be taken over from Newtonian mechanics as $M_{\mu\nu} = p_\mu x_\nu - p_\nu x_\mu$.

7.4. Equations of Motion of a Particle

Next, we want to find the equations of motion of a particle under a given external force. The classical analogue of this is the Newtonian law of motion. Let us tentatively write the same type of equations as Newton's equations but in the four-dimensional space of Minkowski:

$$F_\mu = \frac{d}{dt}(mv_\mu). \tag{7.6}$$

The space components F_x, F_y, and F_z of the force F are just the same as in the Newtonian case. The fourth component F_4 is new. Actually, the equation (7.6) is a *definition* of force in terms of the rate of change of momentum in time. For this reason, it can never be wrong. However, the form of this equation is not properly suited to the spirit of a relativistic law. For example, the time derivative alone appears in the law as though something was special about the time coordinate. To eliminate this asymmetrical situation, we may use the invariant, $d\tau = \sqrt{1 - v^2/c^2} \, dt$ instead of the time differential, dt. This substitution will also modify the force, F. Thus, we write

$$f_\mu = \frac{d}{d\tau}(mv_\mu) \tag{7.7}$$

where f_μ is the Minkowski four-vector

$$f_\mu = \frac{F_\mu}{\sqrt{1 - v^2/c^2}} .$$ (7.8)

The new formula (7.7) is a form-invariant expression. It can be simplified further, by using

$$mv_\mu = m_0 \frac{dx_\mu}{d\tau} ,$$

into

$$f_\mu = m_0 \frac{d^2 x_\mu}{d\tau^2} .$$ (7.9)

However, in many instances it is advisable to keep it in the form (7.6), otherwise, when we deal with more than one particle, it would be necessary to use a different proper time, $d\tau$, for each particle and this is undesirable from the point of view of a general dynamics. Furthermore, in the real world, particles can be created or destroyed. It would be unrealistic to insist on (7.9) which fixes the attention on the individual particles. The form (7.6) fixes attention on the momentum and its change in time. This is more suitable from the point of view of our conservation principles.

7.5. Mass-Energy Relation

One of the most important consequences of the theory of relativity is the relation between mass and energy. The work done on a particle by a given force is, by definition,

$$dE = F_x \, dx + F_y \, dy + F_z \, dz.$$ (7.10)

For simplicity, let the force have only the component F_x. From (7.6) we get

$$dE = \frac{d}{dt} (mv) \, dx = v \, d(mv) = \frac{p \, dp}{m} .$$ (7.11)

Now by differentiating (7.4), we have $p \, dp = c^2 m \, dm$ and, therefore,

$$dE = d \, mc^2 \quad \text{or} \quad E = mc^2 + K$$ (7.12)

where K is an integration constant which is found to be equal to zero by actual comparison with experiment. Thus we have the important formula†

$$E = mc^2.$$ (7.13)

This formula expresses the identity of energy and mass. Any energy, E, possesses the property of inertia E/c^2 and any mass m represents an amount of energy mc^2. A particle at rest has energy $E_0 = m_0 c^2$. When it is set in motion, its kinetic energy will be

$$T = (m - m_0)c^2 = \tfrac{1}{2} m_0 v^2 + \tfrac{3}{8} m_0 \frac{v^4}{c^2} + \ldots$$ (7.14)

whose leading term is the classical formula for the kinetic energy of a particle.

Notice the huge factor c^2 in formula (7.13). How large is the amount of energy which is contained in a piece of ordinary matter, a grain of wheat, a drop of water, or in the pencil

---

† We may also interpret this as follows: E and K are not separately observable. The observable energy is $mc^2 = E - K$. As an application of this, see equation (9.51).

you are holding in your hand? The fantastic energies released by atomic and hydrogen bombs are explained by this formula, by saying that a small fraction of the mass of the material used is converted into energy. Of course, because of the positive definiteness of energy, the mass of a particle is also positive.

According to the mass-energy relation, if two particles are bound together with a certain attractive force, the composite system must have less mass than the sum of the component masses since it takes some energy to separate them again. Indeed, deuteron has less mass than the sum of masses of a neutron and a proton. The difference is called the *mass defect*. It corresponds to the binding energy of the system.

The mass-energy relation makes clear the meaning of the fourth component, $p_4 = imc$, of the momentum. Apart from the factor ic, it represents the energy of the particle. Also, the fourth component, $F_t = (d/dt)\,(imc)$, is, apart from a factor ic, equal to the energy per unit time, that is, the power given to the particle. Using this result, we see that if the rest mass m_0 of the particle is kept constant, the force satisfies

$$F_\mu\,dx^\mu = 0. \qquad (7.15)$$

7.6. The Action Integral for an Isolated Particle

Since the conservation laws apply only to isolated systems, a particle under the influence of an external force does not satisfy them. But when the external force vanishes the particle is isolated and equation (7.6) gives the conservation laws in the form $dp_\mu = 0$. This can also be expressed by saying that a particle left free preserves its energy and momentum. Such a particle will move uniformly in a straight line. This is the expression of *Galileo's Principle of Inertia*. We see that the principle of inertia is a special case of the general conservation principles. We note that in order to express the content of the principles of conservation of energy and momentum we must specify four conditions. One may be interested in expressing these in a *single statement*. To do this, consider the variations δp_μ. These are defined to be variations imagined at will (virtual) so that they do not necessarily vanish. The quantity $\delta p_\mu\,dx^\mu = \alpha$ is a scalar. If we impose the condition $\alpha = 0$, this condition must lead to four statements $\delta p_\mu = 0$, due to the fact that the dx^μ are linearly independent. This shows that if we define an integral

$$A = \int p_\mu\,dx^\mu \qquad (7.16)$$

and impose the condition

$$\delta A = 0, \qquad (7.17)$$

we will obtain our conservation laws. The quantity A is called the *Action*. The condition $\delta A = 0$ tells us that the action integral taken over the actual physical trajectory will be stationary. This statement is called the *principle of stationary action*. It is a single condensed expression of the laws of conservation. In the form considered above we have

$$A = \int_1^2 m_0 \frac{dx^\mu}{d\tau}\,dx_\mu = im_0 c \int_{s_1}^{s_2} ds. \qquad (7.18)$$

Expressed in this way, the condition reduces to $\delta s = 0$, implying that the motion of an isolated particle is such that, between any two points in the four-dimensional space, it follows the shortest possible path, that is, a straight line. Since $ds = ic\,d\tau$ this can be expressed also as being the least possible proper time for the particle.

From the definition of the Action Integral (7.16), we see that the momentum is

$$p_\mu = \frac{\partial A}{\partial x^\mu} \tag{7.19}$$

and putting this into (7.4), we get

$$\left(\frac{\partial A}{\partial x}\right)^2 + \left(\frac{\partial A}{\partial y}\right)^2 + \left(\frac{\partial A}{\partial z}\right)^2 - \frac{1}{c^2}\left(\frac{\partial A}{\partial t}\right)^2 = -m_0^2 c^2. \tag{7.20}$$

This is the Hamilton-Jacobi equation for a relativistic particle. Its classical form may be obtained by separating out the contribution to A of $m_0 c^2$, which is not contained in the classical form

$$A = S - m_0 c^2 t, \tag{7.21}$$

where S is very small as compared to the second term. When we substitute this into (7.20), neglect second-order terms in S, and set $c^2 \to \infty$, we obtain the classical Hamilton-Jacobi equation:

$$\frac{1}{2m}\left[\left(\frac{\partial S}{\partial x}\right)^2 + \left(\frac{\partial S}{\partial y}\right)^2 + \left(\frac{\partial S}{\partial z}\right)^2\right] + \frac{\partial S}{\partial t} = 0. \tag{7.22}$$

The application of the conservation laws and the formulation of the action principle for many-particle systems is complicated. The above, simple forms are not easily generalizable. In fact, to insist on specifying the proper times of individual particles is equivalent to the assumption of permanent particles. In the actual world particles can be created and destroyed. In the following sections we will endeavor to formulate the laws of conservation for an interacting set of particles.

7.7. Interacting Particles in Minkowski Space

There is no essential difficulty, in the theory of relativity, in formulating the conservation principles for systems of particles. The energy-momentum conservation, for example, will simply become

$$dP_\mu = 0, \qquad P_\mu = \sum p_\mu \tag{7.23}$$

where $p_\mu = m_0 u_\mu$. Similarly, the conservation of angular momentum may be expressed as

$$dM_{\mu\nu} = 0, \qquad M_{\mu\nu} = \sum (p_\mu x_\nu - p_\nu x_\mu). \tag{7.24}$$

These laws simply state that the *total energy momentum* P_μ and the *total angular momentum* $M_{\mu\nu}$ of a system never change in time. This statement, of course, is also valid when the particles are in mutual interaction.

In practice the problem usually presents itself in the following form. Initially, there are a number of particles, separated from each other by large distances, so that their interaction is negligible. These particles later converge towards a space-time region where the interaction takes place. They then move away from each other and once again become non-interacting (Figure 7.2). During the period of interaction a number of things can happen. For example, some of the original particles may be transformed into new ones, some may be annihilated, and some others created. Some may simply change their direction, et cetera. Our conservation principles do not tell us anything about how these processes take place. They only state that from the very beginning to the very end the quantities P_μ and

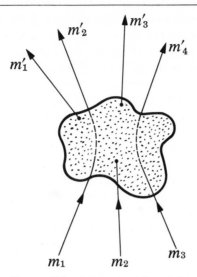

FIGURE 7.2 *Interaction of particles.*

$M_{\mu\nu}$ stay the same. Thus, the *final* values of these quantities are equal to their *initial* values

$$P^{\mu}_{(i)} = P^{\mu}_{(f)} \qquad M^{\mu\nu}_{(i)} = M^{\mu\nu}_{(f)}. \tag{7.25}$$

These statements are powerful tools in practical problems (see Chapter 17, section 3.) In fact, they are among the most secure items of knowledge that we have about the workings of nature. However, as we mentioned above, they do not by themselves determine the way the interaction takes place although, of course, any acceptable hypothesis of interaction must be consistent with them. The problems of how various particles interact and what goes on during the interaction are not completely understood. Today, various possible approaches are being investigated. Later, we will have occasion to discuss these somewhat; the field theory approach especially, will be described at some length.

The way of thinking usually followed in treating interactions is that, in the region of interaction, energy-momentum and angular momentum are being transferred among the particles. Now, according to the theory of relativity, this transfer cannot take place with infinite speed. Therefore, during the interaction there will be some energy momentum and angular momentum in the space between particles. These are quantities which have left some particles and have not as yet reached other particles. We call these the interaction energy-momentum and angular momentum. Thus, in the interaction region, the conservation laws must refer not to the particles alone but to particles plus interaction. The quantities to be conserved are, therefore,

$$P^{\mu} = P^{\mu}_{(p)} + P^{\mu}_{(\text{int})} \qquad M^{\mu\nu} = M^{\mu\nu}_{(p)} + M^{\mu\nu}_{(\text{int})}. \tag{7.26}$$

Henceforth, we shall always understand the conservation laws in this form: namely, when there is interaction the energy-momentum and angular momentum of the agents causing the interaction must be added to those of the particles. The sum total is the quantity that is conserved. When particles are separated by large distances the interaction energy-momentum and interaction angular momentum vanish. Therefore, if initially and finally these conditions are satisfied, equations (7.25) are valid without any modification. In this case, of course, *i* and *f* refer to the infinite past and the infinite future, respectively.

Here, we may point out that the above formulation of the conservation laws is better suited to particles. If matter-energy is continuously distributed in space, a different approach may be better suited for the problem. Of course, the content and the philosophy behind the two formulations would always be the same, although the formulas may now take different forms. In fact, the continuous distributions may be considered as a limiting case of discrete particles, where in each volume element the number of point particles tends to infinity while the mass of each tends to zero. Conversely, a point particle may be looked at as a limiting case of a continuous distribution where at some points (the locations of the particles) the densities become infinitely large. With this understanding, we now consider the energy density $H(x)$. We usually write as the total energy $\mathscr{E} = \int H(x)\, dV$, where dV is the volume element. But this expression is unsatisfactory for two reasons. First, dV is the fourth component of a four-dimensional surface element $dS^4 = dV = dx\, dy\, dz$. For relativistic reasons we must make use of all the components dS^μ. Second, the energy is the fourth component of a vector, the energy-momentum vector. Thus, the general form of the expression for the energy-momentum vector must be of the form (see Chapter 6)

$$P_\mu = \frac{i}{c} \int T_{\mu\nu}\, dS^\nu, \tag{7.27}$$

which reduces to $\mathscr{E} = \int T_{44}\, dV$ when the volume element and the matter in it are at rest. From this it can also be seen that $H(x) = T_{44}$ must always be *positive*. We assume that, in general, the energy-momentum of interaction is also *included* in the tensor so that $T_{\mu\nu}$ includes the whole system. We see that the local densities must form a second order tensor $T_{\mu\nu}(x)$. In a particular coordinate system (volume elements at rest), we then have $P_4 = i/c \int T_{44}\, dV$ and $P_i = i/c \int T_{i4}\, dV$, which shows that T_{44} is the energy density and T_{i4} is the momentum density. The other components, T_{ik}, are usually interpreted as stresses. $T_{\mu\nu}$ is called the *stress-energy tensor*. One may wonder how point particles may be regained from these definitions. For this we assume that at the point where the particle is situated the density becomes infinitely large. For example,

$$P_4 = imc = \frac{i}{c} \int T_{44}\, dV$$

requires a singular distribution, $T_{44} = mc^2\delta(x - x')$, where $\delta(x - x')$ is the Dirac δ-function (see Chapter 6). Thus, actually the $T_{\mu\nu}$ are general enough to describe energy concentrations in the form of (classical) particles.

We now come to the formulation of the conservation laws of energy and momentum. We require

$$dP_\mu = \frac{i}{c} d \int T_{\mu\nu}\, dS^\nu = 0. \tag{7.28}$$

This can be written as

$$dP_\mu = \frac{i}{c} \int \partial^\nu T_{\mu\nu}\, d\Omega = 0, \tag{7.29}$$

from which

$$\partial^\nu T_{\mu\nu} = 0. \tag{7.30}$$

This is the differential form of the conservation of energy-momentum.

We now can proceed to formulate the conservation of angular momentum. We define the angular momentum covariantly as

$$M_{\mu\nu} = \frac{i}{c} \int (T_{\sigma\mu} x_\nu - T_{\sigma\nu} x_\mu) \, dS^\sigma \tag{7.31}$$

Similarly, for this quantity to be conserved the divergence of the expression inside the parentheses must vanish,

$$\partial^\sigma (T_{\sigma\mu} x_\nu - T_{\sigma\nu} x_\mu) = 0, \tag{7.32}$$

which after using (7.30) leads to

$$T_{\sigma\mu} \frac{\partial x_\nu}{\partial x_\sigma} - T_{\sigma\nu} \frac{\partial x_\mu}{\partial x_\sigma} = 0.$$

Now since $\partial x_\nu / \partial x_\sigma = \delta_\nu^\sigma$, we have the equivalent statement for angular-momentum conservation,

$$T_{\nu\mu} = T_{\mu\nu}. \tag{7.33}$$

In other words, the stress-energy tensor must be symmetrical. Equations (7.30) and (7.33) summarize the conservation laws of energy-momentum and angular momentum.

Before we conclude this chapter we would like to try to develop some familiarity and insight into the structure of the stress-energy tensor. As we have pointed out earlier, T_{44} represents the energy density and T_{4k} represents the momentum density. So far, we have not said anything about the T_{ik} components, that is, the space part of the tensor where i, $k = 1, 2, 3$.

$$P_k = \frac{i}{c} \int (T_{k1} \, dy \, dz + T_{k2} \, dx \, dz + T_{k3} \, dx \, dy) c \, dt + \frac{i}{c} \int T_{k4} \, dV \tag{7.34}$$

or

$$\frac{dP_k}{dt} = \int (T_{k1} \, dy \, dz + T_{k2} \, dx \, dz + T_{k3} \, dx \, dy) + \frac{i}{c} \frac{d}{dt} \int T_{k4} \, dV. \tag{7.35}$$

We notice here that dP_i/dt, that is, the force, separated into two parts. The second part is the rate of change of momentum contained in the volume V. The first part may be written as

$$f_i = \int T_{ik} \, dS^k, \qquad i, k = 1, 2, 3. \tag{7.36}$$

This expression is identical with the definition of the force due to elastic stresses in an elastic medium. Therefore, T_{ik}, the space components of the stress-energy tensor, represent stresses, pressures, and shear forces in the space in which the continuous matter-energy distributions exist. The elements of T_{ik} are written as

$$T_{ik} = \begin{pmatrix} T_{11} & T_{12} & T_{13} \\ T_{21} & T_{22} & T_{23} \\ T_{31} & T_{32} & T_{33} \end{pmatrix}. \tag{7.37}$$

Of course, T_{ik} is symmetric, $T_{ik} = T_{ki}$, as is the case for the complete $T_{\mu\nu}$. The diagonal elements T_{ii} are stresses or pressures and the off-diagonal elements, T_{12}, T_{32}, et cetera, are shear forces.

The angular momentum $M^{\mu\nu}$ is an antisymmetric tensor as is evident from its definition. Its space components M_{ik} are the usual angular momenta. For example, in a fixed volume we have

$$M^3 = M_{12} = \frac{i}{c} \int (T^{41}y - T^{42}x)\, dV. \tag{7.38}$$

The space-time component for example, M^{14}, is

$$M^{k4} = \frac{i}{c} \int (T^{44}x^k - T^{4k}ict)\, dV$$

$$= \frac{i}{c} \int T^{44}x^k\, dV - ict \int T^{4k}\, dV,$$

which may be written as

$$M^{k4} = \frac{i}{c}(\mathscr{E}X^k - c^2 tP^k) \tag{7.39}$$

with

$$\mathscr{E}X^k = \int T^{44}x^k\, dV, \qquad P^k = \frac{i}{c}\int T^{4k}\, dV \tag{7.40}$$

where X^k is the center of mass, $\mathscr{E}$ the energy, and P^k the momentum of the system. Since M^{i4}, $\mathscr{E}$, and P^i are all constants, we have

$$\frac{dX^i}{dt} = \frac{c^2 P^i}{\mathscr{E}}. \tag{7.41}$$

This important result tells us that the center of mass of an isolated system moves with constant velocity in all inertial frames. Note, however, that the definition of center of mass

$$X^i = \frac{1}{c^2}\int T_{44}x^i\, dV \tag{7.42}$$

is not an invariant expression. The center of mass relative to one inertial frame does not in general coincide with the center of mass in a different inertial frame. Combining these facts regarding the motion, we see that it is always possible to transform from an inertial frame to the center-of-mass frame of a system by a Lorentz transformation plus a translation. This theorem facilitates the treatment of a large number of practical problems. In particular if two particles move so as to collide, the coincidence being an invariant concept, the transformation and the description of this situation simplifies even further. Because of this, the treatment of a large number of particles colliding two at a time may be reduced in complexity.

Summary: Particle Dynamics in Minkowski Space

(a) The basic principles of dynamics are the conservation of energy-momentum and of angular momentum.

(b) Another basic principle is the positive definiteness of energy: the energy of an isolated system is always positive.

(c) Elementary particles cannot be extended bodies. They must be point particles if the classical motion of an elementary particle is to be retained.

(d) The mass of a particle is not constant. It varies with the velocity according to

$$m = m_0/\sqrt{1 - v^2/c^2},$$

(e) The mass of a body is a measure of its energy. They are related by

$$E = mc^2.$$

(f) An interaction between two systems implies, in general, transfer of energy momentum and angular momentum from one to the other.

(g) The energy-momentum of a system may be thought of as distributed in space. The density functions representing the distribution are the elements of the stress-energy tensor.

(h) The stress-energy tensor must be divergence-free and symmetric in order to assure the conservation of energy-momentum and angular momentum.

8

THE FIELD CONCEPT

8.1. The Field Concept

In the previous chapter we formulated the principles of conservation of energy-momentum and angular momentum. These laws are general and apply to all forms of matter and energy. As applied to particles in interaction, they suggest that during the interaction energy-momentum and angular momentum are transferred from one particle to another, although they do not tell us anything about the mechanism of the interaction itself. The theory of relativity tells us that this transfer cannot take place with infinite speed, but must be propagated with at most the velocity, c. Therefore, as a possible mechanism for the interaction, we may introduce a new element, ϕ, which satisfies a propagation equation and carries energy-momentum and angular momentum between particles. Since the total energy and momentum are conserved, the quantity, ϕ, which we call a *field*, must evidently take full possession of the part being carried and thus act as an independent dynamical element with its own degrees of freedom. From this point of view the interaction energy-momentum and angular momentum must be identified with those of the field. We may therefore write

$$dP^\mu = 0; \qquad P^\mu = P^\mu_{(p)} + P^\mu_{(f)} \tag{8.1}$$

$$dM^\mu = 0; \qquad M^\mu = M^\mu_{(p)} + M^\mu_{(f)} \tag{8.2}$$

where (p) and (f) refer to particles and fields, respectively. One may be tempted to assume that $P^\mu_{(f)}$ and $M^\mu_{(f)}$ are strictly interaction quantities without any meaning on their own account. This, however, is not the case. Since the field is an independent dynamical element, it can exist even when no particles are present. In fact, the field and its associated energy, momentum, et cetera, can exist in a region far from any particles. In this case the field is said to be a *radiation field*. Electromagnetic radiation or light, for example, is an electromagnetic field which has escaped from the region of interacting electrical particles. Splitting the conserved quantities into two parts and recognizing them as belonging to particles and fields is an essential step, but it is still too general to provide a specific mechanism of interaction. We must therefore look for additional statements or *principles* which specify further the general properties which the fields must possess and the particular kind of equation each field must satisfy. One such condition is immediately provided by the principle of the positive definiteness of energy. Since this principle states that the energy of an isolated system is positive, a radiation field must have positive energy. Thus, when no particles are present, the field energy, $P^4_{(f)}$, must never be negative. A second requirement is the so-called principle of *causality*. According to this principle *no observable influence is transmitted from a point Q to a point Q' in less time than $\overline{QQ'}/c$.* In Section 8.6, this principle will be formulated in a usable form. *Together with the principle of relativity and conservation laws, the positive definiteness of energy and the principle of causality are the general principles* *that all fields must satisfy.* In addition, each field, according to its structure, satisfies a propagation equation, although this is not completely independent of the above requirements. These equations, of course, must be chosen so as to provide a reasonable basis for the calculation of the various physical processes.

As we have seen in Chapter 6, there are many types of fields which may be considered. Since this chapter is only an introduction to the ways of thinking and the methods of calculation used in field theory, we consider the simplest case, namely, the case of a scalar field, $\phi(x)$, where x represents all four coordinates unless otherwise stated. The simplest possible relativistic propagation equation for a scalar field is

$$\partial_\mu \partial^\mu \phi = \left(\frac{\partial^2}{\partial x^2} + \frac{\partial^2}{\partial y^2} + \frac{\partial^2}{\partial z^2} - \frac{1}{c^2} \frac{\partial^2}{\partial t^2} \right) \phi = 0. \tag{8.3}$$

This is a scalar field which propagates with the velocity of light; we have some familiarity with such an equation from Chapter 4. But, unfortunately, a scalar field propagating with the velocity of light is not observed in nature.† The next simplest relativistic equation is

$$(\partial_\mu \partial^\mu - \kappa^2)\phi = 0 \tag{8.4}$$

where κ is a constant. The so-called meson field, which is believed to carry the nuclear interaction, is described by such a field. Although a little more complicated mathematically than the case with $\kappa = 0$, we will start our considerations with this equation. Thus we will be dealing with something which we believe to be physical. However, we may set $\kappa = 0$ any time we wish and obtain the result corresponding to the simpler but more speculative situation.

8.2. The Stress-Energy Tensor of the Scalar Field

In order to find the stress-energy tensor of the scalar field, let us consider a region of space where no particles are present. Since in this region there is no transfer of energy-momentum to or from the particles, the field itself must satisfy the conservation requirements. Thus, for such a region the stress-energy tensor, $T^{\mu\nu}$, of the field satisfies

$$\partial_\mu T^{\mu\nu} = 0; \qquad T^{\mu\nu} = T^{\nu\mu}.$$

Furthermore, these equations must be satisfied as a result of the field equation (8.4), and not because of some identities or unrelated reasons. Hence, $\partial_\mu T^{\mu\nu}$ must have the form

$$\partial_\mu T^{\mu\nu} = G^\nu (\partial_\mu \partial^\mu - \kappa^2)\phi \tag{8.5}$$

where G^ν is a nonzero vector depending on the field, ϕ, and its derivatives. These show that $T^{\mu\nu}$ must depend on ϕ and at least on its first derivatives. Our problem is to find a symmetric tensor $T^{\mu\nu}$ $(\phi, \partial_\mu \phi, \dots)$ satisfying the above requirements. A simple calculation shows that the tensor,

$$T^{\mu\nu} = -\frac{1}{4\pi} \{ \partial^\mu \phi \, \partial^\mu \phi - \tfrac{1}{2} \delta^{\mu\nu} (\partial_\alpha \phi \, \partial^\alpha \phi + \kappa^2 \phi^2) \}, \tag{8.6}$$

† Those who believe that nature always realizes the simplest possible forms ought to ponder this fact!

has all these properties. Written explicitly, the components are:

$$T_{11} = \frac{1}{8\pi}\left\{\left(\frac{\partial\phi}{\partial x}\right)^2 - \left(\frac{\partial\phi}{\partial y}\right)^2 - \left(\frac{\partial\phi}{\partial z}\right)^2 - \frac{1}{c^2}\left(\frac{\partial\phi}{\partial t}\right)^2 - \kappa^2\phi^2\right\}$$

$$T_{12} = \frac{1}{4\pi}\frac{\partial\phi}{\partial x}\frac{\partial\phi}{\partial y}, \qquad T_{14} = \frac{1}{4\pi}\frac{1}{ic}\frac{\partial\phi}{\partial x}\frac{\partial\phi}{\partial t},$$

$$T_{44} = \frac{1}{8\pi}\left\{\left(\frac{\partial\phi}{\partial x}\right)^2 + \left(\frac{\partial\phi}{\partial y}\right)^2 + \left(\frac{\partial\phi}{\partial z}\right)^2 + \frac{1}{c^2}\left(\frac{\partial\phi}{\partial t}\right)^2 + \kappa^2\phi^2\right\}, \text{ etc.}$$

Furthermore, when the sign is chosen as indicated, the energy density T^{44} of the field is positive definite. Therefore, we will take this as the stress-energy tensor of the field. The quantities P^μ and $M^{\mu\nu}$ are now given as

$$P^\mu = \frac{i}{c}\int T^{\mu\alpha}\,dS_\alpha, \tag{8.7}$$

$$M^{\mu\nu} = \frac{i}{c}\int(T^{\alpha\mu}x^\nu - T^{\alpha\nu}x^\mu)\,dS_\alpha. \tag{8.8}$$

Note also that with this tensor $G^\nu = \partial^\nu\phi$.

8.3. Equations of Motion of Particles in a Field

Notice that as long as the field satisfies equation (8.4) the energy-momentum of the field itself is conserved, and therefore it cannot transfer energy-momentum to or from the particles. In other words, (8.4) describes the case of no interaction. Therefore, in regions of space containing particles, that is, where the interaction takes place, we must have $\partial_\mu T^{\mu\nu} \neq 0$. From the form of (8.5) we now see that in such regions we must have the more general equation

$$(\partial_\mu\partial^\mu - \kappa^2)\phi(x) = 4\pi\sigma(x) \tag{8.9}$$

where $\sigma(x)$ is a scalar function. This function represents the physical agent situated on the particles that is causing the interaction. It is similar to the electric charge which causes electrons to take up energy and momentum when placed in an electric field. In general, we call $\sigma(x)$ the *source* or the *charge* density. With this, the formulation of the scalar field theory is practically complete in its classical form. We will now start developing the consequences of this theory.

First, we consider the problem of the equations of motion of particles. These will be deduced from the conservation of energy and momentum. Since *when no radiation exists,* the system of particles plus the field is an isolated system, we have

$$dP^\mu = d\sum m_0\frac{dx^\mu}{d\tau} + \frac{i}{c}d\int T^{\mu\alpha}\,dS_\alpha = 0. \tag{8.10}$$

The second term may be evaluated as

$$d\int T^{\mu\alpha}\,dS_\alpha = \int\partial_\alpha T^{\mu\alpha}\,d\Omega = \int\partial^\mu\phi(\partial^\alpha\partial_\alpha - \kappa^2)\phi\,d\Omega.$$

Now substituting $\sigma(x)$ and writing $d\Omega = ic\,dV_0\,d\tau$, we can carry out the integration for the regions where particles are situated. Since the particles are point-like, $\int\sigma\,dV_0 \to \epsilon$, where ϵ

is the source strength of the particle (analogous to electric charge), giving

$$d \sum m_0 \frac{dx^\mu}{d\tau} + \sum \epsilon \, \partial^\mu \phi \, d\tau = 0.$$

Therefore, for each particle we have

$$m_0 \frac{d^2 x^\mu}{d\tau^2} = -\epsilon \frac{\partial \phi}{\partial x^\mu}. \tag{8.11}$$

Note that this equation is the relativistic form of the familiar Newtonian equations. The solution of the problem of motion is in general *not* easy. The difficulty is that the motion of the particles depends on the field and the field in turn depends on the positions and motions of the particles. Thus, the problem becomes one of solving the coupled set of equations:

$$m_0 \frac{d^2 x^\mu}{d\tau^2} = -\epsilon \frac{\partial \phi}{\partial x^\mu}; \qquad (\partial^\mu \partial^\mu - \kappa^2)\phi = 4\pi\sigma. \tag{8.12}$$

This is difficult. Besides, radiation is neglected here. When radiation is also considered, the problem becomes even more complicated.

In certain special cases, however, the problem becomes easy. For example, if the field is static, as in the case of a very heavy body, the radiation term vanishes. Furthermore, if the heavy body carries a very large charge, the other particles do not influence the field much. In this case, the particles can be considered to move in a given external field. Then equations (8.11) alone apply. In the next chapter, the problem of motion will be treated from this point of view.

8.4. Solutions of the Wave Equation

In this section we will discuss the solutions of the wave equation

$$(\partial_\mu \partial^\mu - \kappa^2)\phi = 0. \tag{8.13}$$

This is a second-order, homogeneous partial differential equation. To find its general solution we will use the following relativistic argument: Let us choose a particular coordinate system in which the field depends only on the time, $\phi = \phi(t)$. The equation then reduces to

$$\frac{d^2 \phi}{dt^2} + c^2 \kappa^2 \phi = 0 \tag{8.14}$$

which represents a simple harmonic vibration. The solution of this equation is well known. It is of the form $A \cos(\omega_0 t + \alpha)$ or $A \cos \omega_0 t + B \sin \omega_0 t$ with $\omega_0 = c\kappa$. We will write it in an equivalent form,

$$\phi(t) = a e^{-i\omega_0 t} + a^* e^{i\omega_0 t}, \qquad \omega_0 = c\kappa, \tag{8.15}$$

where a and a^* are the two integration constants and, in general, complex numbers. Since, however, our field is *real*, a^* must be the complex conjugate of a. This solution, of course, refers to the particular reference frame where the wave equation reduces to (8.14). By a Lorentz transformation, we can transform both the function (8.15) and the equation (8.14) into a new reference frame. The transformed function will be a solution of the transformed equation. Consider, for example, a reference frame moving uniformly in the z-direction relative to the original frame. By substituting $t \to (t - vz/c^2)/\sqrt{1 - v^2/c^2}$, we have

$$\phi(z, t) = a e^{i(kz - \omega t)} + a^* e^{-i(kz - \omega t)} \tag{8.16}$$

where

$$\omega = \frac{\omega_0}{\sqrt{1 - v^2/c^2}}, \quad k = \frac{\omega_0 v/c^2}{\sqrt{1 - v^2/c^2}}, \quad \omega^2 = \omega_0^2 + c^2 k^2,$$

while equation (8.14) becomes

$$\left(\frac{\partial^2}{\partial z^2} - \frac{1}{c^2} \frac{\partial^2}{\partial t^2} - \kappa^2 \right) \phi = 0. \tag{8.17}$$

Here, k is called the *propagation vector* or *wave number*. The name, wave number, comes from the fact that if we represent the wave as $A \cos 2\pi(\nu t - z/\lambda + \alpha)$ as we sometimes do, then $k = 2\pi/\lambda$ is 2π times the number of waves per unit length. It is easy to show that the new solution (8.16) does indeed represent a propagation. For this purpose, we write it as

$$\phi(z, t) = a \exp\left[-i\omega\left(t - \frac{z}{V_p} \right) \right] + a^* \exp\left[i\omega\left(t - \frac{z}{V_p} \right) \right] \tag{8.18}$$

which can be put into the form $A \cos \omega(t - \dfrac{z}{V_p} + \alpha)$. From this we see that the wave appears to propagate in the z-direction with the *phase velocity*, V_p.

$$V_p = c^2/v. \tag{8.19}$$

The velocity of propagation seems to exceed the velocity of light, which is contrary to the principle of causality. We will show, however, in the next section that the field energy does not move with the speed V_p, but that it moves with the speed v. Since it is the actual exchange of energy and momentum which causes physical processes, the principle of causality is therefore not violated.

It is evident from the above example that we can generate new solutions by applying new Lorentz transformations, that is, translations, rotations, and reflections. For example, a translation by the amount z_0 changes the phase by kz_0 which in turn may be absorbed into the a and a^*. Reflection of z is equivalent to changing $k_z \to -k_z$, et cetera. Furthermore, since equation (8.13) is linear in ϕ, these solutions can be added to give new solutions. Thus we see that all the solutions of the wave equation can be obtained by applying all possible Lorentz transformations followed by a summation. Hence, the integral

$$\phi(x) = \int_{-\infty}^{+\infty} (a(k) e^{ikx} + a^*(k) e^{-ikx}) \, d^3k \tag{8.20}$$

where

$$\begin{aligned}
x &= (x, y, z, ict) \\
k &= (k_x, k_y, k_z, i\omega/c) \\
kx &= k_x x + k_y y + k_z z - \omega t \\
k^2 &= k_x^2 + k_y^2 + k_z^2 - \frac{\omega^2}{c^2} = \kappa^2 \\
d^3k &= dk_1 \, dk_2 \, dk_3
\end{aligned} \tag{8.21}$$

is the most general solution. This method of finding solutions to wave equations is very general and valid for all fields. For the case $\kappa = 0$ see Chapter 10.

It is to be understood that $a(k)$ is any function of k. The property of linear wave equations that a linear combination of any number of solutions is again a solution is called the *principle of superposition*. The separation of the wave function into the $(+)$ and $(-)$ frequency parts

$$\phi(x) = \phi(x)^{(+)} + \phi(x)^{(-)}$$

where

$$\phi(x)^{(+)} = \int_{-\infty}^{+\infty} a(k)e^{ikx}\, d^3k, \qquad \phi(x)^{(-)} = \int_{-\infty}^{+\infty} a^*(k)e^{-ikx}\, d^3k \qquad (8.22)$$

is invariant under proper Lorentz transformations, although some reflections may mix the two. This separation leads in quantum field theory to the particle-antiparticle concept, but we note carefully that here the negative frequency part does not at all lead to a negative energy. The energy of a scalar field as defined by (8.6) is always positive definite.

The above solutions of the wave equation are written in the Cartesian coordinate system. For certain calculations, such as scattering or radiation, solutions in a spherical coordinate system may be more convenient. To obtain such solutions, one either solves the wave equation in a spherical coordinate system

$$\left(\frac{1}{r^2}\frac{\partial}{\partial r}r^2\frac{\partial}{\partial r} + \frac{1}{r^2\sin\theta}\frac{\partial}{\partial\theta}\sin\theta\frac{\partial}{\partial\theta} + \frac{1}{r^2\sin^2\theta}\frac{\partial^2}{\partial\phi^2} - \frac{1}{c^2}\frac{\partial^2}{\partial t^2} - \kappa^2\right)\phi = 0 \qquad (8.23)$$

or transforms the solution (8.20) into a spherical coordinate system by the transformations

$$\begin{aligned} x &= r\sin\theta\cos\phi \\ y &= r\sin\theta\sin\phi \\ z &= r\cos\theta \end{aligned} \qquad (8.24)$$

with similar equations for k_x, k_y, k_z. In particular, we need

$$d^3k = dk_1\, dk_2\, dk_3 = k^2\, dk\sin\theta\, d\theta\, d\phi. \qquad (8.25)$$

Either of these methods will yield solutions of the type (see Appendix A, $a(k)$ is not arbitrary).

$$\phi(x) = \frac{\mathfrak{f}(\theta, \phi)}{r}\{\alpha e^{i(\omega t - kr)} + \alpha^* e^{-i(\omega t - kr)}\} \qquad (8.26)$$

where $\omega^2 = \omega_0^2 + c^2k^2$, and $\mathfrak{f}(\theta, \phi)$ satisfy the equation

$$\left(\frac{\partial}{\partial\theta}\sin\theta\frac{\partial}{\partial\theta} + \frac{1}{\sin\theta}\frac{\partial^2}{\partial\phi^2}\right)\mathfrak{f}(\theta, \phi) = 0. \qquad (8.27)$$

As is well known, the solutions of this last equation are the spherical harmonics and hence spherical harmonics specify the angular dependence of the waves. In particular, if the field is not angle-dependent (a spherically symmetric field) we have the form

$$\phi(r, t) = \frac{1}{r}\{Ae^{i(\omega t - kr)} + A^* e^{-i(\omega t - kr)}\}, \qquad (8.28)$$

† There are many good books on spherical harmonics. *Methods of Theoretical Physics* by P. M. Morse and H. Feshback (New York: McGraw-Hill Book Co., Inc., 1953), chapter 6, treats the problem of solutions of wave equations in a complete manner.

which satisfies the spherical wave equation

$$\left(\frac{1}{r^2}\frac{\partial}{\partial r}r^2\frac{\partial}{\partial r} - \frac{1}{c^2}\frac{\partial^2}{\partial t^2} - \kappa^2\right)\phi(r, t) = 0. \tag{8.29}$$

Here again, $\omega^2 = c^2\kappa^2 + c^2k^2$. If in addition, the field is time-independent, we have $\omega = 0$, so $k = \pm i\kappa$, leading to a form

$$\phi = \frac{1}{r}(Ae^{-\kappa r} + A'e^{+\kappa r}) \tag{8.30}$$

where A and A' are *real* numbers not necessarily equal. The second term is not acceptable as a solution since it increases indefinitely at large distances. The physically meaningful solution here is of the form†

$$\phi(r) = \frac{Ae^{-\kappa r}}{r}. \tag{8.31}$$

This is the so-called Yukawa potential. Static nuclei are supposed to generate such fields. It can be shown that A is equal to the source strength ϵ of the particle. When $\kappa = 0$, the Yukawa potential reduces to A/r, the Coulomb or Newtonian type as it is expected. Due to the exponential factor the Yukawa potential is short-ranged, the range being defined as $l = 1/\kappa$. Since the nuclear forces are known to be short-ranged, physicists currently believe that they are caused by a field of this type.

In 1935 the Japanese physicist H. Yukawa conjectured that the short-range nuclear forces might arise from such a field. Since the range of nuclear forces is estimated from various sources to be about $l \simeq 1.5 \times 10^{-13}$ cm, Yukawa determined the constant κ to be $\kappa \simeq 7 \times 10^{12}$ cm.$^{-1}$. As we will see in Section 8.6, κ is related to the rest mass of the particle which the field describes. The relation is $\kappa = 2\pi m_0 c/h$ where m_0 is the rest mass of the particle and h is Planck's constant. Therefore, Yukawa predicted that a particle of rest mass $m_0 \simeq 1.8 \times 10^{-25}$ gm (that is, about 200 times the electron mass) must exist if the above conjecture is valid. Indeed, a particle of about 270 electron masses was discovered and called the π-meson. It is also found that there are three kinds of π-meson: π^0, π^+, and π^-, that is, one neutral, one positively charged, and one negatively charged. Although there is no detailed method of calculation available at the present time to extract all the information concerning the nuclear forces, it is believed that the mechanism is fundamentally the π-meson field. The name meson comes from the fact that its mass is intermediate (meso) between the electron and the proton. The content of the present chapter will correspond mainly to a treatment of the neutral, π^0-meson. This particle is described by a real field. The charged π-mesons, on the other hand, require complex fields. For a complex field the integration constants in equation (8.15) would become a and b^*.

8.5. Green's Function Representation of the Solutions

In this section, the solutions of the wave equation will be studied from a different point of view. Although it is equivalent to that of the previous section, the present method will

---

† At first sight it may appear that A and A' in (8.30) have to be equal. This is not so because in (8.28) $A = f(k) + ig(k)$, $A^* = f(k) - ig(k)$. But when $k \to -i\kappa$ both A and A' have to be real. We conclude that $f(k)$ must be an even, and $g(k)$, an odd function of k. Then $A \to f + g$, $A' \to f - g$, so that the choice $f = g$ leads to $A' \to 0$, $A \to 2f$. Thus we see that although we have originally taken a time-dependent solution as (8.15), the superposition of the transforms of this solution is capable of representing even purely space dependent solutions like (8.31). The above relations can be stated as $A(k) = A^*(-k)$ for real k.

bring to light some very important features which are not explicit in the previous method. Again we start by pointing out that the equation

$$(\partial_\mu \partial^\mu - \kappa^2)\phi = 0 \tag{8.32}$$

is a second-order equation and hence its solution must have two arbitrary integration constants. From elementary physics courses, we know that the two integration constants must be chosen so as to satisfy the initial conditions. This is done by giving the initial position and velocity of the system. Here we can do something analogous to this. Let the function $\phi(x)$ and its derivatives $\partial_\mu \phi(x)$ have at the point x' the "initial" and "boundary" values $\phi(x')$ and $\partial'_\mu \phi(x')$. As $x \to x'$ the conditions $\phi(x) \to \phi(x')$ and $\partial_\mu \phi(x) \to \partial'_\mu \phi(x')$ must clearly be satisfied. We look for a solution $\phi(x)$ of the form

$$\phi(x) = \int \{G(x - x') \, \partial'_\mu \phi(x') - \phi(x') \, \partial'_\mu G(x - x')\} \, dS'^\mu. \tag{8.33}$$

Now, in order that $\phi(x)$ be a solution of the wave equation, the function $G(x - x')$ must be a solution of the same wave equation with x as its variable. This and the two other conditions on $\phi(x)$ lead to the defining equations for $G(x - x')$:

$$(\partial_\mu \partial^\mu - \kappa^2)G(x - x') = 0$$
$$\partial'_\mu G(x - x') = -\delta_\mu(x - x') \tag{8.34}$$
$$G(x - x') = 0 \text{ for } x - x' = 0.$$

To solve the inhomogeneous field equation

$$(\partial_\mu \partial^\mu - \kappa^2)\phi(x) = \sigma(x), \tag{8.35}$$

the first of these conditions is generalized as

$$(\partial_\mu \partial^\mu - \kappa^2)G(x - x') = -\delta(x - x') \tag{8.36}$$

so that the solution becomes

$$\phi(x) = \int \sigma(x')G(x - x') \, d\Omega' + \int \{G(x - x') \, \partial'_\mu \phi(x') - \partial'_\mu G(x - x')\phi(x')\} \, dS'^\mu. \tag{8.37}$$

This is the general solution of the field equation. As is well known the general solution of a linear inhomogeneous differential equation is obtained by adding a special solution of the inhomogeneous equation to the general solution of the homogeneous part. The above form does exactly this, the first term being the special solution. The function $G(x - x')$ is called the *Green's Function* and has many useful applications. Here, for simplicity, we have written $4\pi\sigma \to \sigma$.

8.6. The Principle of Causality

When one considers all the possible solutions of the field equations, one sees that some of these solutions may violate the so-called causality principle. This principle states that *from one point to another, physical effects cannot travel faster than with the velocity of light.* Let a wave start out from r' and reach r. We must have the condition that $\phi(r')$ is zero for times smaller than $t = |r - r'|/c$. Only such waves are acceptable. Since the principle involves two points, x and x', rather than one single point, it should be easier to formulate it with the help of the Green's function solutions introduced in the previous section. Indeed,

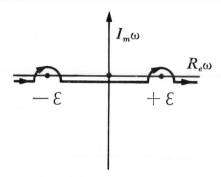

FIGURE 8.1   *Complex ω-plane.*

the principle of causality would be satisfied if

$$G(x - x') = 0 \text{ for } |x - x'|^2 < 0. \tag{8.38}$$

Therefore, the defining equations of $G(x - x')$ may now be written as

$$(\partial_\mu \partial^\mu - \kappa^2)G(x - x') = -\delta(x - x')$$

$$\partial'_\mu G(x - x') = -\delta_\mu(x - x') \tag{8.39}$$

$$G(x - x') = 0 \text{ for } |x - x'| \leqslant 0.$$

The problem of how to determine the Green's function $G(x - x')$ from these conditions is treated in Appendix A. Here, for the sake of completeness, we write it as the relativistically invariant integral

$$G(x - x') = \frac{1}{(2\pi)^4} \int \frac{d^4 k e^{ik(x-x')}}{k^2 + \kappa^2} \tag{8.40}$$

The ω integration is to be carried out first. In order to give a meaning to the integral, the contour followed must be specified. Different contours result in different conditions on the Green's function. It is shown in Appendix A that the contour traced in Figure 8.1 corresponds to our conditions (8.39) if closed in the upper plane for $t < t'$, and in the lower plane for $t > t'$. Thus, for $t < t'$ the function vanishes (causality). For $t > t'$ the $\pm$ poles contribute $(+)$ and $(-)$ frequency parts respectively. If the contour is closed in the lower plane for $t < t'$ and in the upper plane for $t > t'$ the integral leads physically unacceptable solutions.

It is clear from the above development that the principle of causality only results in a restriction on the possible solutions of the field equations. It is, however, one of the most profound properties of our physical world, controlling the cause and effect relationships so deeply imbedded even in our psychological make-up.

One of the immediate consequences of the principle of causality is the so-called *retarded potential* concept. To see this in its simplest form, let us consider the solution (8.28). If the waves are being generated at the center of the coordinate system, $r \to 0$, then at any other point the energy must arrive at a time t *later*; not before the waves are generated.

Thus, in (8.28) k must be positive. Any summation of such waves must therefore be taken from 0 to $+\infty$.

$$\phi(r, t) = \int_0^\infty \frac{1}{r} \{Ae^{i(\omega t - kr)} + A^* e^{-i(\omega t - kr)}\} \, d^3k \tag{8.41}$$

If the argument were of the form $i(\omega t + kr)$ or $i\omega(t + r/V)$, the field energy could reach other points before the waves were generated, thereby violating the principle of *causality*. Such unphysical waves are called *advanced potentials*.

A very important consequence of the causality principle is the analytic property of the expression $e^{ikx}/(k^2 + \kappa^2)$ as a function of the frequency, $\omega = ck_4$, which will be explained in Appendix A.

8.7. Motion of the Field Energy

We mentioned earlier that a stationary oscillation (8.15) appears to be propagated with the phase velocity $V_p = c^2/v > c$ when viewed from a reference frame moving with the velocity v. The question then arises: With what velocity does the field energy move? To answer this question, we may take a volume in the stationary system, define the center of inertia, X, of the energy contained therein, and study how this center moves. As previously derived, the center of inertia of any system has the velocity

$$\frac{dX}{dt} = \frac{c^2 P_x}{\mathscr{E}}. \tag{8.42}$$

Now, from the definition of momentum and energy for a single plane wave, $\phi = ae^{ikx} + a^* e^{-ikx}$, we have

$$P_x = \int Q k_x k_\mu \, dS^\mu, \qquad \mathscr{E} = \int Q \omega k_\mu \, dS^\mu \tag{8.43}$$

where

$$Q = (ae^{ikx} - a^* e^{-ikx})^2; \qquad k_\mu k^\mu = \kappa^2. \tag{8.44}$$

Thus,

$$\frac{dX}{dt} = \frac{c^2 P_x}{\mathscr{E}} = \frac{c^2 k_x}{\omega} \tag{8.45}$$

which, using (8.16), gives

$$\frac{dX}{dt} = v. \tag{8.46}$$

This shows that the field energy moves with the physical velocity, v, and not with the phase velocity V_p. For this reason, we should avoid, as much as possible, the concept of phase velocity (Figure 8.2). Physical effects are connected to the actual transfer of energy and momentum which take place with the physical velocity v. The reader will recall that in Chapter 4 we considered another velocity exceeding the velocity of light which did not carry energy or momentum. Such velocities are purely geometrical concepts which have no physical content. They are sometimes useful mathematically, but their meaning must not be stretched into the physical realm. In Figure 8.2 we show a geometrical construction illustrating the relationship between phase velocity, physical velocity, and the velocity c.

In current quantum mechanics courses, a great deal of attention is often devoted to phase velocity. Since phase velocity does not make physical sense, however, a new velocity

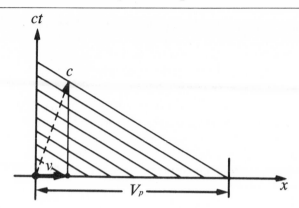

FIGURE 8.2   *The phase velocity V and energy velocity v.   Note that vV = c².*

called group velocity is always defined. Although when defined in a certain way it turns out to be equal to our velocity v, the usual definition of group velocity has ambiguities and lacks immediate physical significance. For the sake of illustration, consider two waves whose frequencies are very close. Let both travel in the x-direction. They will interfere, and the interference is obtained from the relation

$$\phi = A \cos (\omega_1 t - k_1 x) + A \cos (\omega_2 t - k_2 x)$$
$$= 2A \cos \left(\frac{\omega_1 + \omega_2}{2} t - \frac{k_1 + k_2}{2} \right) \cos \left(\frac{\omega_1 - \omega_2}{2} t - \frac{k_1 - k_2}{2} x \right). \qquad (8.47)$$

Now the first cosine oscillates very fast while the second cosine oscillates slowly (Figure 8.3). We see from the figure that the second cosine determines the amplitude of the oscillations given by the first cosine. In fact this amplitude is maximum when the phase of the second cosine is zero, that is,

$$(\omega_1 - \omega_2)t - (k_1 - k_2)x = 0, \qquad v = \frac{dx}{dt} = \frac{d\omega}{dk}, \qquad (8.48)$$

which also gives the velocity of a point where the amplitude is maximum. Now using $\omega^2 = c^2(\kappa^2 + k^2)$ we find

$$v = \frac{d}{dk} c\sqrt{\kappa^2 + k^2} = \frac{ck}{\sqrt{\kappa^2 + k^2}} = \frac{c^2 k}{\omega} \qquad (8.49)$$

which is the same as the velocity of the field energy. This result is indeed expected, since at the points where the field amplitude is maximum, the energy density (mass density) is also

FIGURE 8.3   *Interference of two waves with ω_1 and ω_2.*

maximum. However, in more general cases the center of mass is not necessarily at the point where the field amplitude is maximum. Furthermore, if there is only one wave, the group velocity cannot be defined at all. For these reasons, it is better to deal with the more fundamental concept of the velocity of the energy. It always exists and its definition is unambiguous.

One may object to the above treatment since for a single wave which occupies all of space the center of mass is not well defined. This objection applies for group velocity as well, because any superposition of waves has in principle an infinite number of identical maxima repeating periodically, which again fills all space.

With this, we close this chapter on the fundamental principles of the scalar field concept. In the next chapter, starting from these basic ideas and equations, we will derive some of the most important physical consequences of field theory.

Summary : The Field Concept

The field is an independent dynamic element possessing energy, momentum, and angular momentum. Along with the field concept, new principles are introduced, namely, the positive definiteness of the field energy and the principle of causality. The equation governing the scalar field is $(\partial_\mu \partial^\mu - \kappa^2)\phi = \sigma$. This equation may be made consistent with the above requirements and the conservation laws by suitably choosing the expression for the stress-energy tensor and by imposing conditions on its solutions. Although, when looked at superficially, the field appears to propagate with a velocity $V_p = c^2/v > c$, the theory shows that the energy (and therefore the physical influence) moves with the physical velocity v.

9

CONSEQUENCES OF THE FIELD CONCEPT

In this chapter the most important consequences of the field concept will be exhibited. The field concept has far-reaching implications in physics. In fact, one trend of thought in physics today seems to lead to a general philosophy which regards the field as the basic feature of our world. It is therefore important to study the basic and most general consequences of the field concept. For this purpose the simple scalar field, introduced in the previous chapter, will be used as an example. The results obtained will both illustrate and form the basis for later chapters where we will introduce more complicated field equations. This chapter will introduce the salient aspects of the field concept which is required by relativity.

9.1. Interference and Diffraction

The phenomenon of *interference* is one of the most familiar as well as important consequences of the field concept. Interference occurs when two waves ϕ_1 and ϕ_2, or, more correctly, two solutions of the wave equation, are superposed. Since the wave equation (8.4) is linear in ϕ, the sum $\phi = \phi_1 + \phi_2$ is also a solution of the wave equation. In fact, any linear combination $\alpha\phi_1 + \beta\phi_2$ is also a solution. This fact is called "the principle of superposition" although it is not a basic physical principle.

Consider two points S_1 and S_2 from which emerge two spherical waves ϕ_1 and ϕ_2 of the same frequency and amplitude:

$$\phi_1 = (A/r_1) \cos 2\pi\left(\nu t - \frac{r_1}{\lambda}\right); \qquad \phi_2 = (A/r_2) \cos 2\pi\left(\nu t - \frac{r_2}{\lambda}\right). \qquad (9.1)$$

Here r_1 and r_2 are the distances from the point P where the waves are superposed to the source points S_1 and S_2 (Figure 9.1). It can easily be shown that these are solutions of the

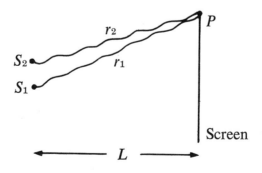

FIGURE 9.1 *Interference.*

wave equation $\partial_\mu \partial^\mu \phi = 0$, which for spherical waves reduces to

$$\frac{1}{r^2} \frac{\partial}{\partial r} \left(r^2 \frac{\partial}{\partial r} \phi \right) - \frac{1}{c^2} \frac{\partial^2}{\partial t^2} \phi = 0. \tag{9.2}$$

Therefore, the superposition of ϕ_1 and ϕ_2,

$$\phi = (A/r_1) \cos 2\pi \left(vt - \frac{r_1}{\lambda} \right) + (A/r_2) \cos 2\pi \left(vt - \frac{r_2}{\lambda} \right), \tag{9.3}$$

is also a solution of $\partial_\mu \partial^\mu \phi = 0$. We want to study the effects of this solution at a screen placed at a distance large compared to the wavelength λ and the distance between S_1 and S_2. This means that $L \gg a$, $r_1 \approx r_2$. Furthermore, since we consider regions over which r_1 and r_2 vary by only a few wavelengths, the r_1 and r_2 may be considered almost constant. Thus, putting $B = A/r_1 = A/r_2$,

$$\phi = B \cos 2\pi \left(vt - \frac{r_1}{\lambda} \right) + B \cos 2\pi \left(vt - \frac{r_2}{\lambda} \right). \tag{9.4}$$

We now see that at a given time, say $t = \bar{t}$, the function ϕ can be zero or maximum at various points. For example, at a point where $2\pi(r_1 - r_2)/\lambda = 0$ or a multiple of 2π, the two cosine functions would reinforce each other because they are in phase. On the other hand, if $2\pi(r_1 - r_2)/\lambda = \pi$ or an odd multiple of π, they would cancel each other because they are 180° out of phase. We describe these reinforcing and cancelling effects with the terms constructive and destructive interference. Thus, if n is an integer,

$$\left. \begin{array}{l} r_1 - r_2 = n\lambda \leftrightarrow \text{constructive interference} \\[2mm] r_1 - r_2 = (n + \tfrac{1}{2})\lambda \leftrightarrow \text{destructive interference} \end{array} \right\}. \tag{9.5}$$

The position of the interference patterns may also be expressed in terms of the angle θ or in terms of the distance x on the screen $x \simeq l \tan \theta$ (Figure 9.1). Since $r_1 - r_2 = a \sin \theta$, and since for small angles $\sin \theta \simeq \tan \theta \simeq \theta$,

$$\left. \begin{array}{l} x = \dfrac{l\lambda}{a} n \leftrightarrow \text{constructive interference} \\[4mm] x = \dfrac{l\lambda}{a} (n + \tfrac{1}{2}) \leftrightarrow \text{destructive interference} \end{array} \right\}. \tag{9.6}$$

These results may also be obtained by a trigonometric transformation of (9.4) into

$$\phi = 2B \cos 2\pi \left(vt - \frac{r_1 + r_2}{2\lambda} \right) \cos 2\pi \left(\frac{r_1 - r_2}{2\lambda} \right), \tag{9.7}$$

from which we see that the second cosine takes its maximum and zero values exactly at the points given by (9.5).

As another example, we may consider two plane waves of different frequencies running in the same direction x.

$$\phi = A \cos 2\pi \left(v_1 t - \frac{x}{\lambda_1} \right) + A \cos 2\pi \left(v_2 t - \frac{x}{\lambda_2} \right). \tag{9.8}$$

Again, by the trigonometric formula we can put this into the form

$$\phi = 2A \cos \pi \left\{ (v_1 + v_2)t - x\left(\frac{1}{\lambda_1} + \frac{1}{\lambda_2}\right)\right\} \cos \pi \left\{ (v_1 - v_2)t - x\left(\frac{1}{\lambda_1} - \frac{1}{\lambda_2}\right)\right\}. \quad (9.9)$$

We see that the field shows reinforcing and cancelling features at distances $\bar{\lambda} = \lambda_1\lambda_2/(\lambda_1 - \lambda_2)$, and at a frequency $\bar{v} = v_1 - v_2$. The latter is called the *beat* frequency.

The phenomenon of *diffraction* is sometimes confused with interference. They are different in origin and the distinction is important. Diffraction is essentially a consequence of Huygens' principle. This in turn may be derived as a consequence of the boundary value solution to the wave equation,

$$\phi(x) = \int \{G(x - x')\partial'^\mu\phi(x') - \phi(x')\partial'^\mu G(x - x')\} \, dS'_\mu. \quad (9.10)$$

To see the connection, let us consider a wave striking a wall which is rigid except at a small opening, S (Figure 9.2). We are interested in the form of the wave passing through the hole and spreading out in the space on the other side of the wall. Our problem is to determine the form of the wave from the knowledge of it in the small volume of the hole. Let us describe the hole with the coordinates x' and t'.

$$\phi(x') = A \cos(\omega t' - kx')$$

$$\frac{\partial\phi}{\partial x'} = kA \sin(\omega t' - kx'); \qquad \frac{\partial\phi}{\partial t'} = -\omega A \sin(\omega t' - kx'). \quad (9.11)$$

For a given point x' and at an instant of time t', these are constants. In fact, for simplicity, we can chose t' such that $\cos(\omega t' - kx') = 0$. Then we have

$$\phi(x) = A\int G(x - x')(\omega \, dx'dy'dz' + k \, dy'dz'c \, dt'). \quad (9.12)$$

Since the range of integration $\Delta x', \Delta y', \ldots$ and so on, is small, and since the function $G(x - x')$ satisfies the wave equation in its x, y, z, ict variables, the function $\phi(x)$ behaves as a wave originating from the small opening S and propagating on the other side of the wall. Thus, the wave will be of the form

$$\phi(x) = (B/r) \cos(\omega t - kr + \alpha). \quad (9.13)$$

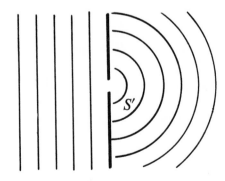

FIGURE 9.2　*Huygen's principle: Diffraction at a small aperture.*

This is the expression of Huygens' principle: Every point of a wave front acts like a source and sends out spherical waves. These are sometimes called secondary waves. Of course, this means in particular that after passing through the hole a wave does not in general propagate on a straight line but spreads in all directions if the opening is very small. When the opening is large compared to the wavelength, however, one can show that the spreading becomes less and less effective due to a subsequent interference of the waves coming from different parts of the hole.

If we use a double hole arrangement instead of the single hole (the holes being small), we can obtain something similar to the previous case of interference of waves from two sources. In fact, this is the usual way of demonstrating the interference phenomenon.

Applying Huygens' principle, if we take a slit of finite width a instead of the hole we again observe a diffraction phenomenon. For from all points of the slit we would get hundreds of secondary waves diffracted into all directions and these would again interfere on their superposition (Figure 9.3). We can give a mathematical treatment of this case by integrating the secondary waves coming from all over the surface of the slit.

$$\phi = C \int_{-a/2}^{a/2} \cos 2\pi \left(vt - \frac{R + y \sin \theta}{\lambda} \right) dy, \tag{9.14}$$

or with $\sin \theta \simeq \theta$,

$$\phi = \frac{C\lambda}{2\pi\theta} \left[\sin 2\pi \left(vt - \frac{R + y\theta}{\lambda} \right) \right]_{-a/2}^{+a/2}$$

$$\phi = \frac{C\lambda}{2\pi\theta} \left\{ \sin 2\pi \left(vt - \frac{R + a\theta/2}{\lambda} \right) - \sin 2\pi \left(vt - \frac{R - a\theta/2}{\lambda} \right) \right\}$$

$$\phi = \frac{2C\lambda}{2\pi\theta} \cos 2v \left(vt - \frac{R}{\lambda} \right) \sin \frac{\pi a\theta}{\lambda}. \tag{9.15}$$

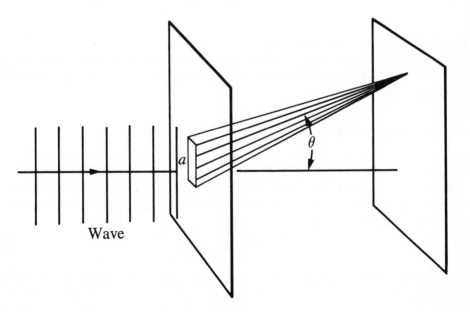

FIGURE 9.3 *Diffraction at a slit.*

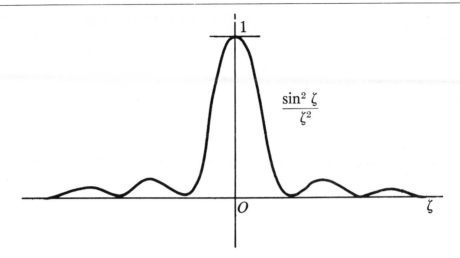

FIGURE 9.4   *A diffraction pattern.*

Since the first cosine is time dependent, the space-dependent features of the field are determined by the sine function. Letting $\zeta = \pi a\theta/\lambda$, we find

$$\phi = Ca\,\frac{\sin \zeta}{\zeta} \cdot \cos\left(\nu t - \frac{R}{\lambda}\right). \qquad (9.16)$$

A plot of the so-called Fresnel function (Figure 9.4),

$$f = \frac{\sin \zeta^2}{\zeta^2}, \qquad (9.17)$$

shows that constructive and destructive interferences occur, although the structure is more complicated than the two-source interference pattern previously considered. The first maximum is at $\zeta \to 0$, $f \to 1$. Thereafter, the maxima are at $\zeta \simeq \pi(n + \frac{1}{2})$, whereas the minima are at $\zeta = n\pi$.

9.2. The Uncertainty Relations

Here we notice an interesting fact: as the width a of the slit becomes larger, the diffraction effects become smaller; as the width becomes smaller, they become more pronounced. This is apparent from the form of the argument $\zeta = \pi a\theta/\lambda$. Since the spreading of the wave is at least as large as the angle between the two minima at $\zeta = \pm\pi/2$, we have for this angular spread $\pi a\theta/\lambda \gg \pi$, $\theta \gg \lambda/a$ or

$$\frac{a\theta}{\lambda} \geqslant 1. \qquad (9.18)$$

Now, the change of direction of a wave is essentially a change in the propagation direction and, consequently, a change in the propagation vector. Thus, the original wave which propagates in the z-direction, as $\cos(\omega t - kz)$, has, after passing through the slit, the form $\cos(\omega t - k_z z - k_y y)$. Here, $k_z = k \cos \theta$ $k_y = k \sin \theta \simeq k\theta = 2\pi\theta/\lambda$. The change in the components of the propagation vector is $\Delta k_z = k_z - k \to 0$, $\Delta k_y = k_y - 0 = k\theta = 2\pi\theta/\lambda$. Comparing this with (9.18) and also using the notation $a = \Delta y$, we obtain

$$\Delta y \cdot \Delta k_y \geqslant 2\pi. \tag{9.19}$$

Here we have derived this relation only for the y-direction, but similar relations are valid also for the other coordinates.

$$\Delta x \cdot \Delta k_x \geqslant 2\pi, \qquad \Delta z \cdot \Delta k_z \geqslant 2\pi, \qquad \Delta t \cdot \Delta \omega \geqslant 2\pi. \tag{9.20}$$

In order to prove it for the x-coordinate, in the above arrangement, one simply takes, instead of a slit, a rectangular window of sides Δx and Δy. To prove the relation in the z-coordinate (the direction of propagation) is more difficult. One accepts, with the help of opening and closing a shutter, a small portion of the wave passing through the slit. This wave will have an extension Δz in space and a duration Δt in time. In other words it is a pulse. A pulse can no longer be described as a single frequency wave like the original wave, but will have a spread $\Delta \omega$ in frequencies and a spread Δk_z in wave numbers. Then, with more elaborate calculations, the above relations can be proved in the z- and t-coordinates. The last equation is the easiest to grasp intuitively. If a periodic phenomenon has a frequency ν and a period T, $T\nu = 1$. If we chose the time Δt smaller than the period, we certainly cannot measure the frequency accurately, for even one period is not completed in that short time. If we want to measure frequency accurately, we must observe the system for a long time. Conversely, if we want to measure time accurately, we must use a frequency which is large (that is, divide the time interval into a large number of small periods).

These facts are completely classical and follow from the wave equation. They are equally true in optics and for sound waves. These relations lead to one of the most celebrated statements in quantum mechanics, where they are called Heisenberg's *uncertainty relations*.

9.3. Formulation of Radiation

In a previous chapter, we mentioned that one of the most important consequences of a field theory is the existance of *radiation*. A system of interacting particles in general will send off energy and momentum in the form of radiation. The *radiated* energy is defined as the energy carried away by the field to infinity. In other words, the radiation is the energy which has escaped from the region of the interacting particles and is carried to infinity by the field. If we consider a spherical surface of infinite radius enclosing the system of interacting particles, the energy carried across this surface is said to be radiated. We can express the radiated energy, by use of the stress-energy tensor, as

$$-\frac{\partial E}{\partial t} = -\int \frac{\partial T_{44}}{\partial t} \, dV = ic \int \partial^k T_{4k} \, dV. \tag{9.21}$$

By virtue of Gauss' theorem, this can be converted into a surface integral

$$-\frac{\partial E}{\partial t} = c^2 \int T_{4k} \, dA^k = (1/4\pi) \int \frac{\partial \phi}{\partial t} \cdot \frac{\partial \phi}{\partial x^k} \, dA^k \tag{9.22}$$

where dA^k are the components of the surface element. Now, making use of the spherical coordinates and choosing the surface at infinity, we have

$$-\frac{\partial E}{\partial t} = (1/4\pi) \int \frac{\partial \phi}{\partial t} \cdot \frac{\partial \phi}{\partial r} \, r^2 \, d\Omega \tag{9.23}$$

where $d\Omega = \sin\theta \, d\theta \, d\phi$ is the element of the solid angle. From this last expression, we conclude that only the solutions of the wave equation which behave at infinity as $(1/r)$ need be considered. Any other dependence will lead either to infinite radiation, which is physically unacceptable, or give zero radiation in which case it will not contribute. Solutions of a wave equation which behave at infinity as $(1/r)$ are called *asymptotic* solutions. A general asymptotic solution for a periodic case can be proved to have the form

$$\phi = \frac{f(\theta, \phi)}{r} \sin(kr - \omega t + \alpha) \tag{9.24}$$

where $f(\theta, \phi)$ is to be determined from the wave equation and depends on the motion of the system of particles. Once this function is determined, the calculation of the radiation is simple. Indeed, we have from (9.23),

$$-\frac{\partial E}{\partial t} = \frac{\omega^2}{8\pi c} \sqrt{1 - \left(\frac{\kappa c}{\omega}\right)^2} \int |f(\theta, \phi)|^2 \sin\theta \, d\theta \, d\phi \tag{9.25}$$

where the fact that the time average of $\sin^2(kr - \omega t + \alpha) \Rightarrow \frac{1}{2}$ is used.

The detailed applications of the *radiation* and another, related phenomenon, the *scattering* of scalar waves, will not be carried out here. However, in the next chapter we will develop further the more interesting and practically important case of radiation and scattering of electromagnetic waves. Since here we are principally interested in the idea of radiation as a part of field theory, we will not go into further detail. Let it suffice to emphasize that the phenomenon of radiation is an effect of field theory which would not exist if the field propagated with infinite velocity, $c \to \infty$.

9.4. Motion in a Static Field

It is well known that scalar fields with $\kappa^2 \neq 0$ term describe various mesons, while no scalar field with $\kappa^2 = 0$ is observed in nature. The static Yukawa solution (8.31) which we obtained earlier would reduce for $\kappa = 0$ to the Newtonian form

$$\phi(r) = \frac{A}{r}. \tag{9.26}$$

It is thus tempting to try to identify the gravitational interaction with a scalar field satisfying the equation

$$\partial_\mu \partial^\mu \phi = 4\pi\sigma(x) \tag{9.27}$$

where $\sigma(x)$ is the matter density in the rest frame. The plausibility of this concept cannot at present be judged from interference, diffraction, or radiation phenomena, because these would be undetectably small owing to the weakness of the gravitational interaction. One of the ways of judging this hypothesis is to study the motion of objects in the field of heavy objects such as the earth or the sun. In this section we will develop the theory of motion in the field of a heavy body. This will serve as a model for $\kappa^2 \neq 0$ type fields as well as providing the solution of the problem of motion in the field of an electrically charged central body. It will be seen, however, that the gravitational field cannot be identified as a special relativistic scalar field with $\kappa = 0$ (propagation with velocity of light c).

During the last two centuries, there have been observed three phenomena of gravitational origin which cannot be explained by the Newtonian theory of gravitation. These are:

(a) The perihelion of the planet Mercury advances at the rate of 43 seconds of arc per century (about one complete revolution every three million years).

(b) Light passing near the surface of the sun is deflected inward by about 1.75 seconds of arc.

(c) The spectral lines of light emitted by atoms on a heavy star are displaced towards the red by an amount which, in the case of the Companion of Sirius, a dense, heavy star, amounts to $\delta\nu/\nu = 6.3 \times 10^{-5}$. (The red shift has been checked in the laboratory by using the newly discovered Mössbauer effect. The experiment was carried out by R. V. Pound and G. A. Rebka of Harvard University.)

We will now try to see whether the scalar field theory developed in this chapter explains the observed effects listed above. First of all, in identifying the field ϕ as the gravitational field we recognize that the source strength ϵ must be equal to $-(Gm_0)$ where G is the gravitational constant. Then, we have

$$\frac{d^2 x_\mu}{d\tau^2} = \frac{\partial \phi}{\partial x^\mu}. \tag{9.28}$$

Since the static field is calculated just as in the usual Galilean case, we have

$$\phi = -\frac{GM_0}{r}. \tag{9.29}$$

Putting this into (9.28), we get

$$\frac{d^2 x_k}{d\tau^2} = GM_0 \frac{x_k}{r^3}; \qquad \frac{d^2 t}{d\tau^2} = 0. \tag{9.30}$$

We see that these equations are similar to Newton's equations. The only difference is that a new parameter τ is used instead of t. Indeed, if $t = \tau$, the latter reduces to Newton's equations. Due to this close analogy, it is possible to solve them as in the Newtonian mechanics. Here, however, we will proceed directly from the conservation laws. This is usually a better way of solving problems. We will see that various fundamental points are clearly exhibited by this approach.

Let us consider two particles, m and m', and choose the coordinate system such that:
(a) The motion of the two particles is in the xy plane.
(b) The system as a whole (center of mass) moves in the x direction.

$$P^4 = \int T^{44} \, dV + m_0 \frac{dt}{d\tau} + m_0' \frac{dt}{d\tau'} = \text{constant},$$

$$P^k = \int T^{k4} \, dV + m_0 \frac{dx_k}{d\tau} + m_0' \frac{dx_k'}{d\tau'} = \text{constant}, \tag{9.31}$$

$$M^{12} = \int (T^{x4}y - T^{y4}x) \, dV + m_0\left(\frac{dx}{d\tau}y - \frac{dy}{d\tau}x\right) + m_0'\left(\frac{dx'}{d\tau'}y' - \frac{dy'}{d\tau'}x'\right) = \text{constant},$$

$$M^{x4} = P^4 X - P^x t = \text{constant},$$

where

$$d\tau^2 = dt^2 - dx^2 - dy^2,$$
$$d\tau'^2 = dt'^2 - dx'^2 - dy'^2. \tag{9.32}$$

For the sake of simplicity, we have adopted here the units $c = G = 1$. We take the M^{x4} equation. By differentiation, we find

$$V_x = \frac{dX}{dt} = \frac{P_x}{P^4} = \text{constant}, \tag{9.33}$$

Since this is a constant velocity, we may transform to a new Lorentz system whose origin coincides with the center of mass. In this new system, $X = V_x = P_x = 0$. Rewriting our equations for this system, we obtain

$$P^4 = \int T^{44} \, dV + m_0 \frac{dt}{d\tau} + m_0' \frac{dt'}{d\tau'}$$

$$M^{12} = \int (T^{4x}y - T^{v4}x) \, dV + (p_x y - p_y x) + (p_x' y' - p_y' x') \tag{9.34}$$

$$M^{x4} = P^4 X = \int T^{44} x \, dV + m_0 x \frac{dt}{d\tau} + m_0' x' \frac{dt'}{d\tau'} = 0$$

where

$$d\tau^2 = dt - dx^2 - dy^2; \qquad d\tau'^2 = dt'^2 - dx'^2 - dy'^2. \tag{9.35}$$

The complete solution of these equations is not known. We will introduce the following simplifications:

1^0) $T^{4k} = 0$, that is, no energy is being radiated;

2^0) $m_0' = M_0 \gg m_0$, that is m_0' is a very heavy body; $\qquad\qquad$ (9.36)

3^0) $\int T^{44} x \, dV \ll m_0 x \frac{dt}{d\tau} + M_0 x' \frac{dt}{d\tau'}$.

Under these assumptions, we see from the M^{x4} equation that

$$m_0 \frac{dx_k}{d\tau} + M_0 \frac{dx_k'}{d\tau'} = 0$$

$$\left| \frac{dx_k'}{d\tau'} \right| = \left| \frac{m_0}{M_0} \frac{dx_k}{d\tau} \right| \ll \left| \frac{dx_k}{d\tau} \right| \tag{9.37}$$

so that the motion of M_0 is confined to a very small region around the center of mass. Therefore, dx'^k and x'^k are small quantities compared to dx^k and x^k. From this, we can assume that $d\tau' = dt$. Our equations reduce to

$$P^4 = \int T^{44} \, dV + m_0 \frac{dt}{d\tau} + M_0$$

$$M^{12} = m_0 \left(\frac{dx}{d\tau} y - \frac{dy}{d\tau} x \right) \tag{9.38}$$

$$d\tau^2 = dt^2 - dx^2 - dy^2$$

which are the simplified forms we want to consider.

In order to solve these equations, we first transform to a polar coordinate system given by

$$x = r \cos \varphi; \qquad y = r \sin \varphi. \tag{9.39}$$

This results in the equations

$$P^4 = \int T^{44} \, dV + m_0 \frac{dt}{d\tau} + M_0 \Bigg\rbrace$$

$$h = \frac{M^{12}}{m_0} = r^2 \frac{d\varphi}{d\tau} \tag{9.40}$$

$$d\tau^2 = dt^2 - r^2 \, d\varphi^2 - dr^2$$

where P^4 and h are constants. Now, due to our assumption $T^{i4} = (1/4\pi)\partial^i\phi(\partial\phi/\partial t) = 0$, we have $\partial\phi/\partial t = 0$; that is, the field is time-independent. If the motion is slow enough, such a field can, at any given moment, be expressed approximately as

$$\phi = -\frac{M_0}{|\vec{r} - \vec{r}_1|} - \frac{m_0}{|\vec{r} - \vec{r}_2|} \tag{9.41}$$

where r_1 and r_2 are the positions of the two particles, respectively. The energy connected to such a static field is, by integration,

$$\int T^{44} \, dV = -\frac{M_0 m_0}{r} + \frac{1}{2}\frac{M_0^2}{0} + \frac{1}{2}\frac{m_0^2}{0}. \tag{9.42}$$

Putting this in, we get

$$E = M_0 + m_0 \frac{dt}{d\tau} - \frac{m_0 M_0}{r} \Bigg\rbrace$$

$$h = r^2 \frac{d\varphi}{d\tau} \tag{9.43}$$

$$d\tau^2 = dt^2 - dr^2 - r^2 \, d\varphi^2$$

where $h = M^{12}/m_0$ and $E = P^4 - \frac{1}{2}(m_0^2/0) - \frac{1}{2}(M_0^2/0)$ are finite constants.

In order to obtain the orbit, we must eliminate dt and $d\tau$ from the above equations. (An orbit is a purely geometrical form, independent of time or proper time.) This elimination yields

$$\left(\frac{dr}{d\varphi}\right)^2 + r^2 = \frac{r^4}{h^2} + \frac{r^4}{h^2}\left(\frac{E - M_0}{m_1} + \frac{M_0}{r}\right)^2. \tag{9.44}$$

Letting $u = 1/r$,

$$\left(\frac{du}{d\varphi}\right)^2 + u^2 = \frac{1}{h^2} + \frac{1}{h^2}\left(\frac{E - M_0}{m_0} + M_0 u\right)^2. \tag{9.45}$$

Differentiating both sides and putting for large r, $E = M_0 + m_0$, we have

$$\frac{d^2 u}{d\varphi^2} + u\left(1 - \frac{M_0^2}{h^2}\right) = \frac{M_0}{h^2}. \tag{9.46}$$

Apart from the small M_0^2/h^2 term (in the usual units this is $G^2 M_0^2/c^4 h^2$), this is the Newtonian form. The solution of the above equation is easy. One can prove by direct substitution that the solution is given by the ellipse (Figure 9.5)

$$u = \frac{1}{r} = \frac{M_0}{h^2}(1 + \epsilon \cos \rho\varphi) \Bigg\rbrace$$

where

$$\rho = \sqrt{1 - \frac{M_0^2}{h^2}} \simeq 1 - \frac{M_0^2}{2h^2} \tag{9.47}$$

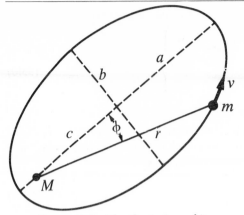

FIGURE 9.5   *The Newtonian orbit for a planet is an ellipse.*

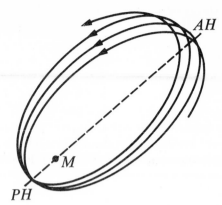

FIGURE 9.6   *Special relativistic orbit is a rotating ellipse. The rate of rotation is $\Delta\phi = 7.2$ seconds of arc per century (wrong). The perihelion (PH) rotates $\Delta\phi = \dfrac{\pi M^2}{h^2}$ per revolution of the planet.*

We see that the difference between the Newtonian (see Problem 19 and Figure 9.5) and the special relativistic laws of planetary motion consists of a slow rotation, in the latter case, of the whole ellipse (Figure 9.6),

$$u = \frac{1}{r} = \frac{M_0}{h^2}(1 + \epsilon \cos \varphi)$$

by the amount $\Delta\dot{\varphi} = 2\pi(1 - \rho)$ per revolution; that is,

$$\Delta\dot{\varphi} = \frac{\pi M_0^2}{h^2} \text{ per revolution.} \tag{9.48}$$

This rotation is called the "advance of the perihelion" of the planetary orbit. When evaluated for the planet Mercury, for example, it gives 7.2 seconds of arc per century. The observed advance, however, is 43 seconds per century, that is, 6 times larger. This shows that the special relativistic theory of gravitation does not correctly explain the observed advance of the perihelion, but there is a certain improvement over the Newtonian theory.

As to the bending of light rays, the theory fails completely. One can see this as follows: The light wave obeys a propagation equation like $\partial_\mu \partial^\mu A_\alpha = 0$ and evidently the wave operator

$$\partial_\mu \partial^\mu = \nabla^2 - \frac{1}{c^2}\frac{d^2}{\partial t^2} \tag{9.49}$$

is not modified by the existence of ϕ in the above theory (although a different theory will bring effects influencing wave equation through a different interpretation of the equivalence principle). Therefore, light propagates in the same manner before and after the ϕ field is considered. Accordingly, the existence of the sun's gravitational field should not influence the propagation of light. This shows that no special relativistic field theory can explain the bending of light rays near the sun as long as the light waves satisfy the usual d'Alembert equation. Special relativity leads to a deflection of light if we are willing to attribute a gravitational action on its equivalent mass, $\mathscr{E}/c^2$. But then the numerical value of the deflection is only half of the observed value. An inconsistency also arises between the wave equation and this (photon) approach.

The shift of spectral lines towards the red is also unexplainable by the above theory. The difficulty can again be traced to the wave equation. According to the wave equation, the only way of obtaining a shift of spectral lines is through the Doppler shift, due to relative motion. In the framework of special relativity, there is no place for a spectral shift between two stationary inertial frames. It becomes clear, therefore, that in order to formulate a *field theory of gravitation*, one must first modify the conceptual framework of the special theory of relativity.

Of course, the possibility that our scalar field ϕ may describe some other physical phenomenon cannot be ruled out. Although at present there is no evidence as to the existence of a special relativistic scalar field of the above type (that is, with zero rest mass) we will carry the analysis a little further. The important features that we are going to point out are valid also for other special relativistic field theories such as the electromagnetic field and the pseudo-scalar field theory of π-mesons.

As the reader may already have noticed, the above calculation of a planetary orbit contains a disturbing fact; namely, the field energy for point particles is infinite. Due to this, the energy of a system of point particles interacting with each other is infinite. Expressed in the simplest terms, the situation is as follows: The theory starts out with a particle of mass m and source strength ϵ, The interaction of the particle with the scalar field ϕ then adds the energy $\int T^{44} \, dV$ to the original energy mc^2. The rest energy of a particle then becomes

$$\bar{m}_0 c^2 = m_0 c^2 + \int T^{44} \, dV \tag{9.50}$$

where m_0 is the mass of the "bare" particle; that is, the particle when $\epsilon = 0$. The mass $\bar{m}_0$ is the mass of the "dressed" particle, that is, when ϵ is switched on. We may say that the effect of the interaction is to increase the rest mass of the particle by an amount δm_0.

$$\bar{m}_0 = m_0 + \delta m_0; \qquad \delta m_0 = (1/c^2) \int T^{44} \, dV. \tag{9.51}$$

The difficulty is that δm_0 is infinite. The result is very unsatisfactory from the physical point of view because we know that particles do not have infinite mass; otherwise, we could not move them at all. We definitely know that particles do not have infinite energies. In the annihilation and creation of particles, we always observe that Einstein's relation (7.13) is obeyed.

In present day theories, the attitude taken toward this difficulty is this: The separation of the mass into two parts $m_0 + \delta m_0$ is not physical. Physically, we have no way of switching off the interaction and of observing m_0 independently of δm_0. Only the sum, $\bar{m}_0 = m_0 + \delta m_0$, is observable, representing the mass of the actual particle. Although physically very plausible, this is an additional statement not contained in the foundations of the theory. Furthermore, the δm_0 is not a small correction to the mass but is infinite. To contend that the mass actually observed is a difference between two infinite quantities m_0 and δm_0 is not a desirable theoretical practice.

This manipulation of the infinite self-energy is the prototype of a process called "Mass Renormalization" in quantum field theories. In quantum field theory, the self-energy divergence survives and there are also other quantities which lead to divergent results.

These must also be renormalized. It turns out that if the field is renormalizable, all infinities may be removed by renormalizing the mass m_0 and the source constant ϵ. The invention of the renormalization technique was one of the decisive advances in field theory. Whether it is a justifiable process or leads to internal contradictions with the basic postulates of field theory is today the subject of much discussion in physics.

9.5. Coulomb Scattering

In the central field problem just discussed, the smaller particle was assumed to revolve around the heavier particle. This is the case if the force between the particles is attractive and the kinetic energy of the smaller particle is not enough to escape the attraction. But if one of these conditions fail, the small particle will approach the heavier one, will be deflected and will go off to infinity in a different direction. In this case the motion is a scattering. The equations of course are the same as before, with a change in sign for the case of repulsion. Thus equation (9.46) can simply be taken over as

$$\frac{d^2u}{d\varphi^2} + u\left(1 - \frac{M_0^2}{h^2}\right) = \pm \frac{M_0}{h^2} \tag{9.52}$$

with the solution

$$u = \frac{1}{r} = \pm \frac{M_0}{h^2}(1 + \epsilon \cos \rho\varphi). \tag{9.53}$$

Now we know that this equation describes (if $\rho = 1$)

$$\begin{aligned}
\epsilon &< 1 \quad \text{ellipse,} \\
\epsilon &= 1 \quad \text{parabola,} \\
\epsilon &> 1 \quad \text{hyperbola.}
\end{aligned} \tag{9.54}$$

Since r is positive, the $(-)$ sign (repulsion) necessarily leads to a hyperbola; for the $(+)$ sign (attraction) all three cases are possible. In this section the case of a hyperbolic trajectory, that is, scattering, will be considered. For simplicity only the nonrelativistic case ($\rho = 1$) will be treated.

We first note that the scattering is studied in terms of the angle θ which is related to φ_∞ as $\theta = \pi - 2\varphi_\infty$ and the φ_∞ is given by $r \to \infty$; that is,

$$\epsilon \cos \varphi_\infty - 1 = 0, \qquad \theta = \pi - 2\varphi_\infty. \tag{9.55}$$

We consider a beam of particles each having a fixed momentum p. If there were no field, the particle would have passed M at a distance l. If at that distance there is a strong enough field, the particle will be scattered. The scattering cross section is defined by the effective area $\sigma = \pi l^2$. For the study of angular dependence of scattering, however, the differential scattering cross section

$$d\sigma = 2\pi l\, dl \tag{9.56}$$

is more suitable. To find l we note that

$$pl = m_0 p^2 \frac{d\varphi}{dt} = m_0 h$$

is the angular momentum, giving

$$l = \frac{m_0}{p} h. \tag{9.57}$$

On the other hand as $r \to \infty$,

$$m \frac{dr}{dt} \to p = \frac{M_0}{h} \epsilon \sin \varphi_\infty.$$

Putting ϵ and $\sin \varphi_\infty$ from (9.55), we find that

$$l = (m_0 M_0/p^2) \tan^{-1} \frac{\theta}{2} \qquad (9.58)$$

$$d\sigma = \frac{1}{4} \left(\frac{m_0 M_0}{p^2} \right)^2 \frac{d\Omega}{\sin^4 \frac{\theta}{2}} \qquad (9.59)$$

where $d\Omega = 2\pi \sin \theta \, d\theta$ is the solid angle. Thus, the scattering into a given direction is inversely proportional to $\sin^4 (\theta/2)$. This is the so-called Rutherford scattering formula. This dependence is characteristic of the Coulomb potential $1/r$. For other types of forces, the dependence would be different. (For example, for the Yukawa potential $Ae^{-\kappa r}/r$, the result is different.) In this way it was found that the Coulomb law is valid down to a distance $\sim 10^{-13}$ cm from the center of a hydrogen nucleus. This shows that the proton has a size of this order. In the nuclear case, instead of M_0 we put $e^2 Z$ where Z is the number of protons. In the relativistic case because of $\rho = 1 - M_0^2/h^2$ these formulas are slightly modified. It would be wrong or unjust to think that the relativistic principles modify the motion only through the small term $(1 - \rho)$. In a sense, the whole concept of field is necessitated by relativity. From the very first chapters it has been apparent that relativity is intimately connected with the field point of view. Fields are simply the quantities which retain their physical meaning under Lorentz transformations. It is therefore justified, perhaps even imperative, to consider not only the waves and their interference, diffraction and radiation but also the $1/r$ Coulomb potential and the classically known Kepler motion and Rutherford scattering as part of the whole relativity concept.

Summary: Consequences of the Field Concept

(a) In Minkowski space, the concept of a field and the point character of elementary particles are both essential.

(b) The self-energy of point particles is infinite. No completely satisfactory solution of this problem has as yet been found.

(c) The simple phenomena of interference and diffraction are consequences of the field concept.

(d) The field equations have retarded and advanced solutions. The principle of causality rules out the advanced solution.

(e) Radiation is a consequence of the field concept and of the fact that the field propagates with finite velocity.

(f) A scalar field theory of gravitation in Minkowski space does not predict correctly the results of the three astronomical observations; namely, the bending of light rays near the sun, the advance of the perihelion of Mercury, and the gravitational red-shift of spectral lines.

10

THE ELECTROMAGNETIC FIELD

10.1. The Basic Equations of the Electromagnetic Field

In this chapter we will present the electromagnetic field. This is probably the most familiar field in physics. In fact, the concept of field theory in its usual sense was first introduced in connection with electromagnetic phenomena. In formulating the laws governing the electromagnetic field, we will benefit from the experience we have gained in the previous two chapters. It will be seen that the main features of this field are similar to those of the scalar field. The essential differences will be analyzed in detail and, in so far as is possible, their origins will be traced.

The source of the electromagnetic field is the charge-current vector defined as

$$j^\nu = (\rho_0/c)u^\nu \tag{10.1}$$

where the real quantity ρ_0 is the electric charge density in the rest frame and $u^\nu = dx^\nu/d\tau$ is the velocity four-vector. The fourth component, $j^4 = i\rho_0(dt/d\tau)$, is imaginary, whereas the first three components are real. Thus, according to the definition of Chapter 6, the charge-current vector is a *real* vector. The charge density is $\rho = (1/i)j^4 = \rho_0/\sqrt{1 - v^2/c^2}$ as observed from the moving frame.

It is an experimental fact that *the total electric charge of an isolated system is conserved.* We will take this statement as a fundamental principle along with the other conservation principles introduced earlier. The principle of charge conservation may be expressed mathematically as

$$\partial_\mu j^\mu = 0. \tag{10.2}$$

Now, consider the problem of constructing the field equation in analogy to (9.27). Since the source term here is a vector, the field must also be a vector. Let us denote the field by the symbol A^ν, the so-called potential four-vector. We have

$$\partial_\mu \partial^\mu A^\nu = -4\pi j^\nu. \tag{10.3}$$

Here we put $\kappa = 0$ since the electromagnetic field propagates with the velocity of light, c. The potential vector, A^ν, is a *real vector field*, that is, its space components A_1, A_2, and A_3 are real and its fourth component $A_4 = i\phi$ is pure imaginary. In other words A_1, A_2, A_3 and ϕ are all real.

In electromagnetic theory we have another principle called the *principle of gauge-invariance*. This principle is formulated mathematically as follows: *The observable quantities of electromagnetic theory are invariant under the transformation*

$$A_\mu \to A_\mu + \partial_\mu \Phi \tag{10.4}$$

where Φ is an appropriate scalar function. The quantities which depend on the gauge function Φ are not observable. This simply means that if we use A_μ and someone else $A_\mu + \partial_\mu\Phi$ to describe electromagnetic phenomena, there should be no difference in the outcome of any experiment or observation between the two descriptions. The principle of gauge invariance has important consequences which will be seen as we go along.

The formulation of the theory is now practically completed. We will develop it on the basis of the preceding equations. First we notice that A^ν itself is not observable since it is gauge dependent. We define a gauge-invariant field $f_{\mu\nu}$ as

$$f_{\mu\nu} = \partial_\mu A_\nu - \partial_\nu A_\mu. \tag{10.5}$$

Secondly, we impose on A_μ the so-called Lorentz condition

$$\partial^\mu A_\mu = 0. \tag{10.6}$$

This condition or a condition equivalent to it is needed (see Section 10.2) because, otherwise, the energy of the electromagnetic field does not stay positive definite. In other words, without the Lorentz condition the principle of the positive definiteness of energy could be violated. Note that the Lorentz condition must be applied to the gauge-transformed potential, $A_\mu + \partial_\mu\Phi$, as well as to A_μ. This leads to

$$\partial_\mu\,\partial^\mu\Phi = 0. \tag{10.7}$$

Hence the gauge function Φ is any scalar function satisfying the wave equation.

Now, if we form $\partial^\mu f_{\mu\nu}$, we see by virtue of (10.3) and (10.6) that

$$\partial^\mu f_{\mu\nu} = -4\pi j_\nu. \tag{10.8}$$

Furthermore, from the definition (10.5) of $f_{\mu\nu}$ we have the identities

$$\partial^\sigma f_{\mu\nu} + \partial^\nu f_{\sigma\mu} + \partial^\mu f_{\nu\sigma} \equiv 0; \qquad \sigma, \mu, \nu = \begin{cases} 123 \\ 234 \\ 341 \\ 412 \end{cases} \tag{10.9}$$

(σ, μ, ν are cyclically permuted). The field $f_{\mu\nu}$ is what we usually call the *electromagnetic field*. The electric field E and the magnetic field H are identified as $f_{12} = -f_{21} = H_z$, $f_{14} = -f_{41} = -iE_x$, et cetera.

$$f_{\mu\nu} = \begin{pmatrix} 0 & H_z & -H_x & -iE_x \\ -H_z & 0 & H_y & -iE_y \\ H_x & -H_y & 0 & -iE_z \\ iE_x & iE_y & iE_z & 0 \end{pmatrix}. \tag{10.10}$$

To find the transformation properties of this antisymmetric tensor, see problems (10.3) and (10.4). The field $f_{\mu\nu}$ (or E, H) is the *physical field* because in an actual physical measurement the components of $f_{\mu\nu}$ can be observed, whereas the A_μ are not observable. We now note that the equations (10.8) and (10.9) are equivalent to the complete set of Maxwell equations. In fact, by direct calculation we can show that equation (10.8) is equivalent to the equations

$$\operatorname{curl} \vec{H} - \frac{1}{c}\frac{\partial \vec{E}}{\partial t} = \frac{4\pi}{c}\vec{j}, \qquad \operatorname{div} \vec{E} = 4\pi\rho \tag{10.11}$$

whereas the identities (10.9) lead to

$$\text{curl}\,\vec{E} + \frac{1}{c}\frac{\partial \vec{H}}{\partial t} = 0, \qquad \text{div}\,\vec{H} = 0. \tag{10.12}$$

These are, as is well known, the complete set of Maxwell equations for a vacuum.

In passing we note here the interesting fact that in writing equation (10.3) in analogy to the scalar field equation (8.9) we could not keep the κ^2 term. This is because with this term, and using equation (10.3), the current j_ν would become nongauge invariant. Since the current is observable, the κ^2 term must vanish. Thus, the fact that the electromagnetic field propagates with velocity c is essentially a consequence of the gauge invariance.

10.2. Energy-Momentum and Angular Momentum

A stress-energy tensor for the electromagnetic field may be obtained in analogy to the scalar field

$$T_{\mu\nu} = -\frac{1}{4\pi}\left(\partial_\mu A^\alpha \partial_\nu A_\alpha - \frac{1}{2}\delta_{\mu\nu}\partial_\alpha A_\beta \partial^\alpha A^\beta\right). \tag{10.13}$$

This tensor is indeed symmetric and divergence-free when no charges are present on account of the field equations (10.3), but it is not explicitly gauge invariant. Nevertheless, the energy-momentum vector defined by the integral

$$P_\mu = \frac{i}{c}\int T_{\mu\nu}\,dS^\nu \qquad dS^4 = dV \tag{10.14}$$

can be shown to be gauge invariant. The definition of the angular momentum cannot be taken over by analogy, since this will not be gauge invariant, but one can show that the integral

$$M^{\mu\nu} = \frac{i}{c}\int (T^{\alpha\mu}x^\nu - T^{\alpha\nu}x^\mu)\,dS_\alpha + \frac{ic}{8\pi}\int(\partial^\alpha A^\mu A^\nu - \partial^\alpha A^\nu A^\mu)\,dS_\alpha \tag{10.15}$$

is actually gauge invariant (see problem 12.4). Thus the angular momentum of the electromagnetic field has a different structure as compared to that of the scalar field. It separates in a natural way into two parts

$$M^{\mu\nu} = L^{\mu\nu} + N^{\mu\nu} \tag{10.16}$$

where

$$L^{\mu\nu} = \frac{i}{c}\int (T^{\alpha\mu}x^\nu - T^{\alpha\nu}x^\mu)\,dS_\alpha \tag{10.17}$$

$$N^{\mu\nu} = \frac{ic}{8\pi}\int(\partial^\alpha A^\mu A^\nu - \partial^\alpha A^\nu A^\mu)\,dS_\alpha. \tag{10.18}$$

The first term, $L^{\mu\nu}$, is the *orbital* angular momentum, and the second term, $N^{\mu\nu}$, is called the *spin* or *intrinsic* angular momentum. This separation, however, is not in general gauge invariant. Consequently, they are not separately observable, except in certain special cases where some gauge-invariant components may be found. We will see by direct calculation that there is no actual spinning of a material body involved, as might be implied by the term "spin." There is a rotating electromagnetic field in circularly polarized light, but the intrinsic angular momentum is independent of the frequency of this rotation, showing that there is no analogy to a spinning mechanical object. The effect depends purely on the fact that the electromagnetic potential gives rise to a multicomponent field. (See Chapter 12 equation 12.17.)

We can construct an explicitly gauge-invariant stress-energy tensor in terms of the $f_{\mu\nu}$

$$\theta^{\mu\nu} = (1/4\pi)(f^{\mu\alpha}f_\alpha^\nu - \tfrac{1}{4}\delta^{\mu\nu}f^{\alpha\beta}f_{\alpha\beta}). \tag{10.19}$$

This tensor is also symmetric and indeed divergence free, not on account of the field equations alone but also on account of the Lorentz condition,

$$\partial^\mu\theta_{\mu\nu} = f_\nu^\alpha\partial_\alpha(\partial^\beta A_\beta) = 0. \tag{10.20}$$

Since the Lorentz condition is not a field equation but only a subsidiary condition, the tensor $\theta_{\mu\nu}$ is not as suitable as $T_{\mu\nu}$ for dynamical considerations. But, of course, they are essentially equivalent and indeed $\theta_{\mu\nu}$ is more useful in most instances since it is gauge invariant and therefore directly observable. We give its components, explicitly below:

$$\begin{aligned}
\theta_{11} &= (1/4\pi)[-E_x^2 - H_x^2 + (E^2 + H^2)/2\,] \\
\theta_{12} &= (1/4\pi)(E_xE_y + H_xH_y) \\
\theta_{41} &= (i/4\pi)(E_yH_z - E_zE_y) \\
\theta_{44} &= (1/8\pi)(E^2 + H^2). \text{ et cetera.}
\end{aligned} \tag{10.21}$$

We see that the θ_{4k} are the components of the Poynting vector, whereas θ_{44} is the field energy density. By direct examination we see from the above that the trace θ_μ^μ of this tensor vanishes,

$$\theta_\mu^\mu = \theta_1^1 + \theta_2^2 + \theta_3^3 + \theta_4^4 = 0. \tag{10.22}$$

Another interesting characteristic of the structure of $\theta_{\mu\nu}$ is the existence of two invariants,

$$\mathscr{L} = (1/16\pi)f_{\mu\nu}f^{\mu\nu} = (1/8\pi)(H^2 - E^2) \quad \text{and} \quad G = \vec{E}\cdot\vec{H}. \tag{10.23}$$

The invariance of the first one is obvious from its definition. The second one may easily be proven to be invariant by a Lorentz transformation. Again, by direct computation one proves

$$\theta_\mu^\alpha\theta_\alpha^\nu = 2\mathscr{L}\theta_\mu^\nu \tag{10.24}$$

The two invariants given above are useful for characterizing the field. For example, if $\mathscr{L} = G = 0$, the field is said to be a "null field." A light wave or an electromagnetic wave is such a field. By means of Lorentz transformations we can give the fields E or H any values we desire, subject only to the condition that $\mathscr{L}$ and G are invariant. If the field is not a null field, it is always possible to find a reference frame in which E and H are parallel so that $G = EH$ (see problem 10.4). The tensors (10.13) and (10.21) are called Fermi and Maxwell tensor, respectively. For further reading see *Theory of Photons and Electrons*, Jauch and Rohrlich, Addison-Wesley Publishing Co. (1955).

Before we conclude this section we note two interesting facts: First, a pure gauge field $A_\mu \to \partial_\mu\Phi$ would possess neither energy, momentum, nor angular momentum. This is clearly seen from the fact that $\theta_{\mu\nu}$ is gauge independent. Thus, the gauge field itself is not a physical field, although it gives rise to drastic conditions on the observability of other physical quantities. Secondly, from (10.14) we find that if we put $A_1 = A_2 = A_3 = 0$, $A_4 = i\phi$; that is, if we had only A_4 components, the energy could become negative unless $\partial A_4/\partial t = 0$. Now, under a Lorentz transformation, finite components A_1, A_2, and A_3 will appear, while the above condition goes over into $\partial_\mu A^\mu = 0$. Thus, the Lorentz condition guarantees the positive definiteness of energy as was stated earlier without proof. Since this condition is invariant, the energy remains positive definite in all frames of reference.

Another way of interpreting the Lorentz condition is that it eliminates the longitudinal vibrations associated with $A_4 = i\phi$ and leaves only the transversal vibrations associated with A_1, A_2, A_3. As a consequence light is a transverse wave.

10.3. Equations of Motion of Charged Particles

If there are charged particles present in the field, energy and momentum may be transferred to the particles from the field and vice versa. In this case neither the field nor the particles alone form a closed system. We take the particles plus the field as our system and apply the conservation laws. The divergence of the stress-energy tensor $T^{\mu\nu}$ of the field is

$$\partial_\nu T^{\mu\nu} = j_\nu f^{\mu\nu} = \frac{e}{c} f^{\mu\nu} u_\nu \tag{10.25}$$

which gives the rate at which momentum is being transferred to the particles. This represents a force. Following the method of Chapter 7, we find the requirement of conservation of energy and momentum leads to

$$m_0 \frac{d^2 x^\mu}{d\tau^2} = \frac{e}{c} f^{\mu\nu} u_\nu. \tag{10.26}$$

The right hand side of this equation represents the relativistic force vector, f^μ

$$f^\mu = \frac{e}{c} f^{\mu\nu} u_\nu, \qquad f^\mu \, dx_\mu = 0 \tag{10.27}$$

$$\vec{f} = \frac{e\vec{E} + e\vec{v} \times \vec{H}}{\sqrt{1 - v^2/c^2}}, \qquad f_4 = -\frac{ie\vec{v} \cdot \vec{E}}{c\sqrt{1 - v^2/c^2}}. \tag{10.28}$$

As we see, the space components of f are components of the Lorentz force. This was discovered by Lorentz before relativity theory was formulated. The equation of motion of the particles plus the field is therefore given by the coupled set of equations

$$m_0 \frac{d^2 x^\mu}{d\tau^2} = \frac{e}{c} f^{\mu\nu} u_\nu, \qquad \partial_\mu \partial^\mu A^\nu = -4\pi j_\nu. \tag{10.29}$$

It is interesting to note that for a given field the rate at which energy is transferred to the particles does not depend on the magnetic field H but depends only on E. This follows from $F^\mu \, dx_\mu = 0$, since

$$d\mathscr{E} = \vec{F} \cdot d\vec{r} = e\vec{v} \cdot \vec{E} \, dt \tag{10.30}$$

$$\frac{d\mathscr{E}}{dt} = e\vec{v} \cdot \vec{E}. \tag{10.31}$$

This means that a static magnetic field by itself does not contribute to the energy balance among moving charges. Another way of saying the same thing is that the absolute value of the velocity of a particle is not influenced by the magnetic field although its direction may be changed. Thus, the magnetic field does not produce an acceleration in the direction of the velocity. A time dependent magnetic field generates electric field and via this field energy can be transferred to particles.

The solutions of problems of motion in a static electric field, such as the Coulomb field of a nucleus, proceed in a fashion similar to those developed in the previous chapter, with minor readjustments. Therefore, such problems as motion in a central field and Rutherford scattering of charged particles will not be treated here. Motion in a magnetic field is different and interesting. For purposes of illustration, consider a uniform magnetic field directed along the z axis.

$$\frac{du_x}{d\tau} = \frac{eH}{m_0 c} u_y, \qquad \frac{du_y}{d\tau} = -\frac{eH}{m_0^c} u_x,$$

$$\frac{du_z}{d\tau} = 0 \qquad \frac{du_t}{d\tau} = 0 \tag{10.32}$$

where $u_\mu = dx_\mu/d\tau$. From the last two equations, we have, after the initial conditions are put in,

$$t = \frac{\tau}{\sqrt{1 - v^2/c^2}} + t_0, \qquad z = v_{oz} t + z_0. \tag{10.33}$$

Now, let

$$\omega = \frac{eH}{m_0^c} \sqrt{1 - v^2/c^2}$$

and substitute for τ in the first two equations, which suggest the form

$$u_x = a \cos(\omega t + \alpha) \qquad u_y = -a \sin(\omega t + \alpha). \tag{10.34}$$

Integrating these and comparing with (10.32) we obtain

$$x = x_0 + R \sin(\omega t + \alpha)$$

$$y = y_0 + R \cos(\omega t + \alpha) \tag{10.35}$$

where $R = a/\omega = mcv/eH$. To find the nonrelativistic approximation we simply put $v^2/c^2 \to 0$, $\omega = eH/m_0 c$. We see that if $v_{oz} = 0$, the particle moves on a circle of radius R centered at the point x_0, y_0, and z_0. On the other hand, if $v_{oz} \neq 0$, we have a helix, the axis of which is parallel to the magnetic field.

An interesting case is the motion of a charged particle in a combination of electric and magnetic fields. Here, for simplicity, we will consider the fields as constant and the motion as nonrelativistic. Let the z axis be along the magnetic field and the electric field be in the zy plane. Equations (10.29) give, in the nonrelativistic limit,

$$m\frac{d^2x}{dt^2} = \frac{e}{c} Hv_y, \qquad m\frac{d^2y}{dt^2} = eE_y - \frac{e}{c} v_x H, \qquad m\frac{d^2z}{dt^2} = eE_z \tag{10.36}$$

The integration of these equations leads, with $\omega = eH/mc$, to

$$x = \frac{a}{\omega} \sin \omega t + \frac{cE_y}{H} t + x_0$$

$$y = \frac{a}{\omega} \cos \omega t + y_0 \tag{10.37}$$

$$z = \frac{eE_z}{2m} t^2 + v_{oz} t + z_0.$$

We see from these that the motion in the z direction is one with a constant acceleration,

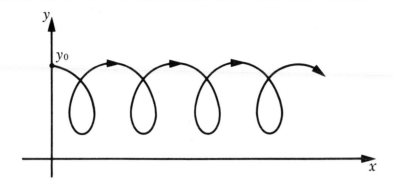

FIGURE 10.1   *Motion of an electron in a combined electric and magnetic field.*

whereas the projection on the xy plane is a trochoid (Figure 10.1). The average values of the coordinates are

$$\bar{x} = \frac{cE_y}{H} t + x_0$$

$$\bar{y} = y_0 \tag{10.38}$$

$$\bar{z} = \frac{eE_z}{2m} t^2 + v_{oz}t + z_0.$$

Thus, it is interesting to note that the particle does not have an overall motion in the y direction but it does in the x direction. The condition that the motion be nonrelativistic is, of course, $\bar{v}_x = (cE_y/H) \ll c$, that is, $E_y \ll H$.

The equations of motion of particles (10.25) can also be obtained from a variational principle by extending the action integral (7.18). From the equations of motion,

$$dm_0 u^\mu - \frac{e}{c} f^{\mu\nu} dx_\nu = 0$$

we have

$$P^\mu + \frac{e}{c} A^\mu - \int \partial^\mu A^\nu \, dx_\nu = \text{constant.}$$

It can be shown that the third term does not contribute to the motion, leaving

$$A = \int \left(P^\mu + \frac{e}{c} A^\mu \right) dx_\mu$$

or

$$A = \int \left(-m_0 c^2 \, d\tau + \frac{e}{c} A^\mu \, dx_\nu \right).$$

This shows, among other things, that for a particle in an electromagnetic field the momentum may be replaced by $P^\mu + (e/c)A^\mu$. An interaction of this type is called a "minimal interaction." It will be shown in Chapter 12 that this is essentially a consequence of gauge invariance.

10.4. Polarization of Light

The electromagnetic field differs from the scalar field in that it is a vector. Since each component of the electromagnetic wave obeys the wave equation, the consequences of the wave equation, namely, wave propagation, interference, diffraction, radiation, causality, uncertainty relations, et cetera, are all valid, although the expression of these may be a little more complicated due to the interplay of the various components. In most instances, however, the previously derived expressions can simply be taken over by analogy.

An important difference between the scalar field and the vector field is the polarizability of the latter (polarization of light). This arises directly from the fact that the scalar field has only one component, whereas the electromagnetic field has more than one. In order to present the polarization as simply as possible, let us consider the plane wave solution of the wave equation $\partial_\mu \partial^\mu A_\nu = 0$. Assuming that the wave propagates in the z direction, we may write, as in the scalar field case,

$$A_\mu = a_\mu e^{i(\omega t - kz)} + a_\mu^* e^{-i(\omega t - kz)}.$$

By a redefinition of a_μ this can also be written as

$$A_\mu = a_\mu \cos(\omega t - kz + \alpha_\mu); \qquad \omega = c |k| \tag{10.39}$$

where a_μ and α_μ are real integration constants. The constant vector a_μ is called the polarization vector. The electromagnetic field may be computed from this as

$$
\begin{aligned}
E_x &= \omega a_1 \sin(\omega t - kz + \alpha_1), & H_x &= -E_y \\
E_y &= \omega a_2 \sin(\omega t - kz + \alpha_2), & H_y &= E_x \\
E_z &= 0, & H_z &= 0.
\end{aligned}
\tag{10.40}
$$

Note that only A_1 and A_2 are used. A_3 and A_4 may be taken as zero. The two invariants are $\mathscr{L} = (1/2)(H^2 - E^2) = 0$ and $G = \vec{E} \cdot \vec{H} = 0$, so that this is a "null" field. Since a_1 and a_2, which are normal to the direction of propagation, z, are nonzero, the plane wave is said to be *transversely polarized*.

We will consider the following special cases:
(1) If $\alpha_1 = \alpha_2$, then at any given point, $z = z_0$, we have

$$\tan \theta = \frac{E_y}{E_x} = \frac{a_2}{a_1} \quad \text{so that } \theta \text{ is constant.} \tag{10.41}$$

In this case, the vector E remains parallel to itself. Its magnitude, of course, oscillates sinusoidally. Such a wave is said to be *linearly polarized*.
(2) If $\alpha_1 = \alpha_2 + \pi/2$, we have $\sin(\omega t - kz + \alpha_1) = \cos(\omega t - kz + \alpha_2)$ and, therefore,

$$
\begin{aligned}
E_x &= \omega a_1 \cos(\omega t - kz + \alpha_2) \\
E_y &= \omega a_2 \sin(\omega t - kz + \alpha_2).
\end{aligned}
\tag{10.42}
$$

The angle θ is now a function of time for any given position, $z = z_0$.

$$\tan \theta = \frac{E_y}{E_x} = \frac{a_2}{a_1} \tan(\omega t - kz_0 + \alpha_2). \tag{10.43}$$

In order to see how the vector E behaves, we obtain from equation (10.42) the relation

$$\frac{E_x^2}{(a_1\omega)^2} + \frac{E_y^2}{(a_2\omega)^2} = 1 \qquad (10.44)$$

which is the equation of an ellipse. This shows that the end point of the electric field vector describes an ellipse with axes ωa_1 and ωa_2. In this case, the field is said to be *elliptically polarized*. If, in addition, $a_1 = a_2$, the ellipse reduces to a circle and the field is said to be *circularly polarized*. In this last case, the angle θ is given as

$$\theta = \omega t - kz_0 + \alpha_2 \qquad (10.45)$$

showing that the field vector rotates at any given position with the angular velocity ω. By superposing unpolarized, linearly polarized, and circularly polarized waves in different proportions, we can obtain various cases of partial polarization.

The material in this section applies equally as well to the vector $\vec{H}$. Here, we must point out that the scalar field which we have considered in the last chapter does not have this property of polarization. The reason is that in that case we have only one field function and, therefore, one a and one α. When a field has more than one component, we may always expect some sort of polarization property.

10.5. The Intrinsic Angular Momentum of Light

Another important difference between the electromagnetic field and the scalar field is that the electromagnetic field has an intrinsic angular momentum. The expression representing this was given in section 10.3 as

$$N^{\mu\nu} = \frac{1}{4\pi} \int (\partial^\alpha A^\mu A^\nu - \partial^\alpha A^\mu A^\nu)\, dS_\alpha. \qquad (10.46)$$

Now, consider again the solution (10.39). We can calculate the components, N^{23}, N^{31}, and N^{12}. These are not, by themselves, gauge invariant. We start from the gauge invariant quantity $M^{\mu\nu}$. If we choose A_μ independent of x and y, we find that $L^{12} = 0$ and, therefore, $M^{12} = N^{12}$ is what is observed. The components which are perpendicular to the direction of propagation do not have this property. Thus, in this case, N^{12} is an observable quantity. A simple calculation gives

$$N^{12} = \frac{1}{8\pi} \int a_1 a_2 \omega \sin(\alpha_1 - \alpha_2)\, dV. \qquad (10.47)$$

From (10.46) we conclude that the plane electromagnetic wave (10.39) has the "intrinsic" angular momentum

$$N^{12} = \frac{1}{8\pi} a_1 a_2 \Gamma \sin(\alpha_1 - \alpha_2). \qquad (10.48)$$

Where $\Gamma = ick^\alpha S_\alpha = \omega V$ is an invariant quantity. For linearly polarized light, this gives $N^{12} = 0$. It is maximum when $\alpha_1 - \alpha_2 = \pi/2$. Since an elliptically polarized light wave may be constructed by superposing two linearly polarized waves with the phase difference $\pi/2$, two linearly polarized waves, which in themselves have no intrinsic angular momentum, will generally give rise to an intrinsic angular momentum. Note that Γ is invariant and therefore N^{12} does not depend on ω. This prediction of the theory is confirmed by experiment. One sends circularly polarized light on to a sensitively suspended blackened circular

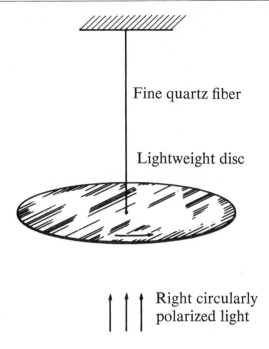

Fine quartz fiber

Lightweight disc

Right circularly
polarized light

FIGURE 10.2 *Spin angular momentum of light.*

disc (Figure 10.2). According to the direction of the polarization, the disc rotates one way or the other.

The intrinsic angular momentum that we have just discussed depends on having two different components with phases α_1 and α_2. Since a scalar field has only one phase α, we see that a scalar field cannot have intrinsic angular momentum. The conclusion is again general: Whenever a field has more than one component, we may expect [see Chapter 12, equation (12.17)] some sort of an *intrinsic* angular momentum. For circularly polarized monochromatic light we have the relation $N^{12} = \pm \mathscr{E}/\omega$.

10.6. Solutions of the Field Equations

A difference between the scalar field of the previous chapter and the electromagnetic field is that, for the latter, $\kappa = 0$. Due to this the electromagnetic field does not have a *rest solution* like equation (8.15). The simplest solution we can get is of the type (8.16) and its equation corresponds to (8.17) with $\kappa = 0$, $\omega^2 = c^2 k^2$

$$A_\mu(z, t) = a_\mu e^{i(kz-\omega t)} + a_\mu^* e^{-i(kz-\omega t)}$$

and the corresponding condition

$$\left(\frac{\partial^2}{\partial z^2} - \frac{1}{c^2}\frac{\partial^2}{\partial t^2}\right) A_\mu = 0$$

where the a_μ are constants. From this point on, however, all the arguments concerning the construction of new solutions (by Lorentz transformations and subsequent summations) and the Green's function formulation, et cetera, are all valid with $\kappa = 0$. For example, the static, spherically symmetric solution for a point particle carrying the charge Q would become the Coulomb potential

$$\phi = \frac{Q}{r}, \qquad A_x = A_y = A_z = 0.$$

Also the velocity of the field energy would reduce to

$$\frac{dX}{dt} = \frac{c^2 P_x}{\mathscr{E}} = c$$

as expected. The gauge function $\partial_\mu \partial^\mu \Phi = 0$ could be constructed conveniently as

$$\Phi(x) = \Lambda e^{ikx} + \Lambda^* e^{-ikx}$$

leading to

$$A_\mu \to A_\mu + k_\mu (\Lambda e^{ikx} - \Lambda^* e^{-ikx})$$

and

$$a_\mu \to a_\mu + k_\mu \Lambda, \qquad a_\mu^* \to a_\mu^* - k_\mu \Lambda^*.$$

Since Λ is arbitrary, this shows that two vectors, A_μ and A'_μ, differing by k_μ times a scalar wave, lead to the same observable results although the transformation has different effects on the positive and negative frequency components.

10.7. Radiation and Scattering

Another difference between a scalar field and a vector field is found in the process of radiation. Although the treatment is similar, the vector field exhibits some interesting features which are worth pointing out here. We start again with the rate of radiation

$$-\frac{\partial \mathscr{E}}{\partial t} = -\int \frac{\partial T^{44}}{\partial t} \, dV = \int T^{4i} \, d\Gamma_i \qquad (10.49)$$

where $d\Gamma_i$ is the surface element. From (10.21) this becomes

$$-\frac{\partial \mathscr{E}}{\partial t} = \frac{c}{4\pi} \int (\vec{E} \times \vec{H}) \cdot \vec{d\Gamma} \qquad (10.50)$$

To calculate E and H we use the solution in a spherical coordinate system,

$$\partial_\mu \partial^\mu A^\nu = -4\pi j^\nu; \qquad A^\nu = \int \frac{\rho(x') u^\nu \, dV'}{cR}. \qquad (10.51)$$

From these, for large R,

$$A^\nu = \frac{1}{cR} \sum (eu^\nu) = \frac{1}{cR} \dot{D}^\nu \qquad (10.52)$$

where

$$D^\nu = \sum ex^\nu; \qquad \dot{D}^\nu = \frac{dD^\nu}{d\tau}. \qquad (10.53)$$

It is clear $\dot{D}_4 = \sum e \, dt/d\tau = \sum e/\sqrt{1 - v^2/c^2}$ depends only on v^2/c^2, and therefore, $\dot{D}_4$ is one order of magnitude smaller than $\dot{D}_1$. This means we may use only the vector potential

$\vec{A}_k$ in calculating the E and H fields for the purpose of deriving the radiation in the lowest approximation.

$$E_k = f_{4k} = -\frac{i}{c} A_k; \qquad \vec{H} = \text{curl } \vec{A} = \frac{1}{c} \dot{\vec{A}} \times \vec{n} = \vec{E} \times \vec{n} \qquad (10.54)$$

The vector $\vec{n}$ is a unit vector in the direction of propagation, which is in the direction of increasing R. Putting these together, we get, at large distances,

$$-\frac{\partial \mathscr{E}}{\partial t} = \frac{1}{4\pi c^3} \int A^2 \sin^2 \theta R^2 \, d\sigma = \frac{1}{4\pi c^3} \ddot{D}^2 \int \sin^2 \theta \, d\sigma \qquad (10.55)$$

where $d\sigma$ is the element of the solid angle $d\sigma = \sin \theta \, d\theta \, d\phi$. Evaluating the integral gives

$$-\frac{\partial \mathscr{E}}{\partial t} = \left(\frac{2}{3c^3}\right) \ddot{D}^2. \qquad (10.56)$$

The quantity $D_i = \Sigma \, e x_i$ is called the "dipole moment" of the charge distribution. A free electron (having a uniform motion, $\ddot{x} = 0$) does not radiate.

The monopole ($Q = \Sigma \, e$) radiation must vanish due to the conservation of charge. Furthermore, if $e = \lambda m$, where λ is a constant, dipole radiation also vanishes due to the conservation of momentum. An isolated system of electrons (electron gas, for example) cannot give dipole radiation. When a system cannot radiate energy due to some conservation laws (charge, momentum, angular momentum, parity, et cetera), the corresponding radiation process is said to be forbidden. In a given system the set of rules, indicating which are the allowed and which the forbidden radiations, is called *selection rules*.

Further approximations in the electromagnetic radiation involve magnetic dipole, electric quadrupole... et cetera, radiations.

10.8. Scattering of Electromagnetic Waves

An effect closely related to radiation is the phenomenon of *scattering* of light. To see it in its simplest form, let a plane electromagnetic wave fall on a charged particle at rest, say an electron. Then the electron would be set into periodic motion by the field. The periodic motion of the electron would, in turn, give rise to dipole radiation. The computation in this case is very simple. Assuming propagation of the original wave in the x direction, $E = B \sin(\omega t - kx)$ and putting the electron at the point $x = x_1$

$$E = B \sin(\omega t - \alpha). \qquad (10.57)$$

The equation of motion then leads to

$$m \frac{d^2 x}{d\tau^2} = m \ddot{x} = eB \sin(\omega t - \alpha)$$

$$\qquad (10.58)$$

$$\ddot{D} = e\ddot{x} = \frac{e^2}{m} B \sin(\omega t - \alpha).$$

If we put this into the radiation formula, we get, for the total amount of energy scattered per unit time,

$$-\frac{\partial \mathscr{E}}{\partial t} = \frac{2E^2 e^4}{3m^2 c^3} \qquad (10.59)$$

This is the energy which is removed from the original wave and scattered in all directions. In other words, we may consider the process as an absorption of energy by the particle and a subsequent reradiation. Note also that an infinitely heavy particle would not scatter electromagnetic waves. One may ask: "What is the equivalent area on the original wave front from which the energy is removed and scattered into all directions?" If we denote this area by σ, we have from (10.50)

$$-\frac{\partial \mathscr{E}}{\partial t} = \frac{c}{4\pi} (E \times H)\sigma = \frac{c}{4\pi} E^2 \sigma. \tag{10.60}$$

Equating this to the above expression, we get

$$\sigma = \frac{8\pi}{3} \left(\frac{e^2}{mc^2}\right)^2. \tag{10.61}$$

The area σ is called the *scattering cross section*. Formula (10.61) is called the Thomson scattering formula. It applies only to free electrons and in the dipole approximation. For bound electrons and for higher order approximations, the treatment is similar, although the formulas become somewhat complicated.

We have treated above the scattering of waves from a free electron. Consider a bound electron, such as one attached to an atom. The electron in this case may be considered as though attached to an elastic spring, so that in equation (10.58) the force of binding may be included

$$m\ddot{x} = -\omega_0^2 x + eB \sin (\omega t - \alpha) \tag{10.62}$$

which gives

$$x = \frac{eB \cos (\omega t - \alpha)}{m(\omega_0^2 - \omega^2)}. \tag{10.63}$$

Now, calculating $\ddot{D} = e\ddot{x}$, we have, following the previous method,

$$\sigma = \frac{8\pi}{3} \left(\frac{e}{mc^2}\right)^2 \frac{\omega^4}{(\omega_0^2 - \omega^2)^2}. \tag{10.64}$$

Here we see that the high frequency limit, $\omega \gg \omega_0$, is the same as before. There is a resonance when $\omega = \omega_0$. At low frequencies $\omega \ll \omega_0$ we have

$$\sigma = \frac{8\pi}{3} \left(\frac{e^2}{mc^2}\right)^2 \frac{\omega^4}{\omega_0^4}. \tag{10.65}$$

The scattering of light by the earth's atmosphere is described by this case. The fact that the sky is blue is explained by this formula, according to which the blue end of the visible spectrum is scattered more than the yellow and red. Scattering according to (10.64) is called Rayleigh scattering.

10.9. Radiation Reaction

Before we conclude this chapter we would like to discuss the interesting concept of *radiation reaction*. According to equation (10.56) an accelerated charge is, in general, expected to radiate ($\ddot{D}$ is the charge times its acceleration). In fact, electrons stopped by the cathode of an X-ray tube, or electrons moving in a circle, as in a synchrotron, do radiate. Generally, electrons passing through a strong electromagnetic field are accelerated and radiate electromagnetic waves. Such radiation is called *bremsstrahlung*. Due to the energy given off in the form of radiation, the electrons must slow down, that is, their motion must be damped. This is called *radiation damping* or, more generally, the *radiation reaction*. For example, electrons in a hydrogen atom have the radial acceleration $\ddot{r} = e^2/mr^2$. The rate of radiation is then $-d\mathcal{E}/dt = (2e^4/3c^2m^2r^4)$. Thus, according to this, the electron should lose energy on each revolution, finally falling onto the nucleus. This prediction of instability for atoms is *not* observed to be the case. When electrons are confined in configurations of the order of $l = 10^{-8}$ cm or less, we need the help of quantum mechanics for their description. Classical theory is no longer adequate. Nevertheless, the radiation phenomenon is essentially a classical concept, governed by the general conservation laws. Therefore, it must be possible to derive at least an approximate formula for the radiation damping. For a single electron, equation (10.56) takes the form

$$-\frac{d\mathcal{E}}{dt} = \frac{2e^2}{3c^2}\,\dot{u}^2.$$

If, because of this radiation, a force f may be said to act on the electron, we have $d\mathcal{E} = f_i\,dx^i$. Thus the equation can be written as

$$\frac{d\mathcal{E}}{dt} = f_i u^i = \frac{2e^2}{3c^2}\,\ddot{u}_i u^i - \frac{2e^2}{3c^2}\frac{d}{dt}\,(u_i \dot{u}^i).$$

It can be shown that the last term fluctuates and therefore, over a sufficiently long time period, gives a zero contribution. Thus, on the average, the equation

$$f_i = \frac{2e^2}{3c^3}\,\dddot{x}_i$$

must be satisfied. Many interesting applications may be made of this equation despite its approximate nature. For example, the equation of motion of an electron performing harmonic oscillations takes the form

$$\ddot{x} + \omega_0^2 x - \frac{2e^2}{3c^3}\,\dddot{x} = 0.$$

Since the damping term is very small, $\dddot{x} \simeq -\omega_0^2\dot{x}$, putting this in we have the form

$$\ddot{x} + \gamma\dot{x} + \omega_0^2 x = 0$$

where $\gamma = 2e^2\omega^2/3c^3$. The solution of this is of the form

$$x = A\cos(\omega_0 t + \alpha)\,e^{-\gamma t/2}$$

showing that the electron loses energy and its motion is damped down by the reaction force.

Summary: Electromagnetic Field

(a) The electromagnetic field is a real vector field. Its source is a real four-vector, namely, the charge-current vector.

(b) The electric charge is a conserved quantity.

(c) Physically observable quantities of electrodynamics are invariant under gauge transformations. Any expression which is not invariant under gauge transformations is not an observable quantity.

(d) The positive definiteness of energy leads to the Lorentz condition.

(e) The polarizability of electromagnetic waves is due to the multicomponent character of the field.

(f) The intrinsic angular momentum is also a result of the fact that the field has more than one component.

(g) The solutions of the wave equation and of boundary value problems are essentially analogous to those corresponding to the scalar field.

(h) Radiation and scattering are the consequences of relativistic field concepts. A field propagating with infinite velocity would not have these properties.

(i) A force, called the radiation reaction, acts on a radiating electron damping down the motion of the electron. A free electron, undergoing unaccelerated motion, does not radiate.

11

SPINOR FIELDS

11.1. Representations of the Lorentz Group

In this chapter we encounter the spinor fields. Although spinor fields are just as natural and necessary as the scalar and vector fields, they are not as familiar from the classical point of view. In fact, it is sometimes said that spinor fields are of quantum mechanical origin and that they do not have a classical field theory analogy. Nevertheless, spinor fields are members of the family of relativistic fields and, when looked at closely, exhibit all the essential features of a field theory, such as interference, diffraction, radiation, et cetera. In the theory of relativity the existence of various types of fields is related to the various representations of the Lorentz group of transformations. A representation of the Lorentz group (see Chapter 6) is a quantity which retains its identity under a Lorentz transformation. For example, a field function $f(x, y, z, t)$ can be such that, in the new frame of reference, we may have

$$f'(x', y', z', t') = f(x, y, z, t).$$

Then we say that the function, f, is a *scalar* representation of the Lorentz transformations. Similarly, we may take a four index field $V_\nu(x, y, z, t)$. If after a Lorentz transformation

$$V'_\mu(x') = \mathscr{L}^\nu_\mu V_\nu(x)$$

where $\mathscr{L}_\mu = \partial x'^\nu / \partial x^\mu$ is an element of the Lorentz transformation, then we say that V_ν is a vector representation of the Lorentz group. Generalizing this idea, we see that a tensor $U_{\mu\nu}...$ is a representation if

$$U'_{\alpha\beta}...(x') = \mathscr{L}^\mu_\alpha \mathscr{L}^\nu_\beta ... U_{\mu\nu}...(x).$$

Any representation of the Lorentz transformations is a possible candidate for a field function. As shorthand, let us disregard indices and write these formally as

$$\psi'(x') = \mathscr{L}^s \psi(x)$$

where $\mathscr{L}^0 = 1$, $\mathscr{L}^1 = \mathscr{L}$, $\mathscr{L}^2 = \mathscr{L}\mathscr{L}$, ... correspond to scalars, vectors, tensors, and so on. Now the question arises: Are there other representations of the Lorentz group corresponding to other values of s, say, $s = \frac{7}{5}$? It was found by mathematicians that all the representations which have a finite number of components correspond either to $s = n$, where n is an integer, or $s = n + \frac{1}{2}$. The latter are generally called spinors. Thus we have

$s = 0$	scalar (or zero-order tensor)
$s = \frac{1}{2}$	spinor (or $\frac{1}{2}$-order tensor)
$s = 1$	vector (or 1st-order tensor)
$s = \frac{3}{2}$	spinor $\frac{3}{2}$ (or $\frac{3}{2}$-order tensor)
$s = 2$	second-order tensor
	and so on.

(We may note, in passing, that in quantum theory s corresponds to spin. For example, a meson field has $s = 0$, so the meson has no spin. On the other hand, the electromagnetic field is a vector and has spin 1. The electron is represented by a spinor $s = \frac{1}{2}$. It therefore has spin $\frac{1}{2}$. But these features become apparent only after quantization. In the previous chapters we have treated the scalar $(s = 0)$ field and the vector $(s = 1)$ electromagnetic field. In this chapter we will treat the case of a spinor $(s = \frac{1}{2})$ field. Higher tensors and higher spinors will not be treated. So far, in nature, only the cases $s = 0$, $\frac{1}{2}$, and 1 appear to exist and therefore we will limit ourselves to these three cases. (Gravitational field is supposed to have $s = 2$ but there is no experimental evidence for this. Furthermore gravitation is purely geometrical in content as will be seen later.)

11.2. Spinor Field Equation

After these preliminaries, let ψ represent the spinor field. In empty space it must satisfy a propagation equation of the form

$$(\partial_\mu \partial^\mu - \kappa^2)\psi = 0. \tag{11.1}$$

This equation is a second-order differential equation. If we use it in the form (11.1) we will have nothing different from a scalar or vector fields. Therefore, we shall inquire about the possibility of having a different field equation which will still satisfy (11.1). For this purpose, let us consider an ψ which, in addition, satisfies the following first-order equation

$$(\gamma_\mu \partial^\mu + \kappa)\psi = 0 \tag{11.2}$$

for our basic equation.† Here the γ_μ are, as yet, unknown. We propose to obtain the propagation equation (11.1) from this after multiplying it by $\gamma^\nu \partial_\nu - \kappa$. We want to have

$$(\gamma^\nu \partial_\nu - \kappa)(\gamma_\mu \partial^\mu + \kappa)\psi = (\partial_\mu \partial^\mu - \kappa^2)\psi = 0 \tag{11.3}$$

from which γ_μ are seen to satisfy

$$\gamma_\mu \gamma_\nu + \gamma_\nu \gamma_\mu = 2g_{\mu\nu}. \tag{11.4}$$

In other words, if the γ's satisfy this relation, the function ψ is a candidate for a possible physical field. Evidently γ's cannot be ordinary numbers since according to (11.4) they do not commute. One can represent them by matrices. (See Appendix B for a short survey of matrices and operators.) For example,

$$
\gamma_1 = \begin{pmatrix} \mathbf{O} & \begin{matrix} 0 & -i \\ -i & 0 \end{matrix} \\ \begin{matrix} 0 & i \\ i & 0 \end{matrix} & \mathbf{O} \end{pmatrix}, \quad
\gamma_2 = \begin{pmatrix} \mathbf{O} & \begin{matrix} 0 & 1 \\ -1 & 0 \end{matrix} \\ \begin{matrix} 0 & -1 \\ 1 & 0 \end{matrix} & \mathbf{O} \end{pmatrix},
$$

$$
\gamma_3 = \begin{pmatrix} \mathbf{O} & \begin{matrix} -i & 0 \\ 0 & i \end{matrix} \\ \begin{matrix} i & 0 \\ 0 & -i \end{matrix} & \mathbf{O} \end{pmatrix}, \quad
\gamma_4 = \begin{pmatrix} \begin{matrix} 1 & 0 \\ 0 & 1 \end{matrix} & \mathbf{O} \\ \mathbf{O} & \begin{matrix} -1 & 0 \\ 0 & -1 \end{matrix} \end{pmatrix}. \tag{11.5}
$$

† Historically, Dirac introduced the equation (11.2) on the ground that it must be first order in time so that $\bar{\psi}\psi$ can represent probability. We know now that this argument can be defended only after field quantization and the use of the exclusion principle (see Chapter 13, section 7).

Actually, this is not the only set which satisfies (11.4). One can find an infinite number of such sets. To see how this is possible, let us subject γ_μ to a similarity transformation $\gamma'_\mu = \Lambda\gamma_\mu\Lambda^{-1}$ where Λ is any nonsingular 4×4 matrix. Then $\gamma_\mu = \Lambda\gamma'_\mu\Lambda$ and (11.4) will become

$$\Lambda^{-1}(\gamma'_\mu\gamma'_\nu + \gamma'_\nu\gamma'_\mu)\Lambda = 2g_{\mu\nu} \quad \text{or} \quad \gamma'_\mu\gamma'_\nu + \gamma'_\nu\gamma'_\mu = 2\Lambda g_{\mu\nu}\Lambda^{-1} = 2g_{\mu\nu}.$$

Thus γ'_μ defined by

$$\gamma'_\mu = \Lambda\gamma_\mu\Lambda^{-1} \tag{11.6}$$

will be just as good, corresponding to the new function $\psi' = \Lambda\psi$.
As an example that will be used later, let

$$\Lambda = \Lambda^{-1} = \frac{1}{\sqrt{2}}\begin{pmatrix} 1 & 0 & 1 & 0 \\ 0 & 1 & 0 & 1 \\ 1 & 0 & -1 & 0 \\ 0 & 1 & 0 & -1 \end{pmatrix};$$

then

$$\gamma'_k = \Lambda\gamma_k\Lambda^{-1} = \gamma_k; \qquad \gamma'_4 = \Lambda\gamma_4\Lambda^{-1} = \begin{pmatrix} 0 & 0 & 1 & 0 \\ 0 & 0 & 0 & 1 \\ 1 & 0 & 0 & 0 \\ 0 & 1 & 0 & 0 \end{pmatrix}. \tag{11.7}$$

$$(\gamma'_k\partial_k + \kappa)\psi' = 0. \tag{11.8}$$

It is clear by now that ψ is not a scalar since, in general, it will be operated on by γ's and Λ's. We may take it as the column matrix,

$$\psi = \begin{pmatrix} \psi_1 \\ \psi_2 \\ \psi_3 \\ \psi_4 \end{pmatrix}. \tag{11.9}$$

We will see that $\psi_1, \psi_2 \ldots$ are not the components of a four vector either. We call ψ a spinor. Equation (11.2) is called a spinor equation or the Dirac equation, after its discoverer. Its properties will be described in this chapter.

The γ-matrices (11.5) are called the Dirac matrices. For the sake of simplicity in calculations, they may be condensed into

$$\gamma_k = \begin{pmatrix} 0 & -i\sigma_k \\ \hline i\sigma_k & 0 \end{pmatrix} \qquad \gamma_4 = \begin{pmatrix} \mathbb{1} & 0 \\ \hline 0 & -\mathbb{1} \end{pmatrix} \tag{11.10}$$

where

$$\sigma_1 = \begin{pmatrix} 0 & 1 \\ 1 & 0 \end{pmatrix}, \qquad \sigma_2 = \begin{pmatrix} 0 & -i \\ i & 0 \end{pmatrix}, \qquad \sigma_3 = \begin{pmatrix} 1 & 0 \\ 0 & -1 \end{pmatrix}, \qquad \mathbb{1} = \begin{pmatrix} 1 & 0 \\ 0 & 1 \end{pmatrix} \tag{11.11}$$

are called the Pauli matrices. They have the following properties:

$$\sigma_j^2 = , \qquad \sigma_1\sigma_2 = -\sigma_2\sigma_1 = i\sigma_3 \text{ (and cyclical perm.)}. \tag{11.12}$$

In concluding this section we note that the row matrix defined by

$$\bar{\psi} = \psi^*\gamma_4 = (\psi_1^*, \psi_2^*, -\psi_3^*, -\psi_4^*) \tag{11.13}$$

satisfies the equation

$$\bar{\psi}(\overleftarrow{\partial}_\mu \gamma^\mu - \kappa) = 0 \tag{11.14}$$

where $\overleftarrow{\partial}_\mu$ indicates that differentiation applies to $\bar{\psi}$ at the left. This remark shows that $(\gamma_\mu \partial_\mu + \kappa)$ and $(\gamma_\mu \partial_\mu - \kappa)$ are being employed equivalently and on the same footing.

At this point we introduce a new principle. The observable quantities depending on a spinor are invariant under the transformation

$$\psi \to \psi e^{i\Lambda} \qquad \bar{\psi} \to \bar{\psi} e^{-i\Lambda}$$

where Λ is a constant or a scalar function. We will refer to this as the *principle of gauge invariance of the first kind.*† As a consequence of this principle the ψ itself is unobservable. In fact, quantities corresponding to any observation can contain only such terms as $\bar{\psi}\psi$, $\bar{\psi}B\psi$, $\bar{\psi}M\psi\bar{\psi}N\psi$, et cetera, so that $\bar{\psi}$ and ψ appear in a bilinear form. Other consequences will be mentioned later.

11.3. Relativistic Invariance

The covariance of the spinor field equation (11.2) is not as evident as for the scalar or vector field equations. For this reason it will be advisable to demonstrate explicitly that this equation is form-invariant under Lorentz transformations. Let a Lorentz transformation be performed. We wish to have in the two inertial frames, respectively,

$$(\gamma_\mu \partial_\mu + \kappa)\psi = 0; \qquad (\gamma_\mu \partial'_\mu + \kappa)\psi' = 0. \tag{11.15}$$

Now, according to (3.24) we have

$$\partial'_\mu = a^\nu_\mu \partial_\nu. \tag{11.16}$$

Let us assume for the transformation of ψ's

$$\psi' = S\psi. \tag{11.17}$$

where S is unitary (see Chapter 6). Putting these in, we have

$$(\gamma_\mu a^\nu_\mu \partial_\nu + \kappa)S\psi = 0. \tag{11.18}$$

Multiplying this from the left by S^{-1} we find

$$(S^{-1}\gamma_\mu a^\nu_\mu S \partial_\nu + \kappa)\psi = 0. \tag{11.19}$$

In order that this be identical with the first equation we must have

$$S^{-1}\gamma_\mu a^\nu_\mu S = \gamma_\nu$$

or

$$S\gamma_\nu S^{-1} = \gamma_\mu a^\nu_\mu. \tag{11.20}$$

In other words, if there exists a unitary matrix S satisfying this condition, the spinor equation will be form-invariant under Lorentz transformations. It may be proven by direct substitution (see also problem 12.1) that

$$S = e^{\frac{1}{4}\gamma^\alpha \gamma^\beta \phi_{\alpha\beta}} \tag{11.21}$$

where $\phi_{\alpha\beta} = -\phi_{\beta\alpha}$ is the angle parameter of the Lorentz group for the x^α, x^β plane. We consider the following special cases:

† The gauge transformation (10.4) is called second kind.

(a). Rotation in the xy plane by an angle ϕ. We have in this case $\phi_{12} = \phi$, $\phi_{21} = -\phi$ all the other components being zero. Expanding S into a Taylor series and collecting similar terms,

$$S_{\alpha\beta} = 1 + \tfrac{1}{2}\gamma^\alpha\gamma^\beta\phi - \tfrac{1}{8}\phi^2 \ldots = \cos\frac{\phi}{2} + \gamma^\alpha\gamma^\beta \sin\frac{\phi}{2}, \tag{11.22}$$

and

$$S_{\alpha\beta}^{-1} = \cos\frac{\phi}{2} - \gamma^\alpha\gamma^\beta \sin\frac{\phi}{2}. \tag{11.23}$$

We may now check equation (11.20)

$$\begin{aligned}
\gamma_1' &= S_{12}\gamma_2 S_{12}^{-1} = \gamma_1 \cos\phi - \gamma_2 \sin\phi \\
\gamma_2' &= S_{12}\gamma_1 S_{12}^{-1} = \gamma_1 \sin\phi + \gamma_2 \cos\phi
\end{aligned} \tag{11.24}$$

which indicates that γ_μ may be considered as a four vector. The transformation of ψ is now given as $\psi' = S\psi$ which leads by evaluating S to

$$S = \begin{pmatrix} e^{-i\phi/2} & & & \bigcirc \\ & e^{i\phi/2} & & \\ & & e^{-i\phi/2} & \\ \bigcirc & & & e^{i\phi/2} \end{pmatrix}$$

$$\psi_1' = e^{-i\phi/2}\psi_1, \quad \psi_2' = e^{i\phi/2}\psi_2, \quad \psi_3' = e^{-\phi/2}\psi_3, \quad \psi_4' = e^{i\phi/2}\psi_4. \tag{11.25}$$

(b). Rotation in the z, t plane by an angle $i\alpha_{34} = -i\alpha_{43} = i\alpha$ (Lorentz transformation with $\tan\alpha = v/c$),

$$S_{34} = e^{\frac{1}{2}\gamma^3\gamma^4\alpha} = \cosh\frac{\alpha}{2} + \gamma^3\gamma^4 \sinh\frac{\alpha}{2}$$

$$S_{34} = \begin{pmatrix} \cosh\dfrac{\alpha}{2} & 0 & \sinh\dfrac{\alpha}{2} & 0 \\ 0 & \cosh\dfrac{\alpha}{2} & \bigcirc & -\sinh\dfrac{\alpha}{2} \\ -\sinh\dfrac{\alpha}{2} & 0 & \cosh\dfrac{\alpha}{2} & 0 \\ 0 & \sinh\dfrac{\alpha}{2} & 0 & \cosh\dfrac{\alpha}{2} \end{pmatrix} \tag{11.26}$$

leading to the transformations

$$\psi_1' = \psi_1 \cosh\frac{\alpha}{2} + \psi_3 \sinh\frac{\alpha}{2}$$

$$\psi_2' = \psi_2 \cosh\frac{\alpha}{2} - \psi_4 \sinh\frac{\alpha}{2}$$

$$\psi_3' = \psi_3 \cosh\frac{\alpha}{2} - \psi_1 \sinh\frac{\alpha}{2} \tag{11.27}$$

$$\psi_4' = \psi_4 \cosh\frac{\alpha}{2} + \psi_2 \sinh\frac{\alpha}{2}.$$

Note the factor $\frac{1}{2}$ in all elements of S. This indicates that when the coordinate axes rotate by an angle ϕ the spinor rotates only by $\phi/2$. This justifies the symbolic way of representing S by the square root of the Lorentz transformations as $S \rightarrow \mathscr{L}^{\frac{1}{2}}$. When the coordinate axes rotate by 2π the spinor rotates by π, that is, it changes sign. Thus the spinor is a double-valued function. Since an observable result cannot be double valued, the ψ field itself cannot be an observable. One can easily see that an expression of the type $\bar{\psi}A\psi$, where ψ appears in a bilinear form, is single valued and can be taken as an observable. To assume that only such quantities will be used as observables we set forth here a new principle: *The observables of the theory are quantities which are invariant under the transformation:*

$$\psi \rightarrow \psi e^{i\Lambda}; \qquad \bar{\psi} \rightarrow \bar{\psi} e^{-i\Lambda}. \tag{11.28}$$

This is called the principle of gauge invariance of the first kind. It simply says that only bilinear combinations of ψ and $\bar{\psi}$ are observable quantities.

Here also we may examine the space reflection (P) and time reversal (T) properties of the spinor equation. For space inversion, we need, according to (11.20), a matrix $S = P$ such that

$$P\gamma_i P^{-1} = -\gamma_i, \qquad P\gamma_4 P^{-1} = \gamma_4$$

which, obviously, gives

$$P = P^{-1} = \gamma_4. \tag{11.29}$$

For time reversal

$$T\gamma_i T^{-1} = \gamma_i; \qquad T\gamma_4 T^{-1} = -\gamma_4$$

leads to

$$T = \gamma_1 \gamma_2 \gamma_3, \qquad T^{-1} = \gamma_3 \gamma_2 \gamma_1. \tag{11.30}$$

We see that

$$P\psi = \gamma_4 \psi = \begin{pmatrix} \psi_1 \\ \psi_2 \\ -\psi_1 \\ -\psi_2 \end{pmatrix}, \qquad T\psi = \begin{pmatrix} \psi_3 \\ -\psi_4 \\ -\psi_1 \\ \psi_2 \end{pmatrix}. \tag{11.31}$$

These show that the Dirac equation is form-invariant under the space-inversion and time-reversal transformations.

11.4. Energy-Momentum and Angular Momentum

The energy and momentum of the spinor field will be taken as the integral.†

$$P^\mu = \frac{i}{2} \int \{\bar{\psi}\gamma^\nu \partial^\mu \psi + \bar{\psi}\gamma^\mu \partial^\nu \psi\} \, dS_\nu. \tag{11.32}$$

Here the second term may be shown to equal the first, and we have

$$P^\mu = i \int \bar{\psi}\gamma^\nu \partial^\mu \psi \, dS_\nu = i \int T^{\mu\nu} S_\nu \tag{11.33}$$

where $T^{\mu\nu} = \bar{\psi}\gamma^\nu \partial^\mu \psi$ is the stress-energy tensor. The divergence of this tensor vanishes due to the field equations (11.2) and (11.14):

$$\partial_\mu T^{\mu\nu} = \partial_\mu \bar{\psi}\gamma^\mu \partial^\nu \psi + \bar{\psi}\partial^\mu \partial_\mu \partial^\nu \psi$$

† Note that in this chapter we will use the system of units in which $c = 1$.

which, by adding and subtracting $\bar{\psi}\kappa\partial^\nu\psi$, may be written as

$$\partial_\mu T^{\mu\nu} = \bar{\psi}(\overleftarrow{\partial}_\mu\gamma_\mu - \kappa)\partial^\nu\psi + \bar{\psi}\partial^\nu(\gamma_\mu\partial_\mu + \kappa)\psi = 0. \tag{11.34}$$

Thus, the divergence vanishes because of (11.2) and (11.12). The angular momentum may be constructed as

$$M^{\mu\nu} = \int(\bar{\psi}\gamma^\rho\partial^\nu\psi x^\mu - \bar{\psi}\gamma^\rho\partial^\mu\psi x^\mu)\, dS_\rho + \tfrac{1}{2}\int \bar{\psi}\gamma^\rho\gamma^\mu\gamma^\nu\psi\, dS_\rho \tag{11.35}$$

which, as in the vector field case, separates into "orbital" and "spin" parts

$$M^{\mu\nu} = L^{\mu\nu} + N^{\mu\nu} \tag{11.36}$$

$$L^{\mu\nu} = \int(\bar{\psi}\gamma^\rho\partial^\nu\psi x^\mu - \bar{\psi}\gamma^\rho\partial^\mu\psi x^\nu)\, dS_\rho \tag{11.37}$$

$$N^{\mu\nu} = \tfrac{1}{2}\int \bar{\psi}\gamma^\sigma\gamma^\mu\gamma^\nu\psi\, dS_\sigma. \tag{11.38}$$

These terms are not separately conserved, although the sum $M^{\mu\nu} = L^{\mu\nu} + N^{\mu\nu}$ is, of course, a conserved quantity (for the origin of spin see Chapter 12).

11.5. The Charge-Current Vector

From the spinor field one can construct still another conserved quantity, which we interpret as the electric charge. Consider the vector $j^\mu = e\bar{\psi}\gamma^\mu\psi$ where e is a constant. (We define e such that the unit charge has the numerical value $e = \sqrt{c\hbar\, 4\pi/137}$ which eliminates factors of c and 4π from all the equations.)

$$\partial_\mu j^\mu = e\partial_\mu\bar{\psi}\gamma^\mu\psi + e\bar{\psi}\gamma^\mu\partial_\mu\psi \tag{11.39}$$

which, by adding and subtracting $e\bar{\psi}\kappa\psi$, may be put into the form

$$e\bar{\psi}(\overleftarrow{\partial}_\mu\gamma^\mu - \kappa)\psi + e\bar{\psi}(\gamma^\mu\partial_\mu + \kappa\psi) = 0. \tag{11.40}$$

Thus due to the field equations the divergence vanishes. This means that j^μ is interpretable as the charge-current vector, if we choose e as the unit of charge; then

$$Q = \int j^\mu\, dS_\mu = \int e\bar{\psi}\gamma^4\psi\, dV \tag{11.41}$$

will represent a conserved quantity, the total electric charge.

11.6. Solutions of the Spinor Wave Equation

The second order spinor equation (11.1) is formally the same as (8.13) and therefore there will be similarities in the solutions. For example, a solution may be written as

$$\psi = ae^{ikx} + b^*e^{-ikx} \tag{11.42}$$

where a and b^* are two integration constants. Since ψ is complex, a and b^* are complex numbers. Since ψ is a column matrix, a and b^* are also column matrices. Furthermore, ψ also satisfies (11.2), so that there will be additional relations between the components of a and b^*. In order to simplify the treatment, we may deal separately with the $(+)$ and $(-)$ frequency parts. These transform separately (independent of each other) under proper Lorentz transformations. Let the field depend on time alone. The $(+)$ frequency part reduces to

$$\psi^{(+)} = ae^{-i\omega_0 t}. \tag{11.43}$$

Putting this into (11.2), we find $\left(-\dfrac{\omega_0}{c}\gamma_4 + \kappa\right)a = 0$, so that

$$\left(-\frac{\omega_0}{c} + \kappa\right)a_1 = 0, \qquad \left(-\frac{\omega_0}{c} + \kappa\right)a_2 = 0, \qquad a_3 = a_4 = 0.$$

Thus, if $\omega_0 = c\kappa$, a solution exists of the form

$$\psi^{(+)} = \begin{pmatrix} a_1 \\ a_2 \\ 0 \\ 0 \end{pmatrix} e^{-i\omega_0 t}. \tag{11.44}$$

But we actually have two linearly independent solutions, since a_1 and a_2 are independent. Let $\psi^{(+)} = \psi^{(+)\uparrow} + \psi^{(+)\downarrow}$

$$\psi^{(+)\uparrow} = \begin{pmatrix} 1 \\ 0 \\ 0 \\ 0 \end{pmatrix} a_1 e^{-i\omega_0 t}; \qquad \psi^{(+)\downarrow} = \begin{pmatrix} 0 \\ 1 \\ 0 \\ 0 \end{pmatrix} a_2 e^{-i\omega_0 t}. \tag{11.45}$$

The reason for distinguishing them this way is that, if we compute the "spin" angular moment in the z-direction, we find $\frac{1}{2}\int a_1^* a_1 \, dV$ and $-\frac{1}{2}\int a_2^* a_2 \, dV$, respectively, so that "spin up" and "spin down" may be characterized by ($\uparrow$) and ($\downarrow$), respectively.

The rest solution (11.43) have associated energy (it is positive) and spin, but no momentum. If the field propagates, say in the z-direction, we should also have a momentum. To find the z-dependent solutions we simply transform them with the matrix (11.26):

$$\psi^{(+)\uparrow}(t,z) = \begin{pmatrix} \cosh\dfrac{\alpha}{2} \\ 0 \\ -\sinh\dfrac{\alpha}{2} \\ 0 \end{pmatrix} a_1 e^{i(kz-\omega t)}, \qquad \psi^{(+)\downarrow} = \begin{pmatrix} 0 \\ \cosh\dfrac{\alpha}{2} \\ 0 \\ \sinh\dfrac{\alpha}{2} \end{pmatrix} a_2 e^{i(kz-\omega t)}. \tag{11.46}$$

These solutions now have, according to (11.33), the energy and momentum.

$$P_\uparrow^\mu = \int a_1^* a_1 k^\mu \, dV; \qquad P_\downarrow^\mu = \int a_2^* a_2 k^\mu \, dV. \tag{11.47}$$

Here $\tanh\alpha = \dfrac{v}{c} = \dfrac{k}{\omega}$ and, therefore,

$$\cosh\frac{\alpha}{2} = \frac{\dfrac{\omega}{c} + \kappa}{\sqrt{2\kappa\left(\dfrac{\omega}{c} + \kappa\right)}}$$

and

$$\sinh \frac{\alpha}{2} = \frac{k}{\sqrt{2\kappa \left(\dfrac{\omega}{c} + \kappa \right)}}$$

may be substituted, if necessary.

In a completely similar fashion we can obtain for the negative frequencies

$$\psi^{(-)\,\uparrow}(t, z) = \begin{vmatrix} \sinh \dfrac{\alpha}{2} \\ 0 \\ \cosh \dfrac{\alpha}{2} \\ 0 \end{vmatrix} b_3^* e^{-i(kz - \omega t)}; \qquad \psi^{(-)\,\downarrow}(t, z) = \begin{vmatrix} 0 \\ \sinh \dfrac{\alpha}{2} \\ 0 \\ \cosh \dfrac{\alpha}{2} \end{vmatrix} b_4^* e^{-i(kz - \omega t)}. \quad (11.48)$$

But the energy and momentum of these solutions are negative. Summarizing, we have the following table (the wave is traveling in the z-direction):

Solution	$\mathscr{E}$	P_3	N^{12}	
$u_1 = \psi^{(+)\,\uparrow}(t, z)$	$\Lambda_1 \omega$	$+\Lambda_1 k$	$+\frac{1}{2}\Lambda_1$	
$u_2 = \psi^{(+)\,\downarrow}(t, z)$	$\Lambda_2 \omega$	$+\Lambda_2 k$	$-\frac{1}{2}\Lambda_2$	(11.49)
$v_1 = \psi^{(-)\,\uparrow}(t, z)$	$-\Lambda_3 \omega$	$-\Lambda_3 k$	$+\frac{1}{2}\Lambda_3$	
$v_2 = \psi^{(-)\,\downarrow}(t, z)$	$-\Lambda_4 \omega$	$-\Lambda_4 k$	$-\frac{1}{2}\Lambda_4$	

where $\Lambda_1 = \int a_1^* a_1 \, dV$ et cetera. Λ being always positive. Now from the outset the negative frequency solutions are unacceptable because, unlike the case of the scalar and vector fields, they lead to a negative field energy, and thereby conflict with the principle of positive-definiteness of energy. One might think that we can simply ignore them by putting $b_3 = b_4 = 0$. After all, we have also ignored some solutions of the wave equation in order to satisfy the causality principle. It turns out, however, that to ignore the negative energy solutions in this way is unsatisfactory because if we consider a $(+)$ frequency part in interaction with, say, an electric field, the $(-)$ frequency modes will be excited. To put it in contemporary terms, transitions will occur from $(+)$ to $(-)$ frequency states. Therefore, we require a different interpretation of the negative frequency states. This is achieved by means of a condition placed on the a and b^* coefficients. This condition turns out to be the quantum condition for spinor fields. After this condition is imposed (see Chapter 13), the negative frequencies no longer lead to negative energies; they lead, as do those of the scalar fields, to positive energies. The particles represented by negative frequencies (which have positive energy) are called antiparticles. It is interesting that this quantization process is equivalent to the exclusion principle of Pauli. It allows only one electron or positron for each state of the field. Thus, without introducing quantization it is difficult to make sense of the spinor equation. It is for this reason that the spinor field is sometimes regarded as quantum mechanical, in contrast to classical, although this is not completely so. Very often, the spin angular momentum is also claimed to be nonclassical which is, as we have seen, somewhat erroneous.

The complete solution of the Dirac equation for given momentum and direction is

$$\psi(k, x) = c_1 \psi^{(+)\uparrow} + c_2 \psi^{(+)\downarrow} + c_3 \psi^{(-)\uparrow} + c_4 \psi^{(-)\downarrow}.$$

By further Lorentz transformations and subsequent summations, one can obtain the general form

$$\psi(x) = \int_{-\infty}^{+\infty} \{c^{(+)}(k)\psi^{(+)}(k, x) + c^{(-)}(k)\psi^{(-)}(k, x)\}\, d^4 k \tag{11.50}$$

which is formally similar to the scalar field solutions.

The Green's function form of the solutions is just as applicable to spinor fields but here, due to the fact that (11.2) is of first order, we require only one initial condition. Let

$$\psi(x) = \int S(x - x')\gamma_\mu \psi(x')\, dS'^\mu. \tag{11.51}$$

Since $\psi(x)$ satisfies (11.1) and (11.2), $S(x - x')$ must also do so. But, since $x \to x'$ leads to $\psi(x) \to \psi(x')$, $S(x - x')$ must behave as a δ-function for $x \to x'$

$$\left.\begin{aligned}
(\gamma_\mu \partial_\mu + \kappa)S &= 0 \\
(\partial_\mu \partial^\mu - \kappa^2)S &= 0 \\
S(x - x') &= \delta(x - x') \quad \text{if} \quad x = x'
\end{aligned}\right\} \tag{11.52}$$

From these it follows that
$$S(x - x') = (\gamma_\mu \partial_\mu + \kappa)\, G(x - x')$$

or, in integral form,

$$S(x - x') = \frac{1}{(2\pi)^4} \int \frac{(\gamma_\mu \partial_\mu + \kappa)e^{ik(x-x')}\, d^4 k}{p^2 + \kappa^2}. \tag{11.53}$$

11.7. Interaction of a Spinor Field with the Electromagnetic Field

The equation (11.2) represents a spinor field which is not in interaction with any other field. The interaction of a spinor field with, say, an electromagnetic field may be formulated as follows: We first substitute the new expression of the current, $j^\mu = e\bar{\psi}\gamma^\mu\psi$ into (10.3) (note the change in units),

$$\partial_\mu \partial^\mu A_\alpha = -e\bar{\psi}\gamma_\alpha\psi. \tag{11.54}$$

This term corresponds, so to speak, to the rate at which energy-momentum, is transferred from the electromagnetic field to the spinor field (which represents the electron). Therefore, we must add something to the wave equation of the spinor to make sure that the energy momentum is absorbed at the proper rate. Forming the divergence of the stress-energy tensor of the electromagnetic field, we have $j^\mu f_{\mu\alpha}$, that is,

$$e\bar{\psi}\gamma^\mu(\partial_\mu A_\alpha - \partial_\alpha A_\mu)\psi,$$

which must be compensated by additional terms to (11.2) and (11.14). A short calculation shows that

$$(\gamma_\mu \partial^\mu + \kappa)\psi = e\gamma_\mu A^\mu \psi; \qquad \bar{\psi}(\overleftarrow{\partial}_\mu \gamma^\mu - \kappa) = -e\bar{\psi}\gamma_\mu A^\mu. \tag{11.55}$$

Equations (11.54) and (11.55) are the complete set of equations of interacting electromagnetic and spinor fields. They are still largely classical in structure, and the negative energy difficulty is not yet resolved. We may point out here that the above interacting set of

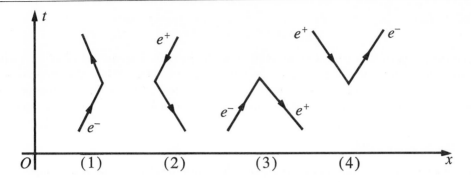

FIGURE 11.1   *Various scatterings of an electron in space and time.*

equations could have been derived from a combination of gauge invariance of the first and second kind. We will leave this derivation to the next chapter, where everything about interacting fields is treated more systematically with the help of the Lagrangian method.

11.8. Particles and Antiparticles. The Positron

Consider again the $(+)$ and $(-)$ frequency solutions

$$a(k)e^{i(k \cdot x - \omega t)} \quad \text{and} \quad b^*(k)e^{-i(k \cdot x - \omega t)}.$$

Since the negative frequency part should not lead to negative energies, one may interpret it, not as a negative energy particle, but as a particle running backward in time. This interpretation puts the two solutions on an equal footing and leads to the interesting and useful concept of the antiparticle. As an example, consider the electron and its antiparticle, the positron. In the space-time diagram (Figure 11.1), the four electron lines represent, respectively: (1) Scattering of an electron, (2) Scattering of a positron, (3) Pair annihilation (scattering of an electron back into past), (4) Pair creation (scattering of a positron back into future). Such processes can take place, of course, only through interaction with other particles, say with photons (electromagnetic field). The real scalar field and the real vector field, as is evident, also has particles and antiparticles, but from the reality condition, the solutions

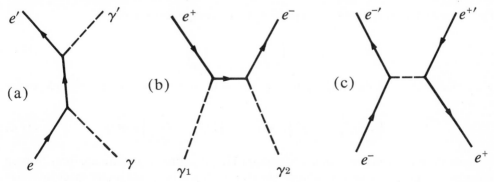

FIGURE 11.2   (a) *Electron scattering.* (b) *Pair creation.* (c) *Electron-positron scattering, and so on.*

are of the form

$$a(k)e^{i(k\cdot x-\omega t)} + a*(k)e^{-k(k\cdot x-\omega t)}$$

so that the antiparticle is *not* distinguishable from the particle. The interaction of light with electrons then can be described by such diagrams as Figure 11.2. (Notice that photons are drawn to have no direction sign.) Due to the conservation of charge in the creation and annihilation of pairs, the positron has a charge equal and opposite to that of the electron.

11.9. The Neutrino Field

As we have just seen, the spinor field which describes the electron has four components. In this section we will introduce a 2-component spinor which many describe a particle called the *neutrino*. In many ways, a 2-component spinor is simpler than the 4-component spinor, but it also has some peculiarities of its own. A convenient way to introduce the 2-component spinor is by a decomposition of the 4-component equation (11.8) into two 2-component spinor equations. Consider again the equation (11.8) (without primes):

$$(\gamma_\mu \partial_\mu + \kappa)\psi = 0 \tag{11.56}$$

where

$$\gamma_k = \begin{pmatrix} 0 & -i\sigma_k \\ \hline i\sigma_k & 0 \end{pmatrix} \qquad \gamma_4 = -\begin{pmatrix} 0 & 1 \\ \hline 1 & 0 \end{pmatrix}. \tag{11.57}$$

Now, by putting

$$\psi = \begin{pmatrix} u_1 \\ u_2 \\ v_1 \\ v_2 \end{pmatrix} = \begin{pmatrix} u \\ v \end{pmatrix} \tag{11.58}$$

we can write the 4-component equation as

$$\left(-i\sigma_k\partial_k + \frac{1}{ic}\frac{\partial}{\partial t}\right)u = \kappa v$$

$$\left(i\sigma_k\partial_k + \frac{1}{ic}\frac{\partial}{\partial t}\right)v = \kappa u. \tag{11.59}$$

This is very interesting because it represents two 2-component spinors

$$u = \begin{pmatrix} u_1 \\ u_2 \end{pmatrix}, \qquad v = \begin{pmatrix} v_1 \\ v_2 \end{pmatrix} \tag{11.60}$$

in interaction through the coupling term κ. If $\kappa = 0$, we have two completely independent equations

$$\left(-i\sigma_k\partial_k + \frac{1}{ic}\frac{\partial}{\partial t}\right)u = 0, \qquad \left(i\sigma_k\partial_k + \frac{1}{ic}\frac{\partial}{\partial t}\right)v = 0. \tag{11.61}$$

It can be shown in a manner similar to Section 11.3, that these equations are form invariant under proper Lorentz transformations, but that neither is invariant under space inversion. Equation (11.59) as a whole is invariant under space inversion because, there, space inversion exchanges u and v as well as the operator, so that the two equations go into each other under the space-inversion operation. In (11.61), however, the two equations are completely independent, and we cannot exchange u and v. Thus, if one or the other of equations (11.61) describes a physical object, that object must be unsymmetric under space inversion. Until 1957, it was assumed that every elementary object in nature must be symmetric with respect to space inversion and, therefore, the field corresponding to u or v was rejected on this ground soon after the discovery of equations (11.61) by the mathematician H. Weyl. In 1957, after the discovery of phenomena violating space-inversion symmetry, it was found that the particle called the *neutrino* can be described by the first of these equations, that is, the equation

$$\left(-i\sigma_k\partial_k + \frac{1}{ic}\frac{\partial}{\partial t}\right)u = 0. \tag{11.62}$$

It turned out, from an analysis of the experimental data, that the second equation is not realized in nature, so we may put $v \equiv 0$. Hence the neutrino field equation is noninvariant under space inversion and, therefore, neutrino interactions in general lead to violations of parity conservation.

The energy, momentum, and spin angular momentum of the neutrino field may be found from (11.33) and (11.38) by putting $\kappa = v = 0$, leading to the expressions

$$\mathscr{E} = i\int u^* \frac{\partial}{\partial t} u \, dV$$

$$P_k = -i\int u^* \partial_k u \, dV \tag{11.63}$$

$$N^{\mu\nu} = \frac{i}{2}\int u^* \sigma^\mu \sigma^\nu u \, dV.$$

We now examine the solutions of the neutrino equation (11.62). Let the field propagate in the z-direction and let us concern ourselves only with the $(+)$ frequency solutions; namely, we take the solution to have the form

$$u^{(+)} = \begin{pmatrix} a_1 \\ a_2 \end{pmatrix} e^{i(kz-\omega t)} \tag{11.64}$$

where a_1 and a_2 are to be determined. Putting this into our equation, we have

$$\left(k - \frac{\omega}{c}\right)a_1 = 0, \qquad \left(k + \frac{\omega}{c}\right)a_2 = 0 \tag{11.65}$$

leading to $a_2 = 0$, so that

$$u^{(+)} = \begin{pmatrix} 1 \\ 0 \end{pmatrix} a_1 e^{i(kz-\omega t)}. \tag{11.66}$$

After evaluation by formulas (11.63), this solution is seen to have $(+)$ energy, $(+)$ momentum and a spin pointing in the $(-)$ z direction. The object under discussion, the neutrino, can then be described by Figure 11.3, and the neutrino is said to be left handed. The so-called *antineutrino* is represented by the $(-)$ frequency solution, so that the exponential must change sign in ω. Again, considering motion in the z-direction, we get

$$u^{(-)\uparrow} = \begin{pmatrix} 0 \\ 1 \end{pmatrix} a_2 e^{-i(kz-\omega t)}. \tag{11.67}$$

FIGURE 11.3   *Neutrino.*   FIGURE 11.4   *Antineutrino.*

This object, the antineutrino, would then have $(-)$ energy, $(-)$ momentum, and spin again directed in the $(-)z$ direction. The difficulty of negative energy is again beyond the classical theory, and is resolved only after proper field quantization. When this is done, the antineutrino has $(+)$ energy, $(+)$ momentum, and spin directed in the $(+)z$ direction, as as shown in Figure 11.4. Thus the antineutrino is a right-handed particle. The complete solution of (11.62), for a given frequency ω and propagating in the z-direction, is given by

$$u = c_1 u^{(+)\downarrow} + c_2 u^{(-)\uparrow}.$$

The neutrino does not carry electric charge and therefore has no electromagnetic interaction. The interactions of the neutrino with other particles such as the electron, μ-meson, proton, neutron, et cetera, are of the form

$$G \psi_p^* u \psi_e^* \psi_N \tag{11.68}$$

where the reaction $N + \bar{e} + \bar{P} + \nu = 0$ or $N = e + P + \bar{\nu}$, that is, the β-decay of the neutron into a proton, electron, and an antineutrino. G is an interaction constant.

This interaction is weak, $G = 10^{-16}$, and it is classified among the weak, Fermi interactions. We will not give a complete description of these interactions here, since this chapter is already rather long. We would like to note in any case, however, that our knowledge of neutrinos is likely to change significantly in the near future. This may be expected as a result of the recent Brookhaven experiment indicating the existence of a new type of neutrino which is not explainable in terms of the above equations. The neutrino considered above should not discriminate between electrons and μ-mesons, whose difference, from the electromagnetic point of view, has so far been completely ignored. However, the Brookhaven experiments indicate a difference between the neutrons associated with electrons and with μ-mesons.

Summary: Spinor Fields

(a) Spinor fields are half integral representations of the Lorentz transformations.
(b) They satisfy relativistic wave equations and give rise to relativistic field theories.
(c) Electron is described by a 4-component spinor with $\frac{1}{2}$ spin, carries mass and electric charge.
(d) Neutrino is described by a 2-component spinor with $\frac{1}{2}$ spin and has zero mass.
(e) The neutrino equation is noninvariant under space reflection.

12

THE ACTION PRINCIPLE

12.1. The Lagrangian Method

In constructing the dynamics of particles or fields, we have so far followed a rather intuitive path. In each case we have first given the equations of motion and then constructed acceptable energy-momentum and angular momentum quantities. Other conserved quantities, such as charge, were also constructed and the whole set of statements and equations were made relativistically covariant. This is a difficult path to follow although we have adopted it for pedagogical reasons. There exists a different method, the so-called Lagrangian method, in which everything is developed from a single function and a single statement. Since this function, the Lagrangian function, is relativistically invariant, everything derived from it automatically satisfies the relativity principle. The Lagrangian method is the most convenient and economical way of formulating dynamical laws. However, it is rather abstract and makes use of the variational calculus for its development. In other words, it lacks intuitive appeal. In fact, historically, no new equation of motion has ever been discovered by this method. It is for these reasons that we have delayed its introduction until this chapter although it would have saved us a great deal of time and effort in our presentation.

The Lagrangian method is based on the observation that the equations of motion of a system can be obtained in the form of the Euler-Lagrange equations of an extremum problem. For example, take $(\partial_\mu \partial^\mu - \kappa^2)\phi = 0$; we can construct a scalar function $\mathscr{L}(\phi, \partial_\mu \phi \ldots)$, such that the action integral

$$W = \int_\Omega \mathscr{L}(\phi, \partial_\mu \phi \ldots) \, d\Omega \tag{12.1}$$

will be stationary (maximum or minimum) when the field equation is satisfied. In fact, the Lagrange function which leads to the field equations for the scalar field is $\mathscr{L} = -\frac{1}{2}(\partial_\mu \phi \partial^\mu \phi + \kappa^2 \phi^2)$. Thus, to any Lagrangian, $\mathscr{L}$, there corresponds a set of equations of motion and vice versa. Although nothing physically new is involved, the Lagrangian method has definite advantages of economy, symmetry, and ease in constructing the conserved quantities such as energy, momentum, and angular momentum.

The essence of the variational treatment is this: Ignore the equations of motion and consider all possible variations of the action integral (12.1) under the symmetry constraints such as Lorentz transformations. In general, these variations will violate the laws of motion. Now formulate a single restricting statement which will allow only those variations which are actually realized by the equations of motion. If we can find such a statement, we would have a right to call it a general principle although it is just a condensation of various laws of motion through the mathematics of the variational calculus.

We will consider Lagrangians which depend only on the field variables and their first derivatives. Due to the homogeneity and the isotropy of the space-time geometry, the

Lagrangian must not depend explicitly on the coordinate variables x^μ; that is, the dependence of $\mathcal{L}$ on x^μ must be through the fields (The dynamics of a system must not depend explicitly on where the system is and how it is oriented). This fact is a consequence of relativity and eventually leads to the laws of conservation of energy-momentum (homogeneity) and angular momentum (isotropy), as will be seen. A field will be denoted generally as ψ, which may mean a scalar ϕ, a vector A_μ, or a spinor ψ_ν. In the case of coupled fields, two or more kinds of fields may be simultaneously present. Now, noting that any four-dimensional volume Ω is bounded by two space-like surfaces σ_1 and σ_2, the action integral may be written

$$W_{12} = \int_{\sigma_2}^{\sigma_1} \mathcal{L}(\psi, \partial_\mu \psi)\, d\Omega. \tag{12.2}$$

The extremum (stationary) condition requires

$$\delta W_{12} = 0. \tag{12.3}$$

This condition is sometimes called the "principle of stationary action" or simply "the action principle." The indices 1 and 2 may be imagined to refer to two observers computing the physical quantities at the two space-like surfaces σ_1 and σ_2 which are essentially 3-dimensional Euclidean volumes. Using the methods of the variational calculus, we have

$$\delta W_{12} = \int_{\sigma_2}^{\sigma_1} \delta_0 \mathcal{L}\, d\Omega + \int_{\sigma_2}^{\sigma_1} \mathcal{L}\delta\, d\Omega$$

$$\delta W_{12} = \int_{\sigma_2}^{\sigma_1} \delta_0 \mathcal{L}\, d\Omega + \left(\int_{\sigma_1} - \int_{\sigma_2} \right) \mathcal{L}\, dS_\mu \delta x^\mu \tag{12.4}$$

where

$$\delta_0 \mathcal{L} = \frac{\partial \mathcal{L}}{\partial \psi} \delta_0 \psi + \frac{\partial \mathcal{L}}{\partial(\partial_\mu \psi)} \delta_0 \partial_\mu \psi. \tag{12.5}$$

The $\delta_0 \psi$ is the variation of the field alone. The total variation $\delta \psi$ of the field receives additional contributions arising from the infinitesimal variations of the reference frame to which ψ is referred. These are of two kinds: (1) a contribution due to the infinitesimal variation δx^μ and (2) a contribution due to the tensorial character of ψ (that is due to its transformation properties). The first of these is of the type $\partial_\mu \psi \delta x^\mu$ and the second is derived from

$$\psi_\alpha'(x') = \mathcal{L}_{\alpha\beta}\psi_\beta(x), \qquad \psi_\alpha' - \psi_\alpha = -\tfrac{1}{2}\sum_{\alpha\beta}^{\mu\nu} \psi^\beta \alpha_{\mu\nu}, \qquad \sum_{\alpha\beta}^{\mu\nu} = -\sum_{\alpha\beta}^{\nu\mu}.$$

The total variation of ψ is then of the form [See Chapter 6, equation (6.50)]

$$\delta \psi = \delta_0 \psi + \partial_\mu \psi \delta x^\mu + \tfrac{1}{2}\sum^{\mu\nu} \psi \alpha_{\mu\nu} \tag{12.6}$$

where (see Problem 12.1)

$$\sum = 0 \qquad \text{for a scalar}$$
$$\sum_{\alpha\beta}^{\mu\nu} = \tfrac{1}{4}(\gamma^\nu \gamma^\mu - \gamma^\mu \gamma^\nu)_{\alpha\beta} \qquad \text{for a spinor} \tag{12.7}$$
$$\sum_{\alpha\beta}^{\mu\nu} = (g_\alpha^\nu g_\beta^\mu - g_\alpha^\mu g_\beta^\nu) \qquad \text{for a vector.}$$

12.2. Field Equations

Before we substitute $\delta_0 \psi$ into (12.4) and (12.5) we want first to derive the equations of the field. Integrating partially the second term of (12.5)

$$\int_\sigma \frac{\partial \mathcal{L}}{\partial(\partial_\mu \psi)} \delta_0 \partial_\mu \psi\, d\Omega = \left[\frac{\partial \mathcal{L}}{\partial(\partial_\mu \psi)} \delta_0 \psi \right]_{\sigma_2}^{\sigma_1} - \int_{\sigma_2}^{\sigma_1} \partial_\mu \frac{\partial \mathcal{L}}{\partial(\partial_\mu \psi)} \delta_0 \psi\, d\Omega$$

and substituting back into (12.4), we obtain

$$\delta W_{12} = \int_{\Omega} \left(\frac{\partial \mathscr{L}}{\partial \psi} - \partial_{\mu} \frac{\partial \mathscr{L}}{\partial(\partial_{\mu}\psi)} \right) \delta_0 \psi \, d\Omega + F(\sigma_1) - F(\sigma_2) = 0 \tag{12.8}$$

where

$$F(\sigma_1) = \int_{\sigma_1} (\pi^{\mu}\delta_0\psi + \mathscr{L}\delta x^{\mu}) \, dS_{\mu}, \tag{12.9}$$

and

$$\pi^{\mu} = \frac{\partial \mathscr{L}}{\partial(\partial_{\mu}\psi)} \tag{12.10}$$

with a similar expression for $F(\sigma_2)$. Thus the variation of W_{12} arises from two distinct sources: (1) from the variations at the boundaries σ_1 and σ_2 and (2) from variations inside the volume Ω. Now, since the Lagrangian is independent of the coordinates, the evaluation of $F(\sigma)$ at σ_1 and at σ_2 corresponds to a redefinition of the integration variables and therefore $F(\sigma)$ is independent of σ.

$$F(\sigma_1) = F(\sigma_2). \tag{12.11}$$

Then the Ω integral in (12.8) must vanish. This leads from (12.8) to the equations of motion of the field.

$$\frac{\partial \mathscr{L}}{\partial \psi} - \partial_{\mu} \left(\frac{\partial \mathscr{L}}{\partial(\partial_{\mu}\psi)} \right) = 0. \tag{12.12}$$

12.3. Conservation Laws

We now show that equation (12.11) contains the conservation principles. Substituting $\delta_0\psi$ into (12.9) from (12.6) and also applying the infinitesimal Lorentz transformations (Chapter 6);

$$\delta x^{\mu} = \alpha^{\mu\nu}x_{\nu} + \epsilon^{\mu}, \qquad \alpha^{\mu\nu} = -\alpha^{\nu\mu} \tag{12.13}$$

we obtain

$$F(\sigma_1) = \int_{\sigma_1} \{\pi^{\alpha}\delta\psi - T^{\alpha\mu}\epsilon_{\mu} - \tfrac{1}{2}(T^{\alpha\mu}x^{\nu} - T^{\alpha\nu}x^{\mu})\alpha_{\mu\nu} - \tfrac{1}{2}\Sigma^{\mu\nu}\pi^{\alpha}\psi\alpha_{\mu\nu}\} \, dS_{\alpha} \tag{12.14}$$

where

$$T^{\alpha\mu} = \pi^{\alpha}\partial^{\mu}\psi - \delta^{\alpha\mu}\mathscr{L}. \tag{12.15}$$

To simplify the expression further, let

$$P^{\mu} = \int T^{\alpha\mu} \, dS_{\alpha}, \tag{12.16}$$

$$M^{\mu\nu} = \int (T^{\alpha\mu}x^{\nu} - T^{\alpha\nu}x^{\mu}) \, dS_{\alpha} + \int \pi^{\alpha} \Sigma^{\mu\nu} \psi \, dS_{\alpha}. \tag{12.17}$$

Then we have

$$F(\sigma_1) = \int_{\sigma_1} \pi^{\alpha}\delta\psi \, dS_{\alpha} + P^{\mu}\epsilon_{\mu} + \tfrac{1}{2}M^{\mu\nu}\alpha_{\mu\nu}. \tag{12.18}$$

Now suppose that we did not change the coordinate system from σ_1 to σ_2, that is, we used the same frame for the initial and final evaluation of $F(\sigma)$. Then ϵ_{μ} and $\alpha_{\mu\nu}$ are the same for $F(\sigma_1)$ and $F(\sigma_2)$, and (12.11) leads to the equation

$$\left(\int_{\sigma_1} - \int_{\sigma_2} \right) \pi^{\alpha}\delta\psi \, dS_{\alpha} + [P^{\mu}(\sigma_1) - P^{\mu}(\sigma_2)]\epsilon_{\mu} + [M^{\mu\nu}(\sigma_1) - M^{\mu\nu}(\sigma_2)]\alpha_{\mu\nu} = 0.$$

Since ϵ_μ and $\alpha_{\mu\nu}$ are all arbitrary, this equation can be satisfied only if

$$P^\mu(\sigma_1) = P^\mu(\sigma_2), \qquad M^{\mu\nu}(\sigma_1) = M^{\mu\nu}(\sigma_2). \tag{12.19}$$

These are expressions of the principles of conservation of energy-momentum and angular momentum. Note that the angular momentum is composed of two parts, the "orbital" and the "spin" parts, which have been introduced earlier on more intuitive grounds. Note also that the spin part is correctly deduced by the present method (compare this with Chapters 10 and 11).

The essential point in the derivation of the conservation laws is the fact that the Lagrangian, $\mathcal{L}$, does not explicitly depend on x. That is, *the conservation laws* (12.19) *are a direct consequence of the relativistic invariance under proper Lorentz transformations.* The invariance of $\mathcal{L}$ under a given transformation leads to some conservation law. Consider, for example, the gauge transformation of the first kind $\psi \rightarrow e^{i\epsilon t}\psi$, where ϵ is infinitesimal, $e^{i\epsilon t} = 1 + i\epsilon t$. For the variation by ϵ we have $\delta\psi = \delta_0\psi + i\epsilon t\psi$

$$F(\sigma) = \int i\epsilon\pi^\alpha t\psi \, dS_\alpha. \tag{12.20}$$

Thus, in the case of spinor field, $t = 1$, and $Q = i\int\bar\psi\gamma^\alpha\psi \, dS_\alpha$ is conserved, leading to the continuity equation

$$\partial_\mu j^\mu = 0, \qquad j^\mu = \bar\psi\gamma^\mu\psi. \tag{12.21}$$

Table 12.1 gives the Lagrangians and other essential quantities for the five most common fields.

TABLE 12.1

	Scalar, Real ϕ	Vector, $\kappa = 0$, Real A_μ	4-Spinor $\bar\psi, \psi$	2-Spinor, $\kappa = 0$ u^*, u	Complex Scalar ϕ^*, ϕ
$\mathcal{L}$	$\frac{1}{2}(\partial_\mu\phi\partial^\mu\phi - \kappa^2\phi^2)$	$\frac{1}{2}\partial_\mu A^\alpha\partial^\mu A_\alpha$	$\bar\psi(\gamma_\mu\partial^\mu + \kappa)\psi$	$u^*\sigma_\mu\partial^\mu u$	$\partial_\mu\phi^*\partial^\mu\phi - \kappa^2\phi^*\phi$
$T^{\mu\nu}$	$\partial^\mu\phi\partial^\nu\phi - \frac{1}{2}\delta^{\mu\nu}\mathcal{L}$	$\partial^\mu A^\alpha\partial^\nu A_\alpha - \delta^{\mu\nu}\mathcal{L}$	$\bar\psi\gamma^\mu\partial^\nu\psi - \delta^{\mu\nu}\mathcal{L}$	$u^*\sigma^\mu\partial^\nu u - \delta^{\mu\nu}\mathcal{L}$	$\partial^\mu\phi^*\partial^\nu\phi - \frac{1}{2}\delta^{\mu\nu}\mathcal{L}$
$\Sigma^{\mu\nu}$	0	$g^\nu_\alpha g^\mu_\beta - g^\mu_\alpha g^\nu_\beta$	$(\gamma^\mu\gamma^\nu - \gamma^\nu\gamma^\mu)/4$	$(\sigma^\mu\sigma^\nu - \sigma^\nu\sigma^\mu)/4$	0
j^μ	0	0	$e\bar\psi\gamma^\mu\psi$	$\lambda u^*\sigma^\mu u$	$e(\partial^\mu\phi^*\phi - \phi^*\partial^\mu\phi)$
t	0	0	1	1	$\begin{pmatrix} 0 & 1 \\ -1 & 0 \end{pmatrix}$

It is interesting and very useful to notice that two Lagrangians differing only by the divergence of a vector describe the same physical system. In other words, the equations of motion are unaltered under the transformation

$$\mathcal{L} \rightarrow \mathcal{L} + \partial_\mu h^\mu. \tag{12.22}$$

The reason is simply that the additional term integrates out at once, giving boundary terms and *not* a volume term,

$$\int_\Omega \partial_\alpha h^\alpha \, d\Omega = \int_{\sigma_2} h^\alpha \, dS_\alpha - \int_{\sigma_1} h^\alpha \, dS_\alpha \tag{12.23}$$

and therefore contributes only to $F(\sigma_1)$ and $F(\sigma_2)$. This changes $F(\sigma_1)$ into

$$F(\sigma_1) \rightarrow F(\sigma_1) - \int_{\sigma_1} h^\alpha \, dS_\alpha. \tag{12.24}$$

This remark is helpful in obtaining equivalent forms of $F(\sigma_1)$. For example, by choosing $h^\alpha = -\delta(\pi^\alpha \psi)$ the expression (12.9) may be transformed into

$$F(\sigma_1) = -\int (\psi \delta \pi^\alpha + T^{\alpha\mu} \, \delta x_\mu) \, dS_\alpha. \tag{12.25}$$

It is also interesting to note that, in electromagnetic theory, the Fermi Lagrangian $\mathscr{L} = (\frac{1}{2})\partial_\mu A^\alpha \partial^\mu A_\alpha$ and the Maxwell Lagrangian $\mathscr{L} = (\frac{1}{4})f_{\mu\nu} f^{\mu\nu}$ differ only by the divergence of a vector. They are therefore dynamically equivalent.

12.4. Interaction Lagrangian

The Lagrangian of two or more fields interacting with each other is given as the sum of the free field Lagrangians and the interaction terms. For example, the electromagnetic field, in its interaction with the electron field, is described by

$$\mathscr{L} = \tfrac{1}{2}\partial_\mu A^\alpha \partial^\mu A_\alpha + \bar{\psi}(\gamma^\mu \partial_\mu + \kappa)\psi + e\bar{\psi}\gamma^\mu A_\mu \psi \tag{12.26}$$

where the last term represents the interaction. Applying the Lagrangian method, by varying A, $\bar{\psi}$ and ψ we obtain, respectively, the three equations

$$\partial_\mu \partial^\mu A_\alpha = -e\bar{\psi}\gamma_\alpha \psi \tag{12.27}$$

$$(\gamma^\mu \partial_\mu + \kappa)\psi = ie\gamma^\mu A_\mu \psi; \qquad \bar{\psi}(\overleftarrow{\partial}_\mu \gamma^\mu - \kappa) = -ie\bar{\psi}\gamma^\mu A_\mu \tag{12.28}$$

which are the same as (11.54) and (11.55). We note that these equations are invariant under the combined gauge transformations of the first and second kind. For a proof, simply substitute

$$\psi \to \psi e^{i\Lambda}, \qquad \bar{\psi} \to \bar{\psi} e^{-i\Lambda}, \qquad A_\alpha \to A_\alpha + \partial_\alpha \Lambda$$

and use $\partial_\mu \partial^\mu \Lambda = 0$. Then, all terms involving Λ cancel out. It can be shown that the above form of the interaction is the only one allowed by the gauge invariance of the first and the second kind. The interaction term of the scalar and spinor fields is not fixed by any such principle. In this case, terms like

$$\bar{\psi}\phi\psi, \qquad \bar{\psi}\phi^2\psi, \qquad \bar{\psi}\phi\psi\bar{\psi}\phi\psi, \quad \text{etc.,}$$

or any linear combination of these, are possible. It is even permissible to consider interactions containing derivatives, or integrals such as

$$\bar{\psi}\gamma_\mu \partial_\mu \phi\psi, \qquad \bar{\psi}\partial_\mu \phi\partial^\mu \phi\psi, \qquad \int \bar{\psi}\gamma_\mu \phi\psi \, dS^\mu \quad \text{etc.}$$

Recently efforts are being made to find similar rules for other interactions by generalizing the gauge transformations. In practice, a choice is made on the basis of simplicity and its consequences are then examined. In case the results do not agree with the observed facts, a different choice is examined. The only requirement on the interaction Lagrangian is invariance under Lorentz transformations and other transformations, as may be required. If ϕ is a pseudo-scalar, as is the case for π-mesons, one includes a γ^5 in the interaction term; for example, $\bar{\psi}\gamma^5\phi\psi$. This is because $\bar{\psi}\gamma^5\psi$ is also pseudo-scalar and $\bar{\psi}\gamma^5\phi\psi$ is then a scalar. The interactions most commonly used are of the type

$$\begin{array}{ll} e\bar{\psi}\gamma^\mu A_\mu \psi & \text{Electromagnetic Interaction} \\ g\bar{\psi}\gamma^5\phi\psi & \text{Yukawa Interaction} \\ G\bar{\psi}_N\bar{\psi}_\nu \psi_P \psi_\nu & \text{Fermi Interaction} \end{array} \tag{12.29}$$

Integral types of interactions lead (due to contributions from separated regions of integration) to nonlocal interactions, which violate the principle of causality.

We must point out at once that with the addition of the interaction terms the field equations are in general nonlinear, as for example, (12.27) and (12.28). It has not been possible to solve such nonlinear equations exactly, either in the classical or in the quantum mechanical form. Hence, it has not been possible to extract all the consequences of these equations to compare them with experiment. It is possible to obtain approximate solutions in the form of series expansions in increasing powers of the coupling constants, e, g, G. These series are called perturbation series and if the coupling constant is small, such as $e^2 \sim \frac{1}{137}$, $G^2 \sim 10^{-14}$, the first few terms can be taken to describe the situation approximately. But, if the coupling constant is large, as in the case of $g^2 \sim 10$, the series expansion does not mean much. Even in the case of small e and G it has not been possible to show that the perturbation series converge. Some people claim that they do not converge, and that a field theory based on an interaction term expressible in terms of ordinary algebraic and mathematical forms has no meaning.

Actually, there is not much justification for talking about an experimental comparison before we quantize the field, since the unquantized theory is not self-consistent. In the next chapter we will discuss the quantization process for fields and discuss some of its consequences. We would like to conclude the present chapter by pointing out that the action principle is a convenient way of condensing a large number of statements into a single statement concerning the scalar action function. Due to the scalar nature of the action function, all equations derived from it are automatically relativistic. Also, a generalization of the classical action principle into an operator form provides a convenient framework for the quantization of the fields. The complete relativistic quantized theory of fields is called *Quantum Field Theory*.

Summary: The Action Principle

(a) Laws of motion of a dynamical system can be formulated in the form of an action principle.

(b) The action is an integral over space and time of a relativistically invariant function, $\mathcal{L}$, called Lagrangian.

(c) The Lagrangian depends only on field variables, not on space and time variables. Independence of the Lagrangian of the space and time leads to conservation laws of energy, momentum, and angular momentum.

(d) Two Lagrangians differing by the divergence of a vector represent the same dynamical system.

(e) The Lagrangian of two interacting systems consists of a sum of their individual Lagrangians plus the interaction Lagrangian. The interaction Lagrangian of electron field and electromagnetic field is determined up to a numerical factor by the combined requirement of gauge invariance of first and second kinds.

13

RELATIVITY AND QUANTUM FIELD THEORY

13.1. Introduction

The method of presentation of this chapter will be markedly different from that of earlier chapters. We will employ essentially a Lagrangian method. There are two reasons for this. First, we would like to give to the reader the flavor of an analytical treatment of relativity and field theory. Second, the material to be covered is so extensive and so complex that a strictly inductive presentation would result in a very long chapter. Needless to say, the Lagrangian treatment, as a manifestly invariant procedure, will save us from errors of intuition that we could easily make in such a complex and abstract subject.

The subject we would like to treat is the quantization of fields. More properly, we should call this "quantum field theory" because we do not know if there is such a thing as an unquantized theory of fields. As we have seen in Chapter 11, the classical form of the theory in the case of a spinor field leads to the inconsistency of negative energy solutions. Therefore, from the beginning we should also orient ourselves toward a basically different attitude suited to the quantum nature of the world as revealed by experiment. At this point one even wonders why we should insist on fields at all. The insistence on fields is essentially due to relativity. According to the theory of relativity, the laws of nature are invariant under the Lorentz group of transformations and the construction of such laws is easiest with the help of the fields which are the representations of the Lorentz group.

13.2. Operator Nature of Observation

In the previous chapters we have treated relativistic field theories from an essentially classical viewpoint. Classically, the energy and momentum of fields are distributed in space in a continuous manner. It is also possible to vary the energy and momentum of a given mode of field vibration by an *infinitesimal* amount by varying the amplitude of that mode infinitesimally. Since, in essence, a measurement is a process of transferring energy and momentum to or from an apparatus, we would expect classically that the measurement of the energy and momentum of a given mode of vibration could yield numbers as small as we wish.

Experiment shows, however, that, in general, observations on a dynamical system yield *discrete numbers*. More specifically, observations on systems of atomic size show that the measurement process does not correspond to a small change in the amplitudes of the modes of vibration but rather to an operation by which the *eigenvalues* of the modes of vibration are extracted. From a classical point of view this is most unexpected.

In developing a physical theory consistent with experiment, we will have to adjust our concepts and symbols and sometimes change our attitude completely, so that the results of experiments are recovered from the theory. In this endeavor the unexpected or unintelligible appearance of certain experimental findings cannot be disregarded. One of the primary aims of science is to *create* new ideas and logical frameworks so that experiments *become* understandable.

The story of how, during the first quarter of this century, a new set of ideas evolved on the basis of experimental facts and how these ideas let to the so-called *quantum mechanics*, and eventually to the present-day quantum field theory, would be very lengthy. In this chapter we will give the final framework with a minimum of inductive reasoning.

In quantum theory an observation or measurement is considered as an operation. Mathematically, an observable is therefore represented by an operator, O, rather than a number. An operator must always be applied to an operand, $\Phi = |\alpha)$, and therefore any physical system is assumed to possess an operand. The operand is usually called a state vector. It is a vector in an abstract space called Hilbert space. More precisely, a dynamical system is described by an operand $\Phi = |\alpha)$ and observations made on the system are represented by operators, O, applied to this operand. Since the ultimate result of an observation is an ordinary real number, the measurement of a quantity, say, energy, is represented by the eignevalues of the energy operator. Therefore we consider the eigenvalue equation

$$O |o') = o' |o') \qquad (13.1)$$

where o' is a real number $o' = o'^*$. The reality condition on the eigenvalues implies that the operator corresponding to an *observable quantity* like energy, momentum, charge, et cetera, is Hermitian

$$O = O^\dagger. \qquad (13.2)$$

In general an operator may have many eigenvalues. In fact many operators have an infinite number of them. In such a case each eigenvalue is a possible result of an observation. From the mathematics of operators it is also known that for each particular eigenvalue, o'_k, there is a particular eigenvector $|o'_k)$, and O gives the number o'_k only when applied to $|o'_k)$. This means that the operand $\Phi = |o')$ actually represents a number of states $|o'_k)$ in which the system can be found. If the system is in a particular state, $|o'_k)$, then the measurement of the quantity represented by O will result in the particular number o'_k.

Thus, for each observable quantity, such as energy, momentum, charge, et cetera, we must find corresponding operator expressions such that the eigenvalues of these operators, obtained mathematically, give the numbers we obtain by actual observation.

13.3. Identification of Observables

The problem just posed is a difficult one. It involves two major steps at once. First we must analyze carefully the results of various experiments and see what sort of numbers are obtained as an outcome of these experiments. Second, we must consider all possible eigenvalue equations and, with the guidance of observed results, make a consistent set of identifications by assigning a particular type of operator to each type of measurable quantity. This is almost a superhuman job.

Here we will turn the question around and try to make the identification of operators with the help of our theoretical knowledge of classical field theory, and see if we can make the scheme work with certain readjustments as required by the experiments. Thus we *assume* that the operators corresponding to observable quantities are essentially the same as the classical expressions given in the previous chapters, especially in Chapter 12. For example, the energy-momentum operator is essentially given by (12.16), the angular-momentum operator by (12.17), the charge operator by (12.21). This identification requires that the field variables ϕ, A, ψ, ... themselves must of necessity, be interpreted as operators although not necessarily observables. Since operators do not, in general, commute, it is also clear that we must pay attention to the order in which they appear in the expressions for the observables. In doing this, we use the methods of matrix algebra. A simple introduction to matrices can be found in Appendix B.

Now a very important point is that when we consider fields as operators, we are making a vast generalization. The theory will not be restrictive enough, after such a generalization, to lead to specific answers for specific questions. Certain conditions will almost always have to be imposed on the formalism. In our present case, the generalization made is from ordinary numbers to operators. The essential difference between ordinary numbers and operators is that the operators do not, in general, commute. Therefore we should expect the restraining statements (if any) to have the form of some conditions on the commutation properties of the field operators.

It is therefore clear that we must follow a line of readjustment somewhat as follows: Convert each classical field into an operator and each classical expression into an operator expression. Construct the expressions representing observables so that they become Hermitian operators. Arrange the field operators in a certain proper order. Impose certain conditions on the commutation properties of the fields. Do all these things in such a manner that the experimental results are recovered from the theory and no general principle of physics is violated.

This was clearly a trial and error program. It was essentially followed, in one form or another, until a general and manifestly relativistic formalism was developed by Julian Schwinger in 1951. Our presentation of quantum field theory in the next section will closely follow Schwinger's method.

13.4. Schwinger's Action Principle

Schwinger's method is essentially a Lagrangian procedure very similar to that used in the previous chapter. The only difference is that the fields are now considered as operators, and therefore the Lagrangian itself becomes an operator expression. Likewise the variations of both the fields and the expressions involving fields all become operators. These operators apply to an operand, $|\alpha\rangle$, which represents the set of all possible states for the system given by the invariant Lagrangian operator $\mathscr{L}(\psi, \partial_\mu \psi)$. Since, apart from minor rearrangements, the variational procedure is similar to that used in the previous chapter, the important new feature consists in the interpretation of the operand, $|\alpha\rangle$, and its relation to the Lagrangian operator. An important point here is that although the system is theoretically given by a Lagrangian, its practical characterization is through the spectrum of eigenvalues of its observables. The eigenvalue spectrum of a system is its observable identity—an image or template of the system. It follows that the time evolution of a system must not alter its eigenvalue spectrum, since the evolution does not alter the Lagrangian itself (The Lagrangian is independent of space and time and its functional form is invariant.) In order to describe the time evolution (the dynamics) of a system, it is therefore necessary to find an evolution transformation, $|t_2\rangle = U_{21}|t_1\rangle$, where U_{21} does not alter the eigenvalue spectrum. We will first prove that U_{21} is a *unitary transformation*.

Let O_1 and O_2 be observables acting on $|t_1\rangle$ and $|t_2\rangle$ at the times t_1 and t_2 but having the same eigenvalue o'. Thus

$$\left.\begin{aligned} O_1 |o', t_1\rangle &= o' |o', t_1\rangle \\ O_2 |o', t_2\rangle &= o' |o', t_2\rangle \\ |o', t_2\rangle &= U_{21} |o', t_1\rangle \end{aligned}\right\} \tag{13.3}$$

from which we see $O_2 U_{21} |o', t_1\rangle = o' U_{21} |o', t_1\rangle$. Comparing with the first of the above equations

$$O_2 = U_{21}^{-1} O_1 U_{21}. \tag{13.4}$$

Furthermore O_1 and O_2 are Hermitian operators, that is,

$$(U_{21}^{-1} O_1 U_{21})^\dagger = U_{21}^\dagger O_1 (U_{21}^{-1})^\dagger = U_{21}^{-1} O_1 U_{21}, \tag{13.5}$$

showing that U_{21} is unitary, that is

$$U_{21}^{-1} = U_{21}, \qquad (U_{21}^\dagger)^{-1} = U_{21}. \tag{13.6}$$

Therefore we can write

$$U_{21} = e^{iF_{21}} = 1 + iF_{21} + \frac{i^2}{2} F_{21}^2 + \cdots \tag{13.7}$$

where F_{21} is called the *generator* of the unitary transformation; it is Hermitian,

$$F_{21} = F_{21}^\dagger \tag{13.8}$$

Now, take any operator, O, not necessarily an observable. We have

$$O_2 = U_{21}^{-1} O_1 U_{21} \tag{13.9}$$

The infinitesimal variation $\delta_{21} O$ of an operator is found from this to be

$$\delta_{21} O = O_2 - O_1 = i(O_1 F_{21} - F_{21} O_1) \tag{13.10}$$

where F_{21} is now considered an infinitesimal operator. For example, specializing to a field operator, ψ, we have

$$\delta\psi = i(\psi F - F\psi). \tag{13.11}$$

All these relations are almost independent of any physical assumption because they have to do with the way we make observations, not with the specific ways physical things behave. They are essentially epistemological in content, rather than physical. Our next problem is to identify physically the generator, F, of the unitary transformation, U. In other words, we want to single out the quantity which causes the dynamical system to evolve from one state to another. This identification must be such that its consequences are consistent with the results of our observations on the system. Thus, in a sense, the identification of F should be equivalent to the specification of the whole dynamics of the system including the quantum postulate which we are trying to formulate. We introduce this identification in the form of an "Action Principle." *The generator F is equal to $\hbar^{-1}$ times the action integral*

$$F_{21} = (1/\hbar) \int_{t_1}^{t_2} \mathscr{L} \, d\Omega \tag{13.12}$$

where $\mathscr{L}$ is the Lagrangian operator and $\hbar$ is Planck's constant divided by 2π, that is, $\hbar = h/2\pi$.

Since the order in which the operators appear in the Lagrangian makes a difference, we must supply a proper ordering rule. Here we choose a symmetrical ordering as follows:

$$ab \rightarrow \tfrac{1}{2}(a^\dagger b + ba^\dagger). \tag{13.13}$$

We will now show that the identification (13.12), together with the principle of causality and the positive definiteness of energy, gives rise to restricting relations (quantum conditions) on the field operators $\psi, \phi, A, \ldots$.

Consider the variation $\delta_0\psi$ of the field alone. From (12.18) we have (note $1/\hbar$ from 13.12)

$$F(t) = \frac{1}{\hbar} \int \pi_\mu \delta_0\psi \, dS^\mu. \tag{13.14}$$

Putting this into (13.11) we obtain*

$$\delta_0\psi = \frac{i}{\hbar} \int (\psi\pi_\mu\delta_0\psi - \pi_\mu\delta_0\psi\psi) \, dS^\mu. \tag{13.15}$$

The problem is then to extract the arbitrary variation $\delta_0\psi$ from the parentheses, so that we can cancel it. There are two natural possibilities:

(a) If ψ and $\delta_0\psi$ commute, $\psi\delta_0\psi = \delta_0\psi\psi$,

$$\int (\pi_\mu\psi - \psi\pi_\mu) \, dS^\mu = i\hbar. \tag{13.16}$$

(b) If ψ and $\delta_0\psi$ anticommute, $\psi\delta_0\psi = -\delta_0\psi\psi$,

$$\int (\pi_\mu\psi + \psi\pi_\mu) \, dS^\mu = i\hbar. \tag{13.17}$$

Therefore, depending on whether $\delta_0\psi$ and ψ commute or anticommute, two different possibilities exist. In other words the fields separate in a natural way into two distinct classes: the ones which satisfy (13.16) and the ones which satisfy (13.17). These two classes turn out to be fields possessing integral spin (Bose fields) and half-integral spin (Fermi fields), respectively. We will indicate that when we introduce Bose fields into (13.16) and Fermi fields in (13.17) the subject can be developed consistently and in agreement with experiment; whereas the reverse substitution leads to a violation of either the principle of positive definiteness of energy or the principle of causality.

For the sake of completeness we note that other commutation relations can be obtained from (13.11). For example if we consider only a translation $\delta x^\mu = \epsilon^\mu$ then $F = P_\mu \delta x^\mu$ and we have $\partial_\mu\psi = i(\psi P_\mu - P_\mu\psi)$. If, in addition, $O = P_\nu$ we have $\delta P_\nu = i(P_\nu P_\mu - P_\mu P_\nu) = O$. Similarly for spin we obtain $S_l = i(S_j S_k - S_k S_j)$.

13.5. Probability Interpretation

Although the physical content is now essentially complete, there remains an important concept which is necessary to incorporate as part of the quantum theoretical formalism. The idea actually belongs to the observational part of the theory but its introduction was left

---

* For simplicity here we are omitting the dependence of ψ on x_1 and x_2. If we include these in (13.15) we would obtain

$$\int (\pi_\mu(x)\psi(x') - \psi(x')\pi_\mu(x)) dS^\mu = i\hbar, \text{ that is, } \pi_\mu(x)\psi(x') - \psi(x')\pi_\mu(x) = i\hbar\delta_\mu(x - x')$$

where x and x' are x_1 and x_2. In addition to these we will also have

$$\psi(x)\psi(x') - \psi(x')\psi(x) = \pi_\mu(x)\pi_\nu(x') - \pi_\nu(x')\pi_\mu(x) = 0.$$

to this section in order not to disturb the continuity of the argument. It is the probabilistic interpretation of measurement.

We said in Section 13.2 that when the system is in a state $|o'_k\rangle$ of the observable O, the observation of O definitely yields the eigenvalue o'_k. Then we may ask: Can the system be found in a mixed state of $o'_0, o'_1, o'_2, \ldots$? In quantum mechanics a linear combination of the states, written as

$$|o\rangle = c_0|o'_0\rangle + c_1|o'_1\rangle + c_2|o'_2\rangle \ldots, \tag{13.18}$$

where $c_0, c_1, \ldots c_n$ are ordinary complex numbers, is considered as a mixed state and the observables assumed as linear operators. When we make an observation on $|o\rangle$, that is when we consider the operation

$$O|o\rangle = c_0 o'_0|o'_0\rangle + c_1 o'_1|o'_1\rangle + c_2 o'_2|o'_2\rangle + \ldots \tag{13.19}$$

the numbers $o'_0, o'_1, o'_2, \ldots$ all appear to be reproduced. But physically this cannot be so. An observation is the recording of a single number. If we record two numbers, there are actually two observations. The equation (13.19) can be taken only in a statistical or probabilistic sense. Therefore we should say that o'_k is a probable result of an observation. On the other hand, if an observation is made, only one of these possible values, o'_k, will be recorded. However, the probabilities of observing all these numbers must add up to unity. We formulate this requirement as follows: First we point out that the eigenstates of a Hermitian operator are all orthogonal and normalizable,

$$(\Phi_k, \Phi_l) = (o'_k \mid o'_l) = \delta_{kl} \tag{13.20}$$

where δ_{kl} is the Kronecker delta.

$$\delta_{kl} = \begin{cases} 1 & \text{if } k = l \\ 0 & \text{if } k \neq l. \end{cases} \tag{13.21}$$

Next we express observation of an observable not strictly as (13.1) but as the more general expression

$$(o|O|o) = c_0^* c_0 o'_0 + c_1^* c_1 o'_1 + c_2^* c_2 o'_2 + \ldots. \tag{13.22}$$

It then becomes evident that if we require

$$(o \mid o) = c_0^* c_0 + c_1^* c_1 + c_2^* c_2 \ldots = 1, \tag{13.23}$$

the $c_k^* c_k$ can be considered as the probability of observing the particular eigenvalue o'_k. For example, if the system is in the pure state $|o'_2\rangle$, all other c_k except c_2 vanish. This leads to $c_2^* c_2 = 1$, that is, to a certainty that in the pure state only o'_2 will be observed. In the general case the probability that any o'_k will be observed is given by

$$(o'_k |o) = c_k^* c_k = |c_k|^2. \tag{13.24}$$

This is the so-called probability interpretation of observation and forms one of the fundamental features of quantum theory. Note in this connection that a unitary transformation, U, preserves the normalization (13.23) and thus the time evolution of a system cannot alter the probability interpretation. In other words the probability interpretation is a consequence of unitarity.

13.6. Experimental Justification: Free Fields

The experimental justification of the quantum formalism lies essentially in its application to free (noninteracting) fields. The predictions of the theory for interacting fields leads to a peculiar difficulty which is not sufficiently understood at the present time. In this section we will present the predictions for free fields in some detail and compare them with experimental facts.

For simplicity, consider a real (that is Hermitian) scalar field $\phi(x)$. Since here $\phi = \phi^\dagger$ the symmetrization of the Lagrangian is not necessary. The classical Lagrangian can be taken over unaltered,

$$\mathcal{L} = -\tfrac{1}{2}(\partial_\mu \phi \partial^\mu \phi + \kappa^2 \phi^2). \tag{13.25}$$

The equation of motion is the same as in the classical case

$$(\partial_\mu \partial^\mu - \kappa^2)\phi(x) = 0. \tag{13.26}$$

We will consider a single plane-wave solution of this equation. More complicated situations can be formed by linear combinations,

$$\phi(x) = \phi^\dagger(x) = a_k e^{i(kx - \omega t)} + a_k^\dagger e^{-i(kx - \omega t)} \tag{13.27}$$

where

$$\omega^2 = \kappa^2 c^2 + k^2 c^2.$$

Since exponential functions are not operators, the operator character of the field is expressed only through the integration constants a_k and $a_k^\dagger$. If we put this operator into (13.16) and integrate by taking $dS^\mu = (0, 0, 0, dV)$, we obtain

$$2\omega V(a_k a_k^\dagger - a_k^\dagger a_k) = \hbar. \tag{13.28}$$

If we redefine $a_k \to a_k \sqrt{\hbar/2\omega V}$ and drop the indices, this becomes [redefinition is related to the δ-function; footnote to equation (13.15)]

$$aa^\dagger - a^\dagger a = 1. \tag{13.29}$$

The energy and momentum operators constructed from our Lagrangian become

$$\mathcal{E} = \int T_{44} \, dV = \hbar\omega\left(\frac{a^\dagger a + aa^\dagger}{2}\right), \tag{13.30}$$

$$P_x = \frac{i}{c} \int T_{41} \, dV = \hbar k_x\left(\frac{a^\dagger a + aa^\dagger}{2}\right). \tag{13.31}$$

Now, according to the postulate of the positive definiteness of energy, there must exist a state of lowest energy. This must correspond either to a positive or zero energy. Call this state the vacuum state and designate it as $\Phi_0 = |0\rangle$

$$(0 \,|\mathcal{E}|\, 0) \geqslant 0 \tag{13.32}$$

or equivalently

$$(0 \,|a^\dagger a + aa^\dagger|\, 0) \geqslant 0 \tag{13.33}$$

A simple representation of a, satisfying the two conditions (13.29) and (13.32) is seen to be

$$a = \begin{pmatrix} 0 & 1 & 0 & 0 & 0 & \cdots \\ 0 & 0 & \sqrt{2} & 0 & 0 & \cdots \\ 0 & 0 & 0 & \sqrt{3} & 0 & \cdots \\ 0 & 0 & 0 & 0 & \sqrt{4} & \cdots \\ \cdot & \cdot & \cdot & \cdot & \cdot & \cdots \end{pmatrix} \quad a^\dagger = \begin{pmatrix} 0 & 0 & 0 & 0 & \cdots \\ 1 & 0 & 0 & 0 & \cdots \\ 0 & \sqrt{2} & 0 & 0 & \cdots \\ 0 & 0 & \sqrt{3} & 0 & \cdots \\ \cdot & \cdot & \cdot & \cdot & \cdots \end{pmatrix} \tag{13.34}$$

which operate on the eigenstates represented by the column matrices*

$$|0\rangle = \begin{pmatrix} 1 \\ 0 \\ 0 \\ \vdots \end{pmatrix} \qquad |1\rangle = \begin{pmatrix} 0 \\ 1 \\ 0 \\ \vdots \end{pmatrix} \qquad |2\rangle = \begin{pmatrix} 0 \\ 0 \\ 1 \\ \vdots \end{pmatrix} \cdots \qquad (13.35)$$

It is then easily seen that the energy and momentum are found to be

$$E' = \hbar\omega(n + \tfrac{1}{2}), \qquad n = 0, 1, 2, 3 \ldots. \qquad (13.36)$$

$$p'_x = \hbar k_x(n + \tfrac{1}{2}), \qquad n = 0, 1, 2, 3 \ldots. \qquad (13.37)$$

To the vacuum state $n = 0$ there corresponds the energy $E'_0 = \tfrac{1}{2}\hbar\omega$. Since, however, this state is the lowest, the energy may be measured from that level. The actual energy that will be measured relative to vacuum will then be

$$E' = n\hbar\omega, \qquad n = 0, 1, 2, \ldots. \qquad (13.38)$$

Note that the vacuum energy is infinite because for each frequency $\omega = c\sqrt{\kappa^2 + k^2}$ we have a contribution $\hbar\omega/2$.

$$E'_0 = \tfrac{1}{2} \sum_{k=1}^{\infty} h\sqrt{\kappa^2 c^2 + k^2 c^2} = \infty. \qquad (13.39)$$

In the case of momentum, k can be positive or negative. When the momenta are computed and added for positive and negative k, we see that

$$p' = \hbar k(n_+ - n_-) \qquad (13.40)$$

where n_+ and n_- are numbers 0, 1, 2, 3, ... In the momentum formula the vacuum part cancels out. These adjustments can be accomplished very simply if we notice that

$$aa^\dagger = n + 1, \qquad a^\dagger a = n. \qquad (13.41)$$

We can simply redefine energy (13.30) and momentum (13.31) as $\mathscr{E} = \hbar\omega a^\dagger a$ and $P_x = \hbar k a^\dagger a$. The energy and momentum of a given state would then be

$$E' = n\hbar\omega, \qquad p' = n\hbar k. \qquad (13.42)$$

The result (13.42) is interpreted as follows: The scalar field is composed of particles (field quanta). Each particle carries an energy $E' = \hbar\omega$ and momentum $p' = \hbar k = h/\lambda$, where λ is the wavelength of the particular field vibration. In this way the empirical Planck formula for the energy, and the de Broglie relation between momentum and wavelength come out of the formalism. Furthermore a given state, $|E'\rangle$, contains an integral number of identical

---

* We can easily see that the following relations hold

$$a\,|0\rangle = 0, \ a\,|n\rangle = \sqrt{n}\,|n-1\rangle, \ a^\dagger\,|n\rangle = \sqrt{n+1}\,|n+1\rangle,$$

$$|n\rangle = \frac{(a^\dagger)^n}{\sqrt{n!}}\,|0\rangle.$$

As a consequence of $a\,|o\rangle = 0$ we find the lowest energy $(|\mathscr{E}_0|) = \tfrac{1}{2}\hbar\omega > 0$. Therefore $a\,|o\rangle = 0$ is equivalent to positive definiteness of energy. Due to the above properties a and $a^\dagger$ are called annihilation and creation operators, respectively. They are also called absorption and emission operators.

quanta. Statistically the state has to be counted as only one state, since the exchange of any two identical quanta would not lead to a new state. This requirement of counting the energy state, $|E'\rangle$, where $E' = n\hbar\omega$, statistically as one single state leads to the Bose-Einstein statistics. Indeed, it is found in nature that particles which are the quanta of scalar fields (scalar particles) obey Bose-Einstein statistics. Despite the complicated nature of the formalism the content is extremely simple. The eigenvalues are simply integer numbers, $n = 0, 1, 2, \ldots$. Therefore the measurable quantities such as energy take on a discrete form, that is, an ordinary function times a number. This is the particle interpretation of the theory.

For the electromagnetic field the analysis can be carried out similarly, although now, due to the vector character and massless nature of the field, we have the wave equation $\partial_\mu \partial^\mu A_\sigma = 0$. In addition the quantity $\partial^\mu A_\mu$ is now an operator. The Lorentz condition in its operator form is to be written as $\partial^\sigma A_\sigma |\alpha\rangle = 0$, which gives

$$k^\mu A_\mu |\alpha\rangle = 0. \tag{13.43}$$

Take the solution (compare with Sections 10.4 and 10.5)

$$A_\sigma(x) = a_{\sigma k} e^{i(kz - \omega t)} + a^\dagger_{\sigma k} e^{-i(kz - \omega t)} \tag{13.44}$$

where $\omega^2 = c^2 k^2$. The condition (13.29) now becomes (again dropping the index k)

$$a_{\sigma'} a^\dagger_\sigma - a^\dagger_\sigma a_{\sigma'} = \delta_{\sigma\sigma'}. \tag{13.45}$$

Here we have four a_σ. However, as in Chapter 10, only two of them are independent due to the Lorentz condition and gauge invariance. We use a_1 and a_2. They satisfy from (13.45)

$$a_1 a^\dagger_1 - a^\dagger_1 a_1 = 1, \qquad a_2 a^\dagger_2 - a^\dagger_2 a_2 = 1, \tag{13.46}$$

$$a_2 a^\dagger_1 - a^\dagger_1 a_2 = a_1 a^\dagger_2 - a^\dagger_2 a_1 = 0. \tag{13.47}$$

The energy and momentum formulas split up into two parts

$$\mathscr{E} = \hbar\omega(a^\dagger_1 a_1 + a^\dagger_2 a_2), \qquad P = \hbar k(a^\dagger_1 a_1 + a^\dagger_2 a_2) \tag{13.48}$$

indicating that $E' = \hbar\omega(n_1 + n_2)$ where n_1 and n_2 are two independent, nonnegative integers. Thus, we have two independent quanta for each electromagnetic wave. The Planck formula, de Broglie-Einstein relation, and Bose-Einstein statistics all remain valid as for the scalar field. The main difference between scalar and vector fields is that the latter has a spin angular-momentum. In the quantized form, Section 10.5 leads to

$$N^{12} = \int (\partial_\mu A^1 A^2 - \partial_\mu A^2 A^1) \, dS^\mu = \hbar(a^\dagger_1 a_1 - a^\dagger_2 a_2). \tag{13.49}$$

$$N'^{12} = \hbar(n_r - n_l). \tag{13.50}$$

We can identify n_r as the number of right circularly-polarized quanta and n_l as the number of left circularly-polarized quanta. Note that for spin the numbers n_r and n_l are not of the form $a^\dagger_1 a_1$. For this reason these integer numbers are related to the commutation relations of spin (see Section 13.4). This prediction of the theory concerning the spin angular momentum is in perfect agreement with what is actually observed.

For the free spinor field-operator, the Lagrangian is given by

$$\mathscr{L} = \tfrac{1}{2}[\psi^\dagger(\gamma_\mu \partial^\mu + \kappa)\psi + \psi(\gamma_\mu \partial^\mu + m)\psi^\dagger]. \tag{13.51}$$

This leads to the equations

$$(\partial_\mu \partial^\mu + \kappa)\psi = 0, \qquad \psi^\dagger(\overleftarrow{\partial_\mu \partial^\mu} + \kappa) = 0. \tag{13.52}$$

Consider a single plane wave solution, for example, the positive frequency spin-up solution in (11.46). We write it as

$$\psi^{(+)\uparrow} = \begin{pmatrix} \cos\dfrac{\alpha}{2} \\ 0 \\ -\sin\dfrac{\alpha}{2} \\ 0 \end{pmatrix} c_1 e^{i(kz-\omega t)}. \tag{13.53}$$

When we introduce this into (13.17), we see (employing also $\pi = \psi^\dagger$, which results from the Lagrangian) that

$$V(c_1^\dagger c_1 + c_1 c_1^\dagger) = \hbar. \tag{13.54}$$

By a redefinition, $c_1 \rightarrow c_1\sqrt{\hbar/V}$, we have (similar to scalar field)

$$c_1^\dagger c_1 + c_1 c_1^\dagger = 1. \tag{13.55}$$

It can be seen that energy is positive in this case and we have

$$\mathscr{E} = \int T^{44}\, dV = \hbar\omega c_1^\dagger c_1, \tag{13.56}$$

$$P = \frac{i}{c} \int T^{14}\, dV = \hbar k c_1^\dagger c_1. \tag{13.57}$$

A solution of the anticommutation equation (13.55) is

$$c_1 = \begin{pmatrix} 0 & 1 \\ 0 & 0 \end{pmatrix}, \qquad c_1^\dagger = \begin{pmatrix} 0 & 0 \\ 1 & 0 \end{pmatrix} \tag{13.58}$$

with only two eigenstates,*

$$|0\rangle = \begin{pmatrix} 1 \\ 0 \end{pmatrix}, \qquad |1\rangle = \begin{pmatrix} 0 \\ 1 \end{pmatrix}. \tag{13.59}$$

The eigenvalues of $c_1^\dagger c_1$ are only two. They are 0 and 1. Thus, for a given momentum, a positive frequency spinor field with spin ($\uparrow$) has only two possible energies, 0 and $\hbar\omega$.

$$E' = n\hbar\omega, \qquad p' = n\hbar k, \qquad n = 0, 1. \tag{13.60}$$

These, therefore. again confirm the Planck and de Broglie relations and, in addition, lead to an expression of the Pauli exclusion principle: *No two identical electrons can be found in the same state.* This, in turn, leads to Fermi-Dirac statistics, which corresponds correctly to what is observed in nature. The analysis is the same for the positive frequency spin ($\downarrow$)

---

* One finds directly that $c|0\rangle = c^\dagger|1\rangle = 0$, $c|1\rangle = |0\rangle$, $c^\dagger|0\rangle = |1\rangle$. Again here c and $c^\dagger$ are called annihilation and creation operators. From these and from the relations satisfied by a, $a^\dagger$ and a_μ, $a_\mu^\dagger$ we can see that the field operator concept adds only a slight complication over the classical theory. The complication is only algebraic, gives integer numbers and can be separated out by the use of their simple algebra.

case. For the negative frequency part, take the solution (11.48)

$$\psi^{(-)\uparrow} = \begin{pmatrix} \sinh\dfrac{\alpha}{2} \\ 0 \\ \cosh\dfrac{\alpha}{2} \\ 0 \end{pmatrix} b_3 e^{-i(kz-\omega t)}. \tag{13.61}$$

By going through the same arithmetics we find

$$b_3^\dagger b_3 + b_3 b_3^\dagger = 1, \tag{13.62}$$

$$\mathscr{E} = \int T^{44}\, dV = -\hbar\omega b_3 b_3^\dagger. \tag{13.63}$$

This seems to indicate that the negative frequency part will have negative energy. Since we cannot allow this, we rewrite the energy with the help of (13.42) as

$$\mathscr{E} = \hbar\omega b_3^\dagger b_3 - \hbar\omega. \tag{13.64}$$

Now the second term is the same for every state. It can therefore be assumed to represent the vacuum energy. It is negative and, when added up for all frequencies it is infinite, $E_0' = -\sum_{k=0}^{\infty} \hbar c\sqrt{\kappa^2 + k^2} = -\infty$. But this infinity does not enter into the observed results if we consider it as the vacuum level. Then, by a redefinition the energy can be taken as

$$\mathscr{E} = \hbar\omega b_3^\dagger b_3. \tag{13.65}$$

We then have $b_3^\dagger b_3 = n$, $n = 0, 1$, which leads to a *positive energy* $E' = n\hbar\omega$ where $n = 0, 1$. The spin ($\downarrow$) case is similar.

In nature the negative frequency electrons are indeed found to have positive energy. They are called *positrons*. Thus, in this respect too, the theory is in agreement with observation.

It is illustrative also to calculate the spin angular-momentum. For $\psi^{(+)\uparrow}$ the formalism leads to

$$N^{12} = (\hbar/2)c_1^\dagger c_1 \tag{13.66}$$

which gives

$$N'^{12} = \frac{\hbar}{2}n, \qquad n = 0, 1. \tag{13.67}$$

Thus, the fact that electrons have a spin which is half of the spin of the light quantum (photon) is also correctly predicted by the theory. In the case of electron spin N^{23}, N^{31} are also observable. For photon only the component along the direction of propagation is observable. The latter statement is true for any field if $\kappa = 0$.

The superpositions of various spin and momentum states are easy to work out. The reader is referred to more advanced books for further details.

If a scalar or a vector field is substituted into (13.17) instead of (13.16), the principle of causality will be violated. This follows from the fact, pointed out in Chapter 12, that a scalar or a vector field can enter linearly into the Lagrangian. This would mean that, in general, the effects of a single scalar or vector field are observable. Since, according to the theory of relativity, no observable effect is transmitted faster than the velocity of light the field must *commute* with itself for spacelike distances. This shows that the *anticommutation* conditions are not proper for scalar and vector fields.

For spinor fields, which do not appear linearly but bilinearly in the expressions for physical quantities, the above argument does not hold. In this case, the anticommutation conditions are permissible. But if we try to calculate the energy of a spinor field with the condition (13.16), it will be easily seen that observable energy cannot be prevented from becoming negative. Thus, for spinor fields we must use (13.17). These arguments can be extended and the following general conclusion reached: All fields with integral spin satisfy commutation relations and all fields with half-integral spin satisfy anticommutation relations. This forms the basis of the so-called spin-statistics connection, and is one of the most brilliant successes of relativistic quantum field theory.

We may now summarize the most important results:

(a) For scalar and vector fields, the theory leads to energy and momentum eigenvalues $P_\mu = n\hbar k_\mu$, $n = 0, 1, 2, \ldots$ where the number n may be interpreted as the number of particles in the state considered. Since these particles are indistinguishable, the whole state has to be counted statistically as one. This leads to Bose-Einstein statistics. Thus scalar and vector particles obey Bose-Einstein statistics in agreement with observation. For example, the Planck black-body distribution law for light is a consequence of this result. Also, one obtains correctly the spins 0 and 1 for scalar and vector fields, respectively.

(b) For spinor fields, the theory leads to $P_\mu = n\hbar k_\mu$ where $n = 0, 1$. This means that in a given state there can be either one particle or none. No two identical particles can be put into one given state, yielding the so-called exclusion principle of Pauli. The consequent counting process leads to Fermi-Dirac statistics and is in agreement with observation. For the electron, μ-meson, neutrino, et cetera, we also have the spin $\frac{1}{2}$ consistent with observation.

13.7. Interacting Fields

Despite these brilliant successes for free fields, the theory meets a peculiar difficulty in the treatment of interacting fields, which has not yet been sufficiently cleared up to analyze its nature or origin and to warrant a final judgment. The situation may be described as follows: The coupled field equations of interacting fields, say (12.27, 12.28), are nonlinear both in the unquantized (classical) and in the quantized (quantum mechanical) form. We are unable to solve them exactly. This forces us to use approximation methods. Approximation methods in the form of perturbation expansions are possible for small coupling constants, that is, for relatively weak interactions. For the electromagnetic interaction the expansion co-efficient is $e^2/\hbar c \sim \frac{1}{137}$ and the expansion is expected to work reasonably well. For Fermi interactions, where $G^2/\hbar c \sim 10^{-10}$, the situation looks even better. For nuclear interactions, however, $g^2/\hbar c \sim 10$ and a perturbation expansion is meaningless since each additional term will be larger than the previous one. But even for the electromagnetic, no one has been able to prove that the perturbation expansion converges. In fact we do not really know if the equations have any solution at all. Under these circumstances what is done is to expand into a perturbation series anyway, and hope for the best. Comparison of the first few terms with experiment gives good results for the electromagnetic and Fermi interactions; whereas, for the strong interactions there is poor agreement, as expected. Even for the electromagnetic and Fermi interactions, certain terms, which are otherwise expected to be small or finite, give infinite results. These infinities normally prevent us from arriving at unambiguous results for the observed quantities. A method of dealing with infinities has been found so that the infinities can be separated from the observed quantities and attached to the two phenomenological constants m and e making them infinite in value. Since these are observed to be finite, one later redefines them to be the observed m and observed e. This process is called mass and charge renormalization. It is only after these readjustments that perturbation theory gives results for the electromagnetic and Fermi interactions which are (for the first few terms of the expansion) in good agreement with observation.

For the sake of completeness, we will indicate briefly how interacting fields are treated. Consider the complete classical Lagrangian (12.26) for the coupled electromagnetic and electron fields. If $e = 0$, there is no interaction. Electrons and photons are independent and free. Therefore the previous results for the free fields apply separately. If the interaction term is not zero, we expect that gradually energy-momentum and angular momentum will be transferred from electrons to photons or vice versa. In the quantized form of the theory this will manifest itself in the following ways: (1) Photons are emitted or adsorbed, that is, the creation operator $a_k^\dagger$ or the adsorption operator a_k operates on the operand. (2) Photons are scattered, that is, a photon is adsorbed and another emitted in a different direction which is represented by the operator $a_{k'}^\dagger$, a_k or $a_k a_{k'}^\dagger$. (3) Electrons are gaining or losing energy or being scattered, that is, the operator $c_{k'}^\dagger c_k$ or $c_k c_{k'}^\dagger$ act on the operand. (4) Electron positron pairs are being created or annihilated, $b_{k'}^\dagger c_k^\dagger$ or $b_{k'} c_k$ act on the operand, and so on. We can see that the interaction term, $\bar\psi \gamma^\sigma A_\sigma \psi$, which causes the system to evolve in time induces a kind of continual emission-adsorption process. The problem, then, is how to calculate the final outcome of a physical process from these concepts.

For this purpose we construct the unitary transformation $U_{t't}$ in terms of the interaction Lagrangian. From the action principle we have

$$U_{t't} = e^{(i/\hbar)\int_t^{t'} \mathscr{L} d\Omega} \tag{13.68}$$

This formal expression is to be understood as a series expansion. Before we make this expansion we note that if the interaction term $\mathscr{L}_I = e\bar\psi \gamma^\mu A_\mu \psi$ did not exist, the initial and final states would be physically the same; that is, $|t\rangle$ and $|t'\rangle$ would differ at most by a constant phase. The physically detectable change is then due entirely to $\mathscr{L}_I$. The unitary transformation can therefore be taken as

$$U_{t't} = e^{(i/\hbar)\int_t^{t'} e\bar\psi \gamma^\mu A_\mu \psi d\Omega} \tag{13.69}$$

The representation this operator refers to is called the interaction representation. When expanded this gives

$$U_{t't} = 1 + \frac{ie}{h}\int_t^{t'} d\Omega \bar\psi \gamma^\mu A_\mu \psi - \frac{e^2}{2\hbar^2}\int_t^{t'} d\Omega \int_t^{t'} d\Omega (\bar\psi \gamma^\mu A_\mu \psi)_2 (\bar\psi \gamma^\mu A_\mu \psi)_1 + \dots \tag{13.70}$$

This expresses the whole interaction process as an interplay of emission and adsorption operators. For example, in the first term there are eight possibilities: $c^\dagger ac$, $c^\dagger a^\dagger c$, $b^\dagger a c^\dagger$, etc. They correspond to scattering of an electron by absorbing a photon, emission of a photon by scattering an electron, creation of an electron-positron pair by adsorbing a photon, etc. Graphical representation of these and more complicated cases lead to the so-called Feynman diagrams. In this way we see that transitions from the initial states to final states take place. From (13.24) it can be deduced that the transition probability per unit time is

$$w_{if} = \frac{1}{\hbar}|\langle f|U|i\rangle|^2 \tag{13.71}$$

If at $t = -\infty$ and $t' = +\infty$ the particles are separated by large distances, the operator $U_{t't}$ is called the *S*-matrix; it is of central importance in scattering theory.

We may wonder how the ordinary quantum mechanics of electrons arise from this complex picture. Consider only the first term in $U_{t't}$. We also assume that the electromagnetic field is given such that the absorption and emission of photons have a negligible effect on the value of the field. Then, the only processes left are scattering of electrons, positrons and the creation and annihilation of electron-positron pairs. If further we assume that there are no positrons present and that energies involved are low enough so that they are not created, we are left only with the scattering of electrons. Due to the exclusion principle, we then always carry a useless state vector $|1\rangle$ with each electron since $a^\dagger a |1\rangle = |1\rangle$ and $a^\dagger |1\rangle$ and $a^\dagger a |1\rangle$ both equal zero. This means that the $|1\rangle$ can be dropped and the normalization can be achieved simply by setting $c^\dagger c = 1$. By a redefinition, this may be written as (see 13.28, 13.29 and footnote for 13.15) a normalization

$$\int \bar\psi\psi \, dV = 1. \tag{13.72}$$

Apart from this normalization all the other features are those of an unquantized theory, which obeys the classical equation (12.28)

$$(\gamma^\mu \partial_\mu + \kappa - ie\gamma^\mu A_\mu)\psi = 0 \tag{13.73}$$

This is the Dirac equation of electron in an electromagnetic field. The Shrödinger equation can be obtained from this as a nonrelativistic limit. We emphasize that no such normalization can be obtained for bosons because they do not satisfy the exclusion principle. As a result, ordinary quantum mechanics in the above sense of normalization does not exist for photons and mesons.

In the past it was possible to extend the Dirac theory to electron-positron systems with a device called hole-theory which also made use of the exclusion principle. In this way ordinary quantum mechanics was able to treat the first order problems, such as scattering of electrons and positrons, energy levels of atoms, creation and annihilation of electron-positron pairs, emission of light, etc.

Problems which require the complete quantized theory are the ones in which higher order terms in the expansion are necessary or the quantum nature of light is important. Three of the most brilliant successes of the quantum field theory in this respect are (1) the calculation of the Lamb-shift, (2) anomalous magnetic moment of the electron, (3) derivation of the Einstein transition probabilities. For an exposition of these we must send the reader to books on quantum electrodynamics.

Summary: Relativity and Quantum Field Theory

(a) In quantum field theory fields are considered as operators. These act on an operand, the so-called state vector.

(b) Observables are Hermitian operators constructed from the fields and act on the state vector. The measurement of an observable yields one of its eigenvalues.

(c) Dynamics of a system is expressed by a unitary transformation on the state vector. This transformation does not alter the eigenvalue spectrum and allows a probability interpretation.

(d) The generator of this unitary transformation is $(1/\hbar)$ times the action integral.

The theory suggests in a natural way two kinds of commutation relations for the field operators. These imply particle properties and lead to the connection between spin and statistics. Fields can be interpreted as emission and absorption operators for the associated particles. This results in a concept of evolution of a field system in time through transitions caused by the interaction term in the Lagrangian. Although the theory is complicated in detail the main ideas and consequences are quite simple. The essential complication over the classical picture is only algebraic and related to the operator interpretation of the fields.

14

MATHEMATICAL AIDS FOR GENERAL RELATIVITY

14.1. Geometry and its Forms

Let $x^1, x^2, \ldots x^N$ be a set of independent continuous variables. The totality of points represented by these variables will be called a *space*. Examples are the ordinary Euclidean space of x, y, and z, and the space of thermodynamic variables P, V, and T. The variables $x^1, x^2, \ldots x^N$ are called the coordinates. The independence of these variables means that no one of them depends on any other, that is $(\partial x^2/\partial x^1) = 0, \ldots$ et cetera. We have

$$\frac{\partial x^\nu}{\partial x^\mu} = \delta_\mu^\nu = \begin{cases} 1 & \text{if} \quad \mu = \nu \\ 0 & \text{if} \quad \mu \neq \nu. \end{cases} \tag{14.1}$$

If it is possible to describe the space concerned by a new set of independent variables x'^ν, these new variables must be functions of the old ones, that is, $x'^\nu(x^\mu)$. If this description is in all respects equivalent to the old description, we must be able to obtain the x^μ as functions of the new variables, that is $x^\mu(x'^\nu)$. This simply means that nothing is lost by the first transformation; that is, if we wish, we can recover everything by the inverse transformation. Such transformations are called *one to one*. The complete description of a space and its transformations is called a *geometry*. The set of coordinates x^μ and x'^ν are called the *coordinate systems* S and S', respectively.

Consider the increments, dx^μ, of the coordinate x^μ. Corresponding to these there are the increments dx'^ν. Differentiating partially the $x'^\nu(x^\mu)$ we obtain the transformation law for the differentials

$$dx'^\nu = \frac{\partial x'^\nu}{\partial x^\mu} dx^\mu, \qquad \mu, \nu = 1, 2 \ldots N. \tag{14.2}$$

A summation over the repeated index μ is implicit. Since the transformation is assumed to be reversible, the dx^μ must be obtainable from (14.2) which implies that the determinant of the coefficients must not vanish

$$\det \left\| \frac{\partial x'^\nu}{\partial x^\mu} \right\| \neq 0. \tag{14.3}$$

Any aggregate of N quantities U^μ, which transform from the coordinate system S to the coordinate system S', like the dx^μ in (14.2), is called a *contravariant vector*.

$$U'^\nu = \frac{\partial x'^\nu}{\partial x^\mu} U^\mu. \tag{14.4}$$

Consider a function $\Phi(x^\mu) = \Phi(x'^\nu)$. Since $d\Phi(x^\mu) = d\Phi(x'^\nu)$, we have

$$\frac{\partial \Phi}{\partial x^\mu} dx^\mu = \frac{\partial \Phi}{\partial x'^\nu} dx'^\nu \tag{14.5}$$

which, by substituting

$$dx^\mu = \frac{\partial x^\mu}{\partial x'^\nu} dx'^\nu,$$

gives

$$\left(\frac{\partial \Phi}{\partial x'^\nu} - \frac{\partial x^\mu}{\partial x'^\nu}\frac{\partial \Phi}{\partial x^\mu}\right) dx'^\nu = 0. \tag{14.6}$$

Since the dx'^ν are independent increments,

$$\frac{\partial \Phi}{\partial x'^\nu} = \frac{\partial x^\mu}{\partial x'^\nu}\frac{\partial \Phi}{\partial x^\mu}. \tag{14.7}$$

Any aggregate of N quantities V_μ, which transform from the coordinate system S to the coordinate system S' like $\partial\Phi/\partial x^\mu$, is called a *covariant vector*.

$$V'_\nu = \frac{\partial x^\mu}{\partial x'^\nu} V_\mu. \tag{14.8}$$

Note that so far *covariant* and *contravariant* vectors have nothing to do with each other except that their *inner product*, defined as $V_\mu U^\mu$, is an *invariant*, that is, independent of the coordinate system.

$$V'_\mu U'^\mu = \frac{\partial x^\alpha}{\partial x'^\mu}\frac{\partial x'^\mu}{\partial x^\beta} V_\alpha U^\beta = \frac{\partial x^\alpha}{\partial x^\beta} V_\alpha U^\beta = \delta^\alpha_\beta V_\alpha U^\beta$$

so that

$$V'_\mu U'^\mu = V_\alpha U^\alpha = \text{Inv.} \tag{14.9}$$

For example, equation (14.5) expresses the invariance of $d\Phi$. Such invariant quantities are called *scalars*. A space in which covariant and contravariant vectors exist separately is called *affine*. In other words, in an affine space a *vector* does not exist; but covariant and contravariant vectors exist independently of each other. Such spaces are very general and have been extensively studied by mathematicians. In fundamental physical theories we deal with objects or quantities which are independent of the particular choice of the mode of description. In other words it is desirable to deal with a space in which the concept of a *vector* exists as an objective physical reality, independent of the possible choices of covariance or contravariance. Such spaces are called *metric*. We will introduce metric spaces a little farther on. For the sake of generality let us go a little farther with affine spaces. Consider a two index quantity $U_{\mu\nu}$ which behaves like a covariant vector in each of its indices. For example, if we fix $\mu = 2$, $U_{2\nu}$ behaves like a covariant vector in its ν index, and so on. Such a quantity will transform as

$$U'_{\mu\nu} = \frac{\partial x^\alpha}{\partial x'^\mu}\frac{\partial x^\beta}{\partial x'^\nu} U_{\alpha\beta}. \tag{14.10}$$

This is called a *second order covariant tensor*. Generalizing this idea to contravariant situations and to more indices, we have tensors of the type

$$U'^\tau_{\mu\nu\cdots} = \frac{\partial x^\tau}{\partial x'^\mu}\frac{\partial x^\alpha}{\partial x'^\nu}\frac{\partial x^\beta}{\partial x'^\gamma} \cdots U^\gamma_{\alpha\beta\cdots}. \tag{14.11}$$

Such a quantity is called a *mixed tensor with covariance* $\mu, \nu, \ldots$ *and contravariance* $\tau, \ldots$. The total number of the indices of a tensor is called its *order*.

$$
\begin{array}{lll}
U & \text{0th} & \text{order tensor} \\
U_\mu & \text{1st} & \text{order tensor} \\
U_{\mu\nu} & \text{2nd} & \text{order tensor} \\
U^{\alpha\tau}_{\mu\nu\lambda} & \text{5th} & \text{order tensor}
\end{array}
\tag{14.12}
$$

and so on. A tensor symmetric in any pair of indices remains symmetric in all coordinate systems.

There are spaces in which covariant and contravariant vectors do not exist independently; they can be converted into each other. Such spaces have a further property that the index of a contravariant vector U^ν can be lowered to become U_μ.

$$
U_\mu = g_{\mu\nu}U^\nu.
\tag{14.13}
$$

Such a space is called *metric*. In a metric space there exists the concept of a vector $\vec{U}$ which may be described by *contravariant indices* U^μ, or by covariant indices U_μ. These two descriptions must be equivalent if the vector $\vec{U}$ is to have an independent objective meaning. This is primarily a physical requirement, because the outcome of an experiment should not depend on the mode of description (covariance or contravariance). Thus the reverse of transformation (14.13) must exist,

$$
U^\nu = g^{\nu\mu}U_\mu.
\tag{14.14}
$$

Equations (14.13) and (14.14) will be taken as the definition of a *vector*. The tensor $g_{\mu\nu}$ is called the *metric tensor* of the space concerned, and $g^{\mu\nu}$ is the contravariant form of it. By combining the two preceding transformations, we have

$$
U_\mu = g_{\mu\nu}g^{\nu\alpha}U_\alpha
$$

which means

$$
g_{\mu\nu}g^{\nu\alpha} = \delta^\alpha_\mu.
\tag{14.15}
$$

In other words, $g^{\mu\nu}$ is the inverse of $g_{\mu\nu}$ and vice versa, that is,

$$
g^{\mu\nu} = \frac{M^{\mu\nu}}{|g|}
\tag{14.16}
$$

where $|g|$ is the determinant of $g_{\mu\nu}$ and $M^{\mu\nu}$ is the minor of the element $g_{\mu\nu}$. It goes without saying that any index of a tensor $U^\alpha_{\mu\nu\cdots}$ may be lowered by the metric tensor just as is the case for vectors. In the following, we will deal exclusively with metric geometries.

The *square* of a vector is defined by the *inner product*

$$
\vec{U}^2 = U_\mu U^\mu = g_{\mu\nu}U^\mu U^\nu = g^{\alpha\beta}U_\alpha U_\beta.
\tag{14.17}
$$

Similarly we can define the square of the differential dx^μ

$$
ds^2 = d\vec{x}^2 = g_{\mu\nu}\, dx^\mu\, dx^\nu.
\tag{14.18}
$$

The quantity ds is called the *line element* of the metric space concerned, and equation (14.18) expressing the invariance of ds^2 is called the *fundamental quadratic form*. It is about the most important equation used in the study of metric geometries. An important assumption, which is not explicitly expressed in the usual textbooks, is that the *basic observable of a metric geometry is the distance ds*. This means, among other things, that we can take

$g_{\mu\nu}$ as symmetric, since in (14.18) only symmetric terms contribute to ds^2. As an example we give here the $g_{\mu\nu}$ and ds^2 for the Euclidean 3-space in both Cartesian and spherical coordinates (Figure 14.1).

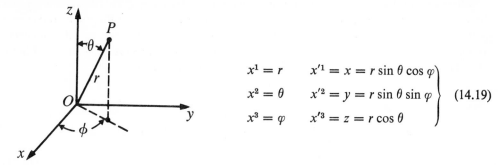

$$x^1 = r \qquad x'^1 = x = r \sin \theta \cos \varphi$$
$$x^2 = \theta \qquad x'^2 = y = r \sin \theta \sin \varphi \qquad (14.19)$$
$$x^3 = \varphi \qquad x'^3 = z = r \cos \theta$$

FIGURE 14.1 *Spherical polar coordinates.*

Now for Cartesian coordinates we know the square of the vector dx, dy, dz, is $ds^2 = dx^2 + dy^2 + dz^2$. Substituting, we find

$$ds^2 = dx^2 + dy^2 + dz^2 = dr^2 + r^2\, d\theta^2 + r^2 \sin^2 \theta\, d\varphi^2. \qquad (14.20)$$

Hence we see that for Cartesian and for spherical coordinates we have, respectively,

$$g'_{\mu\nu} = \begin{pmatrix} 1 & 0 & 0 \\ 0 & 1 & 0 \\ 0 & 0 & 1 \end{pmatrix}; \qquad g_{\mu\nu} = \begin{pmatrix} 1 & 0 & 0 \\ 0 & r^2 & 0 \\ 0 & 0 & r^2 \sin^2 \theta \end{pmatrix}. \qquad (14.21)$$

Thus, in order to define a metric geometry it is sufficient to give the coordinates x^μ and the metric tensor $g_{\mu\nu}$ for one particular frame S. Equivalently, one may give *the fundamental metric form ds^2*. As another example consider the Lorentz space x, y, z, and t, and its transformation x', y', x', and t', by a Lorentz transformation given by

$$x^1 = x \qquad x'^1 = x' = x \cosh \alpha - ct \sinh \alpha$$
$$x^2 = y \qquad x'^2 = y' = y$$
$$x^3 = z \qquad x'^3 = z' = z \qquad (14.22)$$
$$x^4 = t \qquad x'^4 = t' = \frac{x}{c} \sinh \alpha - t \cosh \alpha$$

$$ds^2 = dx^2 + dy^2 + dz^2 - c^2\, dt^2 = dx'^2 + dy'^2 + dz'^2 - c^2\, dt'^2$$

$$g_{\mu\nu} = \begin{pmatrix} 1 & 0 & 0 & 0 \\ 0 & 1 & 0 & 0 \\ 0 & 0 & 1 & 0 \\ 0 & 0 & 0 & -c^2 \end{pmatrix}, \qquad g'_{\mu\nu} = \begin{pmatrix} 1 & 0 & 0 & 0 \\ 0 & 1 & 0 & 0 \\ 0 & 0 & 1 & 0 \\ 0 & 0 & 0 & -c^2 \end{pmatrix}. \qquad (14.23)$$

In this case $g_{\mu\nu}$ and $g'_{\mu\nu}$ are of the same form. In this example if we choose $x^4 = ct$, $x'^4 = ct'$, the last element, g_{44}, would become $g_{44} = -1$. If we choose $x^4 = ict$, $x'^4 = ict'$, then it would become $g_{44} = +1$.

Notice that in these examples $g_{\mu\nu}$ has only diagonal elements, $g_{\mu\mu}$. This means simply that the coordinate surfaces $x^1 = $ constant, $x^2 = $ constant, et cetera, are orthogonal, and consequently coordinate lines meet at right angles. Such coordinates are called *orthogonal coordinates*. We can construct systems with *oblique* axes. As an example consider Figure 14.2. The expression for the line element (square of the distance) is

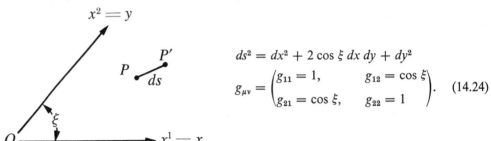

$$ds^2 = dx^2 + 2 \cos \xi \, dx \, dy + dy^2$$

$$g_{\mu\nu} = \begin{pmatrix} g_{11} = 1, & g_{12} = \cos \xi \\ g_{21} = \cos \xi, & g_{22} = 1 \end{pmatrix}. \qquad (14.24)$$

FIGURE 14.2   *Oblique coordinates.*

A more important point to notice is that when the coordinate surfaces are planes (that is, when the coordinate lines are straight lines), the $g_{\mu\nu}$ are all constants. On the other hand, when coordinate lines are curves, as in spherical coordinates, the $g_{\mu\nu}$ are functions of x^μ. These two cases are distinguished from each other by the names *rectilinear* and *curvilinear* coordinates respectively. If a space can be given by a rectilinear system it is called a *flat space*. All the preceding examples are flat spaces. If a space can never be brought into a rectilinear coordinate system, it is called *curved* or *Riemannian*. As an example, consider the surface of a sphere, $r = a$; then the variables are $x^1 = \theta$, $x^2 = \varphi$. The line element on the surface of the sphere is (Figure 14.3),

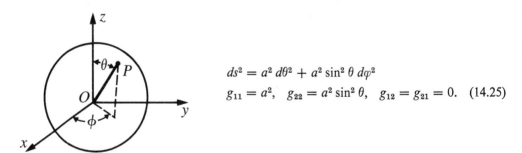

$$ds^2 = a^2 \, d\theta^2 + a^2 \sin^2 \theta \, d\varphi^2$$

$$g_{11} = a^2, \quad g_{22} = a^2 \sin^2 \theta, \quad g_{12} = g_{21} = 0. \quad (14.25)$$

FIGURE 14.3   *Surface of a sphere.*

Now this is in curvilinear form and it happens that it can never be put into rectilinear form by any transformation. This is essentially because one cannot draw straight lines on the surface of a sphere. The surface of a sphere, the surfaces of an ellipsoid, paraboloid, et cetera, are examples of curved spaces. Note that the surface of a cylinder or a cone is *not* a curved space. This is evident from the fact that a cylinder or a cone can be formed out of a plane, which is a flat space. A sphere or a hyperboloid cannot be shaped from a plane without stretching, and hence cannot be transformed into rectilinear coordinates. The so-called *Riemannian Geometry* is the science of curved spaces.

In an affine space, the tensor $g_{\mu\nu}$ cannot be defined. The equivalence of covariant and contravariant descriptions of geometry by $g_{\mu\nu}$ is a property of metric spaces. With the help of this tensor, line element, the concepts of distance, length, angle, perpendicularity, and many other familiar geometrical concepts, may be defined. In an affine space these are not definable. The tensor $g_{\mu\nu}$ operates essentially as an operator to lower a contravariant index, as in (14.13). This works also for tensors of any rank. However, for tensors, it is necessary to remember the position from which the index was lowered or raised. For example,

$$\left.\begin{aligned} T_\mu^\nu &= g_{\alpha\mu}T^{\alpha\nu} \\ T_\mu^\alpha &= g_{\mu\nu}T^{\alpha\nu} \end{aligned}\right\}. \tag{14.26}$$

The reason for this is that when we bring the index back to its original site, we do not want to interchange the order of indices since, in general, $T^{\mu\nu} \neq T^{\nu\mu}$.

14.2. Tensor Analysis

In the rectilinear coordinate system of a flat space the differentiation of a scalar Φ, $\partial\Phi/\partial x^\mu$, creates a covariant vector. If we differentiate any tensor in these coordinates, we get a new tensor. For example,

$$\partial_\mu U^\alpha = U^\alpha_{,\mu}. \tag{14.27}$$

This definition is not general. In curvilinear coordinate systems one cannot, in general, form a new tensor from other tensors by ordinary partial differentiation. In rectilinear coordinate systems the ordinary differentiation of a tensor yields a tensor of the same rank $dT_\mu^\alpha = \partial_\nu T_\mu^\alpha dx^\nu$. In curvilinear coordinates (and this is also true in curved spaces), differentiation in the ordinary sense does not give a new tensor. For example, $dA_\mu = d(g_{\mu\nu}A^\nu) = dg_{\mu\nu}A^\nu + g_{\mu\nu}dA^\nu$ where $dg_{\mu\nu} \neq 0$ destroys the vector character of dA_μ and dA^ν. In order to obtain new tensors with these operations, the concept of *ordinary differentiation* must be generalized into a new concept called *absolute differentiation*, denoted by D. It is evident from the definition of a vector that such an operation should give

$$DA_\mu = D(g_{\mu\nu}A^\nu) = g_{\mu\nu}DA^\nu, \qquad Dg_{\mu\nu} = 0. \tag{14.28}$$

Thus, absolute differentiation, D, may be defined by

$$Dg_{\mu\nu} = 0, \qquad Dg^{\mu\nu} = 0. \tag{14.29}$$

Since a scalar Φ, say, $A^\mu A_\mu$ does not involve $g_{\mu\nu}$, absolute differentials of scalars equal their ordinary differentials,

$$D\Phi = d\Phi \tag{14.30}$$

$$DA^\mu A_\mu + A^\mu DA_\mu = dA^\mu A_\mu + A^\mu dA_\mu. \tag{14.31}$$

This last formula is satisfied if we assume the forms

$$DA^\mu = dA^\mu + \{^\mu_{\alpha\,\nu}\}A^\alpha\,dx^\nu, \tag{14.32}$$

$$DA_\mu = dA_\mu - \{^\alpha_{\mu\,\nu}\}A_\alpha\,dx^\nu, \tag{14.33}$$

where $\{^\mu_{\alpha\,\nu}\}$ are differential coefficients called Christoffel symbols. They are not tensors because when added to dA^μ, which is not a tensor, they yield a tensor DA^μ. Applying the same process to the scalar $U^\nu_\mu U^\mu_\nu$, we find that for each contravariant index a $\{^\mu_{\alpha\,\nu}\}$ term, and for each covariant index a $-\{^\mu_{\alpha\,\nu}\}$ term is added. For example,

$$DU^\nu_\mu = dU^\nu_\mu + \{^\nu_{\alpha\,\lambda}\}U^\alpha_\mu \, dx^\lambda - \{^\alpha_{\mu\,\alpha}\}U^\nu_\alpha \, dx^\nu. \tag{14.34}$$

To find the Christoffel symbols we use the equations

$$Dg_{\mu\nu} = dg_{\mu\nu} - \{^\alpha_{\mu\,\alpha}\}g_{\alpha\nu} \, dx^\alpha - \{^\alpha_{\alpha\,\nu}\}g_{\mu\alpha} \, dx^\alpha = 0. \tag{14.35}$$

Permuting cyclically the indices α, μ, and ν, and adding the resulting equations, using the relation $g_{\mu\nu}g^{\mu\alpha} = \delta^\alpha_\nu$, we find

$$\{^\alpha_{\mu\,\nu}\} = \tfrac{1}{2}g^{\alpha\lambda}(\partial_\nu g_{\lambda\mu} + \partial_\mu g_{\lambda\nu} - \partial_\lambda g_{\mu\nu}) \tag{14.36}$$

where $\{^\alpha_{\mu\,\nu}\}$ is symmetric in $\mu\nu$. Since (14.32) and (14.33) can be written as

$$DA^\mu = (\partial_\nu A^\mu + \{^\mu_{\alpha\,\nu}\}A^\alpha) \, dx^\nu \tag{14.37}$$

$$DA_\mu = (\partial_\nu A_\mu - \{^\alpha_{\mu\,\nu}\}A_\alpha) \, dx^\nu \tag{14.38}$$

we find that the *covariant derivative*, defined by

$$A^\mu_{;\nu} = D_\nu A^\mu = \partial_\nu A^\mu + \{^\mu_{\alpha\,\nu}\}A^\alpha \tag{14.39}$$

$$A_{\mu;\nu} = D_\nu A_\mu = \partial_\nu A^\mu - \{^\alpha_{\mu\,\nu}\}A_\alpha, \tag{14.40}$$

produces a new tensor and may be taken as the generalization of the ordinary partial derivative. Note that

$$D_\nu A_\mu - D_\mu A_\nu = \partial_\nu A_\mu - \partial_\mu A_\nu. \tag{14.41}$$

This indicates that the ordinary *curl* is still a tensor in curvilinear coordinates, with its definition being taken over without change; it still produces antisymmetric tensors.

One can generalize the concept of *divergence* in curvilinear coordinates,

$$D_\mu A^\mu = A^\mu_{;\mu} = \partial_\mu A^\mu + \{^\mu_{\alpha\,\mu}\}A^\alpha. \tag{14.42}$$

This operation produces a scalar. Now let $A_\mu = D_\mu\Phi = \partial_\mu\Phi$. Then $A^\mu = g^{\mu\nu}\partial_\nu\Phi$ and we have as a generalization of the *Laplace-d'Alembert* operator $\partial_\mu\partial^\mu$

$$D_\mu D^\mu\Phi = \Phi^{;\mu}_{;\mu} = \partial_\mu(g^{\mu\nu}\partial_\nu\Phi) + \{^\mu_{\alpha\,\mu}\}g^{\alpha\nu}\partial_\nu\Phi. \tag{14.43}$$

These formulas may be put into more compact form with the help of differentiation of the determinant g

$$\partial_\alpha g = M^{\mu\nu}\frac{\partial g_{\mu\nu}}{\partial x^\alpha} = gg^{\mu\nu}\partial_\alpha g_{\mu\nu} \tag{14.44}$$

Now, from

$$\{^\mu_{\alpha\,\mu}\} = \tfrac{1}{2}g^{\mu\lambda}(\partial_\mu g_{\lambda\alpha} + \partial_\alpha g_{\lambda\mu} - \partial_\lambda g_{\mu\alpha}), \tag{14.45}$$

by exchanging μ and λ indices (they are running indices, and can be interchanged), we have

$$\{^\mu_{\alpha\,\mu}\} = \tfrac{1}{2}g^{\mu\lambda}\frac{\partial g_{\mu\lambda}}{\partial X^\alpha} = \frac{1}{2g}\partial_\alpha g = \partial_\alpha \log\sqrt{g}. \tag{14.46}$$

Thus, the $A^\mu_{;\mu}$ and $\Phi^{;\mu}_{;\mu}$ become, respectively,

$$A^\mu_{;\mu} = (1/\sqrt{g})\partial\mu(\sqrt{g}A^\mu), \tag{14.47}$$

$$\Phi^{;\mu}_{;\mu} = (1/\sqrt{g})\partial_\mu(\sqrt{g}g^{\mu\nu}\partial_\nu)\Phi. \tag{14.48}$$

These formulas will be useful later.

In Cartesian coordinates the constancy of a vector is expressed by $du^\mu = 0$. In the curvilinear coordinates of a flat or Riemannian space, this becomes $Du^\mu = 0$. In particular, let $u^\mu = dx^\mu/ds$, where ds is the invariant line element. Since u^μ is a constant vector

$$Du^\mu/Ds = 0 \qquad \text{or} \qquad \frac{d^2x^\sigma}{ds^2} + \{^{\sigma}_{\mu\,\nu}\}\frac{dx^\mu}{ds}\frac{dx^\nu}{ds} = 0. \tag{14.49}$$

This is the generalization of a straight line which in Cartesian coordinates reduces to $d^2x^\sigma/ds^2 = 0$. We call (14.49) the *geodesic equations*. Later we will derive them from the condition of the shortest distance.

The generalization of the invariant four volume is given by $d\Omega \to \sqrt{g}\, d\Omega$. Gauss's theorem (6.37) takes the form

$$\int A^\mu_{;\mu}\sqrt{g}\, d\Omega = \int A^\mu \sqrt{g}\, ds_\mu. \tag{14.50}$$

In a flat space the second derivative $\partial_\mu\partial_\nu A_\sigma$ is equal to $\partial_\nu\partial_\mu A_\sigma$. In a curved space in general $D_\mu D_\nu A_\sigma$ is not equal to $D_\nu D_\mu A_\sigma$. From the difference, we define a new tensor $R^\lambda_{\mu\nu\sigma}$, called the curvature tensor,

$$D_\mu D_\nu A_\sigma - D_\nu D_\mu A_\sigma = R^\lambda_{\sigma\mu\nu}A_\lambda. \tag{14.51}$$

We can easily evaluate it, using this definition:

$$R^\lambda_{\sigma\mu\nu} = \partial_\nu\{^{\lambda}_{\mu\,\nu}\} - \partial_\mu\{^{\lambda}_{\nu\,\sigma}\} + \{^{\lambda}_{\alpha\,\nu}\}\{^{\alpha}_{\mu\,\sigma}\} - \{^{\lambda}_{\alpha\,\mu}\}\{^{\alpha}_{\sigma\,\nu}\}. \tag{14.52}$$

The significance of this tensor now becomes clear, since it depends only on Christoffel symbols and their derivatives. In a flat space all $g_{\mu\nu}$ can be transformed into constants (rectilinear coordinates) where all Christoffel symbols vanish; hence, $R^\lambda_{\mu\nu\sigma} = 0$. Being a tensor equation, it holds in all coordinate systems (Cartesian, oblique, curvilinear) of a flat space. In curved spaces, that is, in a Riemannian geometry, $R^\lambda_{\mu\nu\sigma}$ will not vanish. Therefore it is a *measure of the curvature of space*.

The curvature tensor is antisymmetric in $\mu\nu$. This tensor has other symmetry properties which we will not go into here. However, we point out that by contracting it,

$$R_{\sigma\mu} = R^\lambda_{\sigma\mu\lambda} = R_{\mu\sigma}, \tag{14.53}$$

we get the so-called symmetric Ricci tensor. By contracting again we obtain the curvature invariant R defined as

$$R = g^{\sigma\mu}R_{\sigma\mu}. \tag{14.54}$$

One of the most important tensors in the study of gravitation is the Einstein tensor defined by

$$G_{\mu\nu} = R_{\mu\nu} - \tfrac{1}{2}g_{\mu\nu}R. \tag{14.55}$$

It is important to know that this is the only tensor which satisfies the following:

1. It is purely geometric in character, being built up from only the $g^{\mu\nu}$ and their first and second derivatives; it is linear in the second derivatives of $g_{\mu\nu}$.

2. It is second order and symmetric, $G_{\mu\nu} = G_{\nu\mu}$.

3. Its covariant divergence vanishes identically, $D^\mu G_{\mu\nu} \equiv 0$.

This latter property, namely, the vanishing of the covariant derivative, will be used to formulate the gravitational field equations.

This chapter has contained a very brief survey of the tensor calculus and the nature of different geometries. We have omitted a discussion of spinors in curved spaces, since these have not found much useful applications in the study of gravitation. For further reading we recommend the literature listed at the end of the book.

15

PRINCIPLE OF GENERAL COVARIANCE

15.1. The Shortcomings of Special Relativity

It is strange that one of the primary functions of a physicist is that of a fault-finder. We have demonstrated this attitude repeatedly in the previous chapters. We have tried to point out the deficiencies of a theory, whenever we have had the chance to do so. Let us now summarize the most important points where the special theory of relativity seems to meet with serious difficulties.

(a) The special theory of relativity is applicable only to a special class of observers, namely, to inertial observers. The Minkowskian space-time structure cannot be used to describe natural phenomena in a noninertial frame. The so-called clock paradox, and the variation of the ratio of a circumference to its diameter for a noninertial system (Figure 15.1) indicate that special relativity has only a limited applicability. Thus, there arises the necessity of extending the kinematical framework so that it applies generally. This extension should enable us to treat physics from any reference frame, inertial or non-inertial. Such a generalization of the theory is called *general relativity*. Consideration of the clock paradox alone is not a sufficient guide for determining the form of the required change. A new principle called *the principle of equivalence* will be introduced in order to complete the new structure. This principle, however, is closely connected to the nature of gravitation. In fact, when we complete the theory we will also obtain a relativistic theory of gravitation. For this reason, the theory of general relativity may alternatively be called *the theory of gravitation*. In developing the new theory, it is thus helpful to analyze the predictions of the special theory of relativity with regard to gravitational phenomena.

(b) The special relativistic theory of gravitation leads to an inward deflection of light passing near the surface of the sun, amounting to 0.88 seconds of arc. Observationally, the deflection is found to be about 1.75 seconds of arc, that is, twice the special relativistic result.

(c) The special relativistic theory of gravitation leads to a precession of the perihelion of a planet. In the case of Mercury, the theory predicts a *retardation* amounting to 7.2 seconds of arc per century. Observation shows that the perihelion of the planet Mercury *advances* at the rate of 43 seconds of arc per century; that is, the effect is six times larger in magnitude than is predicted by special relativity.

(d) Unless its kinematics is modified, the special relativistic theory of gravitation presented in Chapter 8 does not predict any shift of the spectral lines emitted by atoms in strong gravitational fields, whereas observation shows that there is a shift of the spectral lines towards the red. In the case of the companion of Sirius (a dense, heavy star), the shift is observed to amount to $\delta\nu/\nu = 6.3 \times 10^{-5}$. Also, the gravitational red shift in the field of the earth was recently measured by R. V. Pound and G. A. Rebka at Harvard University, using the Mössbauer effect, and was found to agree with the theory.

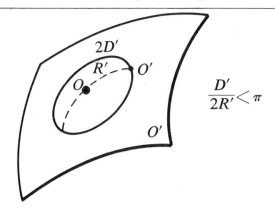

$$\frac{D'}{2R'} < \pi$$

FIGURE 15.1 *To the observer, O', the figure appears to be drawn on a curved surface.*

One may claim that it is unjust to judge special relativity on the basis of gravitation. Why not consider electrodynamics, where the theory has so far not led to a single experimental difficulty? Furthermore, the precession of the perihelion of electronic orbits was considered in conjunction with quantum theory by Sommerfeld and led to Sommerfeld's fine structure formula, which was confirmed by experiment. We have an answer to this, namely, that the quantum effects cannot be separated from the relativistic in this case. For a large macroscopic body with a large orbit, quantum effects do not play an appreciable role, so that we are in a better position to judge special relativity macroscopically. No macroscopic result of electrodynamics has been tested to an accuracy comparable to the above-mentioned astronomical observations of the perihelion of Mercury.† Furthermore, the same fine structure formula of Sommerfeld was derived by Dirac from a completely different fusion of quantum mechanics and relativity which does not even employ the picture of an orbit or a perihelion. There is no need to emphasize, of course, that the two theoretical shortcomings of special relativity, namely, the clock paradox and the self-energy difficulty, apply to electrodynamics just as well as to gravitation. Also, the bending of light rays and shift of spectral lines must be counted as partly electromagnetic because light itself is an electromagnetic phenomenon.

15.2. The Curved Space Concept

Of course, the special relativistic theory of gravitation cannot be altogether wrong because, in the limit of small velocities, it reduces to Newton's theory which is valid to a high degree of precision. For velocities approaching the velocity of light, the theory must be slightly wrong as is clear from its failure to account correctly for the small deflection of light. But the existence of a gravitational red shift of spectral frequencies shows that the theory must also be wrong for fixed particles in gravitational fields. The red shift is the effect of the gravitational field on a fixed periodic phenomenon in a gravitational field. Since no velocity is involved here, the effect is due to the gravitational field alone. The precession of the perihelion of planetary orbits must be due to both the velocity of the

† Gravity is the weakest known interaction and the perihelion advance is a second-order consequence of it. Here the observed result represents the detection of the second order term $(G/C^2)^2 \simeq 10^{-56}$.

planet and the strength of the gravitational field since planets such as Neptune, which are in a weaker gravitational field and move more slowly than Mercury, do not show appreciable perihelion precession.

The special theory of relativity and the corresponding Minkowski space were originally advanced to account for effects due to relative velocities comparable to or approaching the velocity of light. We now see, from the above analysis, that the presence of the gravitational field modifies the Minkowskian structure of space and time. This is especially clear from the experimentally observed red shift; for the shift of spectral lines implies that in a gravitational field periodic phenomena run slower than do the same periodic phenomena in a gravitation-free part of space. In fact, the proof of the existence of the gravitational red shift on the earth rules out the possibility of a theory of gravitation in Minkowski space. This departure from the Minkowskian structure is, of course, expected to be a gradual one, depending upon the value of the gravitational field and possibly on its derivatives. As soon as we postulate that time is influenced by the gravitational field, we must also assume the possibility of its influencing the measure of length. For space and time coordinates must be treated on equal footing without any intrinsic preference of one over the other, as in Minkowski space, to which we expect the theory to reduce in the limit of the gravitational field. Thus, we expect the Minkowskian line-element

$$ds^2 = -dx^2 - dy^2 - dz^2 + c^2\,dt^2 \tag{15.1}$$

to become

$$ds^2 = -A\,dx^2 - B\,dy^2 - C\,dz^2 + Dc^2\,dt^2 \tag{15.2}$$

where A, B, C, and D depend on the gravitation and reduce to unity at large distances from the gravitational source. The coefficients A, B, C, and D are functions of the space-time variables. The space-time variables x, y, z, and t are themselves the same variables as in Minkowski space; the distortions caused by the presence of the gravitational field are separated out and contained in the coefficients. If we were to show such a line element to a mathematician, without even suggesting to him what we have in mind is actual space and time, he would immediately tell us that this line element represents, in general, a curved geometry (Figure 15.1). Furthermore, he will not be content with the simple form of (15.2), but will write it in the more general quadratic form

$$ds^2 = \sum_{\mu,\nu} g_{\mu\nu}\,dx^\mu dx^\nu \tag{15.3}$$

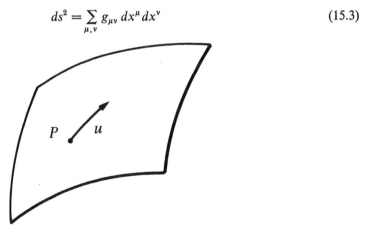

FIGURE 15.2   *Curved space.*

where the $g_{\mu\nu}$ are functions of the space-time variables which characterize gravitation. In the preceding chapter on mathematical aids we introduced some of the most important concepts of curved geometry. That chapter and some additional reading, say, from Weatherburn's book on *Tensor Calculus* (see reference section) will enable the reader to follow the remainder of this book without difficulty. The book by Einstein, *The Meaning of Relativity*, is strongly recommended both for its lucid treatment of the tensor calculus and for the masterly exposition of the theory of general relativity. We will also essentially follow Einstein's notation.

15.3. The Principle of General Covariance

Instead of the Minkowskian geometry, we now have a curved space-time geometry given by the line element

$$ds^2 = g_{\mu\nu} \, dx^\mu \, dx^\nu \tag{15.4}$$

Although we do not as yet know the precise functional forms of the coefficients $g_{\mu\nu}$, we can readily draw some general conclusions. Mathematicians have shown that if we have a tensor, say T^ν_μ, defined in the coordinate system S, the tensor will transform into

$$T'^\nu_\mu = \frac{\partial x^\alpha}{\partial x'^\mu} \frac{\partial x'^\mu}{\partial x^\beta} T^\beta_\alpha \tag{15.5}$$

where the primes indicate quantities associated with the new system. Since this is a completely linear form in the components of the tensor T^ν_μ, the vanishing of all of its components in one coordinate system leads, as a consequence, to the vanishing of all of its components in any other coordinate system. Therefore, let us consider, say in S, the tensor equation

$$A^\nu_\mu = B^\nu_\mu \tag{15.6}$$

and assume that this represents a law of nature. We can certainly write

$$G^\nu_\mu = A^\nu_\mu - B^\nu_\mu;$$

then transforming this into a new coordinate system, we obtain

$$A'^\nu_\mu - B'^\nu_\mu = \frac{\partial x^\alpha}{\partial x'^\mu} \frac{\partial x'^\nu}{\partial x^\beta} (A^\beta_\alpha - B^\beta_\alpha).$$

In other words, we have in the primed coordinate system S', as a consequence of the tensor character of the law,

$$A'^\nu_\mu = B'^\nu_\mu. \tag{15.7}$$

The complete similarity between (15.6) and (15.7) shows that by using tensorial quantities for expressing the laws of nature, we will have generally covariant laws, that is, we will generally satisfy the requirement of the relativity principle.

The requirement that, under a coordinate transformation, the laws of nature must remain covariant (that is, form invariant) is called the *principle of general covariance*.

15.4. Laws of Nature in a "Given" Space

The problem of generalizing a particular law from the flat Minkowski space to a general curved space does not at all have a unique solution. In fact, the problem is highly complicated since, in general, there will be an interaction between the space (the $g_{\mu\nu}$) and the physical phenomenon whose laws we are trying to formulate. But if the object under consideration does not appreciably influence the $g_{\mu\nu}$, that is, if the $g_{\mu\nu}$ are determined by objects much larger and heavier than the object under consideration, we may consider the $g_{\mu\nu}$ as *given* functions of the space-time variables, $g_{\mu\nu}(x)$. In this case the geometry is rigidly determined and the reaction of the physical object under study on the geometrical structure may be neglected. Under these circumstances, we may take over the special relativistic laws by substituting

$$d \to D; \qquad \partial_\mu \to D_\mu; \tag{15.8}$$
$$d\Omega \to \sqrt{|g|}\, d\Omega.$$

As an example, consider the motion of a free particle. This can be written in Minkowski space as

$$\frac{d^2 x^\sigma}{ds^2} = 0, \tag{15.9}$$

which is the expression for uniform motion in a straight line. (15.9) can be derived from the requirement that the motion between two points A and B corresponds to the shortest distance

$$\delta \int_A^B ds = 0. \tag{15.10}$$

The generalization of the free motion of a particle to curved spaces and to general coordinates may be accomplished by using the expression

$$\frac{D^2 x^\sigma}{Ds^2} = 0, \tag{15.11}$$

which is equivalent to equation (14.49), that is,

$$\frac{d^2 x^\sigma}{ds^2} + \left\{ {}^{\sigma}_{\mu\ \nu} \right\} \frac{dx^\mu}{ds} \frac{dx^\nu}{ds} = 0. \tag{15.12}$$

This motion also corresponds to the shortest distance between the two points A and B (Figure 15.3),

$$\delta \int_A^B \sqrt{g_{\mu\nu}\, dx^\mu\, dx^\nu} = 0. \tag{15.13}$$

We can show this by writing (15.13) as

$$\delta \int_A^B \sqrt{g_{\mu\nu} u^\mu u^\nu}\, ds = 0$$

where $g_{\mu\nu} = g_{\mu\nu}(x)$ and $u^\mu = dx^\mu/ds$. Comparing the above with (15.10) we see that $\sqrt{g_{\mu\nu} u^\mu u^\nu} = 1$. Since this quantity is constant, its absolute derivative must vanish, that is,

$$D(g_{\mu\nu} u^\mu u^\nu) = 0. \tag{15.14}$$

This leads, as is shown in the previous chapter on mathematical aids, to the geodesic equation

$$Du^\sigma = 0 \quad \text{or} \quad \frac{d^2 x^\sigma}{ds^2} + \left\{ {}^{\sigma}_{\mu\ \nu} \right\} \frac{dx^\mu}{ds} \frac{dx^\nu}{ds} = 0. \tag{15.15}$$

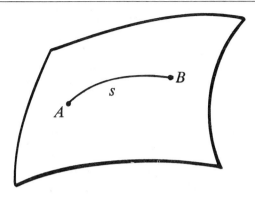

FIGURE 15.3 *Shortest distance between two points of a curved space is a geodesic.*

Geodesic motion corresponds to the shortest distance between the two points A and B. It also corresponds to the constancy of u^σ, since $Du^\sigma = 0$. Putting these conditions together, a *free particle* moves in curved space-time with a constant velocity and on a geodesic of the geometry. This is the *generalization* of Galileo's *principle of inertia*, which says that a free particle moves (in flat space) on a straight line with constant velocity.

As another example, consider electromagnetic theory. Equations (10.2), (10.3), (10.6), and (10.7) now become

$$\left.\begin{array}{ll} j^\mu_{;\mu} = 0 \ ; & A^{\nu;\mu}_{;\mu} = -4\pi j^\nu \\[6pt] A^\mu_{;\mu} = 0 \ ; & \Phi^{;\mu}_{;\mu} = 0 \end{array}\right\} \tag{15.16}$$

whereas (10.1), (10.4), and (10.5) remain unchanged. As in Chapter 10, the rest of the theory can be developed from these relations, assuming the proper generalization of all equations concerned. For example, the equations of motion of a charged particle become

$$\frac{d^2x^\sigma}{ds^2} + \left\{{}^{\ \sigma}_{\mu\ \nu}\right\} \frac{dx^\mu}{ds}\frac{dx^\nu}{ds} = ef^{\sigma\alpha}\frac{dx_\alpha}{ds}. \tag{15.17}$$

When the charge vanishes, that is, for an uncharged particle, we have

$$\frac{d^2x^\sigma}{ds^2} + \left\{{}^{\ \sigma}_{\mu\ \nu}\right\}\frac{dx^\mu}{ds}\frac{dx^\nu}{ds} = 0,$$

which is again the equation of a geodesic. A neutral particle moves along a geodesic in the given space-time structure.

The stress-energy tensor of a field or of matter is generalized into curved space according to the relations

$$T_{\mu\nu} = T_{\nu\mu}, \qquad T^\nu_{\mu;\nu} = 0. \tag{15.18}$$

The divergence equation $T^\nu_{\mu;\nu} = 0$ leads in a general way to the equations of motion. The generalization of scalar and spinor field theories into curved spaces may be accomplished along similar lines. However, spinors in curved spaces and other such details will not be treated in this book.

Thus we have seen how to generalize any given law into curved space-time, although we do not in general know what these generalizations mean or how their effects might be observed. In particular, we do not know, as yet, to what physical phenomena the $g_{\mu\nu}$ and the curvature of space correspond, although we have gravitation in mind. In the next chapter, we will introduce the principle of equivalence and with its help we will identify the $g_{\mu\nu}$ as the gravitational field and the geodesic equations of motion as the equations of motion of free particles in a gravitational field. Then curved spaces will mean gravitational fields.

Summary: Principle of General Covariance

(a) The laws of Nature are covariant, that is, form-invariant under all coordinate transformations. This requires tensorial equations for the expression of physical laws.

(b) The shortcomings of special relativity indicate that space-time, in general, is not flat but curved. That is, the geometry of space-time is Riemannian.

(c) Laws of Nature which are written down in a flat space-time coordinate frame, may be taken over intact by replacing tensors and all tensorial operations, such as absolute and covariant differentiation, by their curved space generalizations.

16

PRINCIPLE OF EQUIVALENCE

16.1. The Principle of Equivalence

In the previous chapter we generalized the space-time framework of the special theory of relativity into a curved space-time geometry. We have also shown how to generalize a law of nature into a given curved space-time so that the law holds in a generally covariant way. However, we have not as yet made any interpretation of what these things mean physically or described how they can be observed if they mean anything. In this chapter we will show that the effects of the $g_{\mu\nu}$ may be considered to correspond to the physical phenomenon of *gravitation*. This identification will be accomplished through the so-called *principle of equivalence*.

In the Newtonian theory of gravitation the inertial mass, m_i, of a body (the one which enters into $\vec{f} = m_i \vec{\gamma}$) and the gravitational mass, m_g, of the same body (the one which enters into the gravitational attraction $\vec{f} = m_g \vec{g}$) cancel out, because m_i and m_g are implicitly assumed equal. Thus from

$$m_i \frac{d^2 x^k}{dt^2} = m_g g_k, \qquad m_i = m_g, \tag{16.1}$$

an equation is obtained which is *independent of the mass of the body considered*:

$$\frac{d^2 x^k}{dt^2} = g_k; \qquad g_k = -\frac{\partial \phi}{\partial x^k}. \tag{16.2}$$

This fact is by no means physically trivial. It is a simple but profound mark distinguishing gravitation from all other natural phenomena. For example, the electric charge of an electron or of a proton is not equal to its inertial mass. Since the equation of motion is independent of the mass of the body, all bodies move in the same way in a gravitational field. A piece of iron and a piece of cotton fall in exactly the same way. This is the statement of Galileo's famous experiment; namely, *in an evacuated room, all bodies fall in the same way*. Evacuation is mentioned here to eliminate possible complications arising from the friction of the air. Until this point, we still have nothing of particular importance. Galileo's experiment is a trivial consequence of Newton's law of gravitation. Now see what happens in the following.

Consider a room fixed on the earth. Take an apple and a piece of iron. Let them simultaneously fall out of your hands (Figure 16.1a). According to the above result, they will fall in exactly the same way and reach the floor at exactly the same time.

Consider another room which is identical to the first one except that it is placed out in space far from all massive bodies, so that no gravitational field exists. A piece of iron and an apple left free will obviously not fall anywhere in such a room. Now imagine that a practical joker has tied a rope to the top of the room and started pulling the whole room

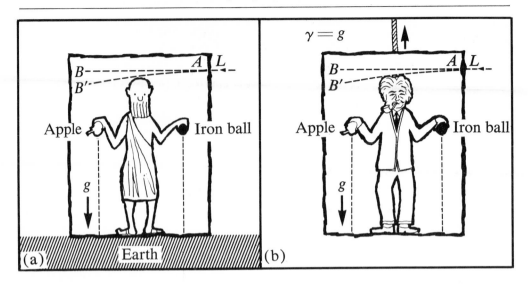

FIGURE 16.1 *A system which is stationary in a uniform gravitational field of strength g is physically equivalent to a system which is in a gravitation-free space but accelerated in the opposite direction with an acceleration γ = g.*

with an acceleration $\gamma = g$. To a man in such a room, the apple and the iron would appear to be moving downward with an acceleration $\gamma = g$ (Figure 16.1b). Since the room is moving upward, the floor of the room would eventually hit the apple and the iron at exactly the same instant. Thus the motion of the apple and the iron in such a room would be indistinguishable from their motion in a gravitational field. More precisely, the equation of motion of all material bodies would be exactly the same [equation (16.2)] in both rooms! All appearances would be the same in both systems. Stated in this way, the problem takes on a definitely relativistic form:

"It is impossible to tell whether a system (room) is in a state of accelerated motion by experiments performed in that system alone. For the observer in the room can claim that his room is stationary but there is a gravitational field present in the room."

One may think that this interpretation goes too far. Because in the gravitational field, in addition to the motions of bodies that an observer kinematically sees, there is an additional fact, namely, that he himself feels that gravity is pulling his body downward with a force which he experiences as his weight. Will he also have such a sensation of weight in the second room? The answer is yes. Furthermore, his weight will be identical to his weight in the other room. Everyone knows that in a car accelerated forward, we feel a backward force. This force, called the inertial force, is calculated by the formula

$$-f = m_i \frac{d^2 x}{dt^2} = m_i \gamma \tag{16.3}$$

where m_i is the inertial mass of the body and γ is the acceleration of the car (here the room). But $m_i = m_g$, and since we (practical joker) have chosen $\gamma = g$, we see that the weight of the body in the second room will be

$$W = m_i \gamma = m_g g. \tag{16.4}$$

This is identical to the weight of the body in the gravitational field. We see that a spring balance, for example, will give exactly the same value for the weight of an object in both of these rooms. Putting everything together, we arrive at the following general conclusion:

"A system which is stationary in a gravitational field of strength g is physically equivalent to a system which is in a gravitation-free space but accelerated in the opposite direction with an acceleration g."

Here, we have motivated this conclusion from Newtonian equations. However, since the conclusion actually depends only on the principle of equivalence $m_i = m_g$, it can be valid even when we reject the Newtonian equations. The above statement of the equality of gravitational fields to accelerated systems is identical in content with the principle of the equivalence of inertial and gravitational mass. They are two different ways of formulating the same principle.

At this point, the reader may have an uncomfortable feeling. The principle is *derived* from the Newtonian expressions which we know are not rigorously valid. What is the sense of obtaining something from a wrong theory and then holding that the derived result is the more fundamental truth? The answer to this question is that we do not derive it at all. We are only *motivated* towards it by the approximately valid Newtonian theory. Seeing, however, that the result so motivated may have a more fundamental significance, we wish to hold on to it even if we reject the rest of the theory. We simply assert the equality $m_i = m_g$ as a principle. A principle is, by definition, "something which is not derived from anything, except possibly from experiment." Thus, a postulate or a principle is a vulnerable statement which is always open to disproof by direct or indirect experimental evidence. Therefore, the only question that may be asked in adopting a principle is the extent of our present-day experimental evidence supporting it. The Hungarian physicist Eötvös, using a torsion balance, carried out extremely sensitive experiments which proved the equality of inertial and gravitational mass to one part in one hundred million. The experiments are done with all possible forms of matter found on earth—elements, chemical compounds, organic matters, radioactive isotopes, et cetera. Recently, R. H. Dicke of Princeton University extended the accuracy of R. Eötvös' experiment to one part in 10^9 (see reference section). To this accuracy, therefore, the principle is experimentally sound.

16.2. Immediate Consequences of the Principle of Equivalence

This principle is a very powerful tool. In order to appreciate its power, let us ask a rather peculiar question. Does the presence of a gravitational field influence the propagation of light? We cannot answer this question as long as we deal with the gravitational field itself. But let us first work with the accelerated room. Consider the ray of light, L, traveling in gravitation-free space (Figure 16.1a). This ray is obviously a straight line. It enters the room and hits the wall opposite the opening. Suppose L was parallel to the floor when the room was stationary. Will the light hit the same spot when the room is accelerated upward? Of course not. The room will move upward while the light ray is travelling from A to B so that the light will hit the wall at B', a little below B. Thus, to a man inside the room, the light ray will appear curved. Now using our equivalence, we conclude that in a gravitational field, light will not propagate along straight lines, but its path will be curved (Figure 16.1)!

We now see why, in the gravitational field of the sun, light rays should be deflected.

As another example, consider an accelerated frame of reference. Let P and P' be two fixed points on a straight line parallel to the direction of acceleration. Suppose a light wave emitted by an atom fixed at P proceeds toward P'. Will it have the same frequency when it reaches P'? To analyze the situation we point out first that the light ray will take a time $\Delta t = \Delta x/c$ to reach P' and during this time the point P' gains an additional velocity $V = \gamma \Delta t$. This is an apparent relative velocity with respect to P. It will cause a Doppler shift:

$$\nu' = \nu \frac{\left(1 - \dfrac{V}{c}\right)}{\sqrt{1 - V^2/c^2}} = \nu e^{-\gamma \Delta x/c^2} \simeq \nu\left(1 - \frac{\gamma \Delta x}{c^2}\right). \tag{16.5}$$

Thus, the frequency of the light wave will be different when it reaches P'. This is a purely special relativistic effect due to the acceleration of the extended body. The existence of this effect was demonstrated experimentally in 1960 by T. E. Cranshaw, J. P. Schiffer, and A. B. Whitehead of Harwell Laboratories, England, using the Mössbauer effect.

Now it follows from the principle of equivalence that the same thing must be observed in a reference frame fixed in a gravitational field, say, in a room on earth. Substituting g for γ

$$\nu' = \nu\left(1 - \frac{g \Delta x}{c^2}\right) = \nu\left(1 + \frac{\Delta \phi}{c^2}\right), \tag{16.6}$$

where $\Delta \phi$ is the gravitational potential difference between the two points. This is the so-called gravitational red shift we mentioned in the previous chapter. Its existence was demonstrated also in 1960 by R. V. Pound and G. A. Rebka of Harvard University, U.S.A., using the Mössbauer effect (See Chapter 17, Section 17.4). The accuracy of the experiment at present is of the order of 3 per cent but it definitely shows the existence and the correct order of the effect.

Note that the gravitational red shift provides a resolution of the clock paradox of special relativity. The existence of the red shift means that in a gravitational field, clocks placed at different localities run at different rates. Since, in the clock paradox, the system that did not stay inertial now has an equivalent gravitational field during the reversing of its velocity, the resulting difference of time readings may provide the resolution of the clock paradox. That this is indeed so is demonstrated in the problem section of this book (problem 17.3).

16.3. Gravitation of Energy

According to the special theory of relativity, there is the relation $m_i = E/c^2$ between energy and inertial mass. It then follows from the principle of equivalence that an amount of energy E must participate in gravitational phenomena equivalently to an amount of gravitating mass $m_g = E/c^2$. If this were not so, the theory of gravitation that we are trying to develop would evidently be in conflict with special relativity. Since we want our gravitation theory to be a natural generalization of special relativity, the above assertion must be guaranteed. In this section, we will establish the theorem of gravitation of energy. The demonstration will also show some subtle relations between special relativity and the principle of equivalence.

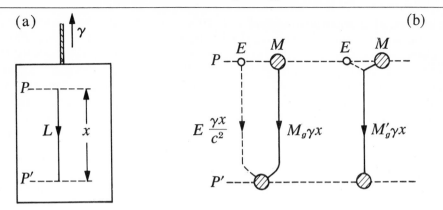

FIGURE 16.2 *Energy takes part in the gravitational phenomena. To an amount of energy E there corresponds a gravitational mass $M_g = E/c^2$.*

Let E be the energy of radiation contained in a light wave. We assume that it is being propagated downward from a point P to a point P' in a constant gravitational field (Figure 16.2a). Will this energy be the same upon arrival at the point P'? To answer this question, we first replace the gravitational field γ with a uniformly accelerated frame of reference. In this frame, there is no gravitational field but every point in the system is accelerated upward at the rate γ. If light starts from P at a certain instant $t = 0$, it will reach P' at $\Delta t = \Delta x/c$ and thus it will find P' at a different velocity then P, the difference being $V = \gamma \Delta t = \gamma \Delta x/c$. Thus, according to special relativity, the points P and P' can be considered as two reference frames moving with respect to each other with the apparent velocity $V = \gamma \Delta x/c$.

Now in Chapter 5, we have seen that energy and momentum together form a four-vector. The transformation formulas between the energy and the x-component of the momentum are

$$E' = \frac{E + Vp_x}{\sqrt{1 - V^2/c^2}} \; ; \quad p'_x = \frac{p_x + \dfrac{V}{c^2} E}{\sqrt{1 - V^2/c^2}} \tag{16.7}$$

where

$$V = c \tanh \alpha.$$

Since, for light propagating in the x-direction, $p_x = E/c$, we have to first order

$$E' = E \frac{1 + \dfrac{V}{c}}{\sqrt{1 - V^2/c^2}} = Ee^\alpha \simeq E\left(1 + \frac{V}{c}\right). \tag{16.8}$$

At the point P', the energy is therefore given approximately by

$$E' = E\left(1 + \frac{\gamma x}{c^2}\right). \tag{16.9}$$

Due to the principle of equivalence, this same relation must hold in a gravitational field.

If we write (16.8) in the suggestive form

$$E' = E + \left(\frac{E}{c^2}\right)\gamma x, \tag{16.10}$$

the interpretation is obvious: The energy E, in its journey from P to P', gained from the gravitational field the amount of energy $(E/c^2)\gamma x$, as though it possessed the gravitational mass

$$m_g = E/c^2. \tag{16.11}$$

The theorem can be particularly clearly demonstrated if we consider the following two processes (Figure 16.2b):

1. The body M is lowered from P to P'. The energy is then sent downward and absorbed by the body M.

2. The energy E is first absorbed by the body M at P, then the body is lowered to P'.

Assuming that by the transfer of energy the gravitational mass of the body is changed from M_g to M_g' the energy balance at P' gives

$$E\left(1 + \frac{\gamma x}{c^2}\right) + Mc^2 + M_g\gamma x = E + Mc^2 + M_g'\gamma x. \tag{16.12}$$

Hence

$$M_g' - M_g = E/c^2. \tag{16.13}$$

16.4. Identification of $g_{\mu\nu}$ as a Gravitational Field; Geodesic Equation of Motion

We have still not made the essential step toward the merging of the space-time structure with the gravitational field. We have only made certain things plausible. We now will provide the expressions governing the union of geometry and gravitation by identifying certain key equations. This will be done through the geodesic equations of motion. Let us consider the Newtonian equation of motion in a gravitational field and the geodesic equations of motion in a curved-space geometry:

$$\frac{d^2 x^\sigma}{dt^2} + \frac{\partial \phi}{\partial x^\sigma} = 0; \qquad \frac{d^2 x^\sigma}{ds^2} + \left\{{}^{\sigma}_{\mu\,\nu}\right\}\frac{dx^\mu}{ds}\frac{dx^\nu}{ds} = 0. \tag{16.14}$$

These two equations have a fundamental similarity in that both are *independent of the mass of the moving body* considered. In other words, both equations satisfy the principle of equivalence. Therefore, we would like to *identify* the geodesic equations as the equations of motion in a gravitational field. Since the Christoffel symbols $\left\{{}^{\sigma}_{\mu\,\nu}\right\}$ are constructed from the $g_{\mu\nu}$ this means that we interpret $g_{\mu\nu}$ as the generalization of the gravitational field ϕ. We must first show that this interpretation is consistent with the Newtonian equations; namely, we must demonstrate that in the limit of ordinary velocities the geodesic equations reduce to the Newtonian equations. To see this, let the velocity $dx^\sigma/dt \ll c$. Then $ds^2 \simeq g_{44}c^2\,dt^2$, $ds \simeq \sqrt{g_{44}}\,c\,dt$, so that

$$\frac{d^2 x^\sigma}{dt^2} + \left\{{}^{\sigma}_{4\,4}\right\}c^2 = 0, \tag{16.15}$$

where

$$\left\{{}^{\sigma}_{4\,4}\right\} = \frac{\partial g_{44}}{\partial x^\sigma}.$$

From this we see that in this limit $g_{44} = K + 2\phi/c^2$. Since in the flat space $g_{44} = 1$, $\phi = 0$, we have $K = 1$.

$$g_{44} = 1 + \frac{2\phi}{c^2} \tag{16.16}$$

This shows that the identification postulated above is possible. Therefore, from now on we will assume that the gravitational field is represented by the metric tensor $g_{\mu\nu}$ and that the equations of motion of a particle in a gravitational field are given by the geodesic equations of motion. This is the culmination of the curved-space concept and the principle of equivalence. We could actually have derived this conclusion from the principle of equivalence in conjunction with the curved-space concept. This derivation proceeds along the following lines: As a corollary of the equivalence principle, a gravitational field can be modified at any point by a suitably chosen accelerated frame. Consider the space of a fixed room on the earth. We have here a gravitational field of strength g. In an elevator accelerated relative to this room we will have the resultant field strength

$$g' = g - \gamma, \tag{16.17}$$

where γ is the acceleration of the elevator. Thus, if the elevator is accelerated upwards (opposite to g), the field will become stronger and the weights of objects will become larger. If the elevator is accelerated downward, the field will become weaker. If γ is larger in magnitude than g and downward, the resultant will become negative, or everything will appear to be falling towards the roof of the elevator!

The most interesting case is the situation of the freely falling elevator where $\gamma = g$,

$$g' = g - \gamma = 0. \tag{16.18}$$

Since, in such a room there is no gravitation, the system may be considered as an inertial frame in which special relativity is valid. In such a frame objects become weightless. A satellite, for example, is an object moving freely around the earth. The small room in the satellite is an inertial frame where objects are weightless. The special theory of relativity is valid there, whereas it is only approximately valid in a room fixed on the earth! A freely moving object in a gravitational field is called a *local inertial frame*. It is a local situation since, when we make the room larger, various parts should be assumed to be moving with different accelerations which would be inconsistent with the solid nature of the room. The curved-space interpretation of this is the *local flat space in a curved space*. In the same way as a small area on the curved surface of the ocean may be considered as a plane, so in a curved space a small four-dimensional volume (say, the space-time of a satellite's room) can be considered flat (Figure 16.3). But in a flat space we know that the equations of motion satisfy the variational principle

$$\delta \int_A^B ds = 0. \tag{16.19}$$

Since (16.19) holds at each point of space-time, the integral holds even if A and B are a finite distance apart (Figure 16.4). Now, ds is an invariant. That is, it is the same whether measured in the local inertial frame or in the noninertial frame. Therefore, the variational equations (16.19) can be taken over without change in noninertial frames and in gravitational fields. However, it was proved in Chapter 4 that this variational problem leads to the geodesic equations of motion.

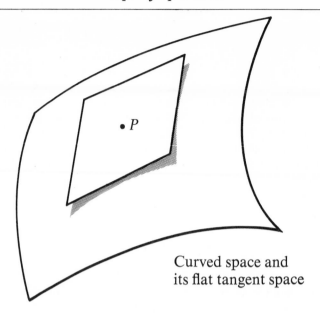

Curved space and
its flat tangent space

FIGURE 16.3 *Just as a small part of the surface of the ocean looks like a plane, the vicinity of a nonsingular point of the curved space-time geometry is a flat Minkowski space.*

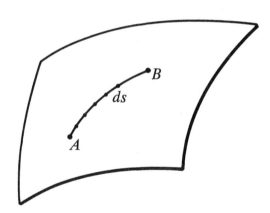

FIGURE 16.4 *Equations of a geodesic follow from the condition of minimal distance between two points.*

We should be careful to note that the physical content of the two equations (16.14) are entirely different. In Newton's equation we have a field ϕ, which causes the motion. The particle is under a *force* and its velocity changes in time. In the geodesic equations, on the other hand, there is no physical agent such as ϕ. The particle is free and under no force. It follows a geodesic, which is a straight line in that geometry. It *does not change* the magnitude or direction of its four velocity u^μ. In fact, the geodesic equations follow from the absolute constancy of u^μ, that is from $Du^\mu = 0$, as we have shown in Chapter 14. This profound change in interpretation is actually a conceptual simplification, since *inertia* and *gravitation* are unified and the concept of external force is eliminated from the theory of gravitation. In other words the theory of gravitation has become *pure geometry*!

Summary: Principle of Equivalence

(a) The principle of equivalence can be formulated in two different ways:
    (1) The inertial mass of a particle is equal to its gravitational mass.
    (2) An accelerated frame of reference is equivalent to a suitably chosen gravitational field.

(b) Acceleration, as well as velocity, is relative. Since any motion can be reduced to these, all motion is relative.

(c) A gravitational field is a relative concept. By suitable transformations it can be created or eliminated at any given point.

(d) In a gravitational field, light rays are deflected.

(e) In a gravitational field, the rates of clocks are different at different localities.

(f) The expression $m_g = E/c^2$ relates energy and gravitational mass.

(g) The equations of motion of a free particle are given by the geodesic equations of motion.

17

FIELD EQUATIONS AND THE THREE
EXPERIMENTAL TESTS

17.1. Formulation of Field Equations

We have now arrived at a moment of great excitement. We have generalized the Minkowskian geometry into a curved, four-dimensional space-time geometry and we have
adopted the physical interpretation that the curvedness of space-time corresponds to
gravitation. We also know how to calculate the trajectories of particles, the propagation
of waves, and the kinematical relationships of clocks and measuring roads when the space-
time structure, that is, the metric tensor $g_{\mu\nu}$, is given. For example, the space of a kinematically accelerated frame or the space of a rotating frame may be considered as known
because they can be obtained from flat Lorentz space by coordinate transformations. In
order to obtain the kinematics of a rotating frame, for example, we first take the Lorentz
line element in the cylindrical form

$$ds^2 = dr^2 + r^2\,d\varphi^2 + dz^2 - c^2\,dt^2 \tag{17.1}$$

and then transform to the rotating frame by the substitution

$$\varphi \rightarrow \varphi + \omega t. \tag{17.2}$$

We obtain

$$ds^2 = dr^2 + dz^2 + r^2\,d\varphi^2 + 2\omega r^2\,d\varphi\,dt - \left(1 - \frac{\omega^2 r^2}{c^2}\right)c^2\,dt^2. \tag{17.3}$$

The geodesic equations of motion for the line element (17.1) will give a straight line, since
when we transform back to Cartesian form, $ds^2 = dx^2 + dy^2 + dz^2 - c^2\,dt^2$, the geodesic
is a straight line. In the rotating frame the motion will appear as a sort of spiraling motion
(if started from the origin). These paths can be shown explicitly by solving the geodesic
equations. Furthermore, it is possible to calculate the inertial force acting on a point fixed
to the rotating frame (the centrifugal force). This is given from (d^2x/dt^2) in the geodesic
equations when we put $dr = d\varphi = dz = 0$ (point is fixed). Thus, from the geodesic equations

$$\frac{d^2r}{dt^2} = -\left\{\begin{matrix}1\\4\ 4\end{matrix}\right\} = \frac{1}{2}\frac{\partial}{\partial x}\,g_{44} = -\omega^2 r$$

$$\frac{d^2z}{dt^2} = \frac{d^2\varphi}{dt^2} = 0 \tag{17.4}$$

which is just what we expected! When we consider the particle as moving, the geodesic
equations also lead to the Coriolis force because of $g_{34} = 2\,\omega r^2\,d\phi\,dt$.

Generally the geometry of a flat space-time is given by the equations

$$R^{\lambda}_{\mu\nu\sigma} = 0. \tag{17.5}$$

These equations are satisfied in Minkowski space since all $g_{\mu\nu}$ are constants; they are satisfied in a rotating frame since the rotating frame is obtained from the former by a coordinate transformation.

All this is very well, but it does not help us much. The solutions we have been considering are obtainable from the solutions in a Minkowski frame simply by transformation. Is it possible to obtain the motion of a particle in a gravitational field by such a transformation? The answer is no, because this would require a rigid frame moving in such a way that at every point in it the gravitational field can be reduced to zero. This is obviously impossible in general and we must consider intrinsically curved spaces. *Our problem is how to determine the $g_{\mu\nu}$ of such a curved space given the matter distribution generating it (such as the Sun or the Earth).*

Evidently the equations (17.5) are too restrictive since they allow only flat spaces. Here we must be guided by Newtonian theory as we were guided by it in the previous chapter. The Newtonian analogue of our problem is the Poisson's equation. Taking notice of (16.16) we write, with $c = 1$,

$$\nabla^2\phi = \tfrac{1}{2}\nabla^2 g_{44} = 4\pi\sigma \tag{17.6}$$

where σ is the density of matter. In the theory of relativity σ is the fourth component, T_{44}, of the stress energy tensor. Thus, for the right-hand side we may consider the tensor $T_{\mu\nu}$. The left-hand side must depend purely on the geometrical structure, $g_{\mu\nu}$, since we now consider gravitation as a property of space-time alone. Furthermore, because of the principle of general covariance we must write a tensor equation. Let $G_{\mu\nu}$ be a tensor depending on the geometry alone, that is, depending on $g_{\mu\nu}$ and its derivatives, such that its 44 component, G_{44}, reduces to $\nabla^2 g_{44}$ in the Newtonian limit. Let us write tentatively

$$G_{\mu\nu} = 8\pi T_{\mu\nu}. \tag{17.7}$$

In order that this equation may be admissible we must require of $G_{\mu\nu}$ the following additional properties:

(a) It must be symmetric in $\mu\nu$ since $T_{\mu\nu}$ is symmetric.
(b) $D^{\mu}G_{\mu\nu} = 0$, since $D^{\mu}T_{\mu\nu} = 0$.
(c) It must be linear in the second derivatives of $g_{\mu\nu}$ since (17.6) is so linear.

We have mentioned at the end of Chapter 14 that the only tensor satisfying all these requirements is the *Einstein tensor*, $G_{\mu\nu} = R_{\mu\nu} - \tfrac{1}{2}g_{\mu\nu}R$. Thus we take as our field equations

$$R_{\mu\nu} - \tfrac{1}{2}g_{\mu\nu}R = 8\pi\kappa T_{\mu\nu}, \tag{17.8}$$

where κ is the gravitational constant and $T_{\mu\nu}$ is the matter tensor. These are the fundamental equations of Einstein's theory of gravitation. In the following we will solve these equations and calculate the trajectories of particles and the propagation of waves and compare them with observation. If we find the results to be valid we may then claim that the simple and generally covariant geometrical theory thus obtained represents gravitational phenomena and, indeed, unifies gravitation and inertia in a satisfactory way.

17.2. Solution of the Field Equations

Consider a large body, such as the Sun, at rest. In solving the field equations we may consider a frame in which the $g_{\mu\nu}$ are all independent of time, that is, in which they are all static. Furthermore, if the body is spherically symmetric, as the Sun is, the field will depend on r alone and not on θ and ϕ. We will take the line element in the form

$$ds^2 = -B(r)\,dr^2 - r^2\,d\theta^2 - r^2 \sin^2\theta\,d\varphi^2 + A(r)c^2\,dt^2. \tag{17.9}$$

Thus, we are making the assumption that

$$g_{11} = -B(r), \qquad g_{22} = -r^2, \qquad g_{33} = -r^2 \sin^2\theta, \qquad g_{44} = A(r)c^2, \tag{17.10}$$

all other $g_{\mu\nu}$ being zero. Referring to equations (17.8), there is matter at the origin (the Sun is assumed very small in volume); but everywhere else $T_{\mu\nu} = 0$. Furthermore, $T_{44} = \sigma$ at the origin, but all other components of $T_{\mu\nu} = 0$ (the matter is assumed stationary and stress-free). We have

$$R_{\mu\nu} - \tfrac{1}{2}g_{\mu\nu}R = 0 \qquad\qquad \text{for } r \neq 0$$

$$R_{\mu\nu} - \tfrac{1}{2}g_{\mu\nu}R = 8\pi\kappa T_{44} \qquad \text{for } r \to 0. \tag{17.11}$$

Now, if we put

$$A = e^\nu; \qquad B = e^\lambda \tag{17.12}$$

the Christoffel symbols for the line element (17.9) are

$$\left\{ \begin{matrix} 1 \\ 1\ 1 \end{matrix} \right\} = \frac{1}{2}\lambda' \qquad\qquad \left\{ \begin{matrix} 3 \\ 2\ 3 \end{matrix} \right\} = \cot\theta$$

$$\left\{ \begin{matrix} 2 \\ 1\ 2 \end{matrix} \right\} = \left\{ \begin{matrix} 3 \\ 1\ 3 \end{matrix} \right\} = \frac{1}{r} \qquad \left\{ \begin{matrix} 1 \\ 3\ 3 \end{matrix} \right\} = -r \sin^2\theta^{-\lambda}$$

$$\left\{ \begin{matrix} 1 \\ 2\ 2 \end{matrix} \right\} = -re^{-\lambda} \qquad\qquad \left\{ \begin{matrix} 2 \\ 3\ 3 \end{matrix} \right\} = -\sin\theta\cos\theta \tag{17.13}$$

$$\left\{ \begin{matrix} 4 \\ 1\ 4 \end{matrix} \right\} = \frac{1}{2}\nu' \qquad\qquad \left\{ \begin{matrix} 1 \\ 4\ 4 \end{matrix} \right\} = e^{\nu-\lambda}\frac{1}{2}\nu'$$

where primes mean derivatives with respect to r.

Now, constructing the equations (17.11) we find

$$8\pi\kappa T_1^1 = -e^{-\lambda}\left(\frac{\nu'}{r} + \frac{1}{r^2}\right) + \frac{1}{r^2} = 0$$

$$8\pi\kappa T_2^2 = 8\pi\kappa T_3^3 = -e^{\lambda}\left(\frac{\nu''}{2} + \frac{\lambda'\nu'}{4} + \frac{\nu'^2}{4} + \frac{\nu'-\lambda'}{2r}\right) = 0 \tag{17.14}$$

$$8\pi\kappa T_4^4 = e^{-\lambda}\left(\frac{\lambda'}{r} - \frac{1}{r^2}\right) + \frac{1}{r^2} = \begin{cases} 0 & \text{if } r \neq 0, \\ 8\pi\kappa M\delta(0) & \text{if } r = 0. \end{cases}$$

all other components being identically zero. Let us solve these equations at $r \neq 0$, that is, for points away from the origin. From the first and third equations we have

$$\nu' + \lambda' = 0. \tag{17.15}$$

Putting this into the second equation one has

$$\nu'' + \nu'^2 + \frac{2\nu'}{r} = 0. \tag{17.16}$$

This equation is nonlinear in ν but it can be reduced to a linear equation in terms of $A = e^\nu$, that is by the substitution $\nu = \log A$. In fact, we get the simple equation

$$A'' + \frac{2A'}{r} = 0 \tag{17.17}$$

which immediately gives the solution

$$A = K_1 + \frac{K_2}{r}. \tag{17.18}$$

Here K_1 and K_2 are integration constants to be determined from the physical situation. First of all, we assume that as $r \to \infty$ the gravitational effect of the central body becomes negligible, and the reference frame reduces to a Lorentz frame. This leads to $K_1 = 1$. Secondly, the constant K_2 must be related to the mass of the body generating the field. Referring to (17.6) we find that $K_2 = -2\kappa M = -2GM/c^2$. So we have

$$A = 1 - \frac{2GM}{c^2 r} \tag{17.19}$$

where G is the gravitational constant. In a system of units where $G = c = 1$ we have

$$A = 1 - \frac{2M}{r} \tag{17.20}$$

and the line element is then given by

$$ds^2 = \left(1 - \frac{2M}{r}\right) dt^2 - r^2 \, d\theta^2 - r^2 \sin^2 \theta \, d\varphi^2 - \left(1 - \frac{2M}{r}\right)^{-1} dr^2. \tag{17.21}$$

This solution is called the *Schwarzschild line element*. We note that if we had chosen the form of the line element as isotropic, say,

$$ds^2 = e^{-2\alpha} dt^2 - e^{2\beta}(dr^2 + r^2 \, d\theta^2 + r^2 \sin^2 \theta \, d\varphi^2) \tag{17.22}$$

after going through a similar process we would have obtained

$$e^{-2\alpha} = \left(\frac{1 - \dfrac{M}{2r}}{1 + \dfrac{M}{2r}}\right)^2; \quad e^{2\beta} = \left(1 + \frac{M}{2r}\right)^4. \tag{17.23}$$

Or equivalently we could transform the solution (17.21) into (17.23) by the coordinate transformation

$$r \to \left(1 + \frac{M}{2r}\right)^2,$$

showing that these two line elements are kinematically equivalent. Therefore the problem of the motion of particles or the propagation of waves may be studied either in the non-isotropic form (17.21) or in the isotropic form

$$ds^2 = \left(\frac{1 - \dfrac{M}{2r}}{1 + \dfrac{M}{2r}}\right)^2 dt^2 - \left(1 + \frac{M}{2r}\right)^4 (dr^2 + r^2 \, d\theta^2 + r^2 \sin^2 \theta \, d\varphi^2) \tag{17.24}$$

of the Schwarzschild solution.

17.3. Planetary Motion

The planets move in the spherically symmetric gravitational field of a much heavier sun. Considering planets as small particles compared to the sun, we can now apply the geodesic equations of motion. We shall use the isotropic line element (17.22) although other authors prefer the nonisotropic form. The Christoffel symbols for the isotropic line element are

$$\begin{Bmatrix} 1 \\ 1\ 1 \end{Bmatrix} = \beta' \qquad\qquad \begin{Bmatrix} 3 \\ 2\ 3 \end{Bmatrix} = \cot\theta$$

$$\begin{Bmatrix} 2 \\ 1\ 2 \end{Bmatrix} = \frac{1}{r} + \beta' \qquad\qquad \begin{Bmatrix} 1 \\ 3\ 3 \end{Bmatrix} = -(r + r^2\beta')\sin\theta$$

$$\begin{Bmatrix} 1 \\ 2\ 2 \end{Bmatrix} = (r + r^2\beta') \qquad \begin{Bmatrix} 2 \\ 3\ 3 \end{Bmatrix} = -\sin\theta\cos\theta \qquad (17.25)$$

$$\begin{Bmatrix} 3 \\ 1\ 3 \end{Bmatrix} = \frac{1}{r} + \beta' \qquad\qquad \begin{Bmatrix} 4 \\ 1\ 4 \end{Bmatrix} = -\alpha'$$

$$\begin{Bmatrix} 1 \\ 4\ 4 \end{Bmatrix} = e^{-2(\alpha+\beta)}\alpha',$$

where primes denote derivatives with respect to r.

Since the planet moves in a plane we can specialize the line element so that $\theta = \pi/2$; that is, the line element for the planet reduces to

$$ds^2 = e^{-2\alpha}\,dt^2 - e^{2\beta}(dr^2 + r^2\,d\varphi^2). \qquad (17.26)$$

Now the geodesic equations of motion for this line element are

$$\left.\begin{aligned}
\frac{d^2r}{ds^2} + \beta'\left(\frac{dr}{ds}\right)^2 - 2(r + r^2\beta')\left(\frac{d\varphi}{ds}\right)^2 - e^{-2\alpha-2\beta}\alpha'\left(\frac{dt}{ds}\right)^2 &= 0 \\[4pt]
\frac{d^2\phi}{ds^2} + 2\left(\frac{1}{r} + \beta'\right)\frac{d\varphi}{ds}\frac{dr}{ds} &= 0 \\[4pt]
\frac{d^2t}{ds^2} - 2\alpha'\frac{dt}{ds}\frac{dr}{ds} &= 0
\end{aligned}\right\} \qquad (17.27)$$

where $\alpha' = d\alpha/dr, \beta' = d\beta/dr$. The first of these will not concern us here.

From the second equation we obtain (first putting $\eta = d\varphi/ds$ and solving for η)

$$\frac{d\varphi}{ds} = h\frac{e^{-2\beta}}{r^2}, \qquad (17.28)$$

and from the third equation

$$\frac{dt}{ds} = ke^{2\alpha}. \qquad (17.29)$$

Equation (17.28) corresponds, for slow motion, to Kepler's law of areas, while equation (17.29) corresponds to the law of conservation of energy. Now, if we substitute $dt = ke^{2\alpha}\,ds$ and then $ds = r^2e^{2\beta}\,d\varphi/h$ into the line element (17.26), we obtain (here we are trying to find the trajectory; since the trajectory is a geometrical figure, independent of time, we want to eliminate dt and ds from the line element):

$$\left(\frac{dr}{d\varphi}\right)^2 + r^2 = \frac{r^4}{h^2} e^{2\beta}(k^2 e^{2\alpha} - 1). \tag{17.30}$$

Now we expand $e^{2\alpha}$ and $e^{2\beta}$ to second order in $M/r \ll 1$

$$e^{2\alpha} = 1 + \frac{2M}{r} + \frac{2M^2}{r^2} \cdots,$$

$$e^{2\beta} = 1 + \frac{2M}{r} + \frac{3}{2}\frac{M^2}{r^2} \cdots, \tag{17.31}$$

$$k = e^{-2\alpha} dt/ds \simeq 1,$$

$$\left(\frac{dr}{d\varphi}\right)^2 + r^2 = \frac{r^4}{h^2}\left(2\frac{M}{r} + 6\frac{M^2}{r^2}\right). \tag{17.32}$$

Substituting $u = 1/r$, $dr = -r^2 du$, we obtain

$$\left(\frac{du}{d\varphi}\right)^2 + u^2 = \frac{1}{h^2}(2 Mu + 6M^2 u^2). \tag{17.33}$$

Differentiating and canceling $2 \, du/d\varphi$ we finally have

$$\frac{d^2u}{d\varphi^2} + u = \frac{M}{h^2} + \frac{6M^2}{h^2} u. \tag{17.34}$$

Newtonian theory corresponds to

$$\frac{d^2u}{d\varphi^2} + u = \frac{M}{h^2}, \tag{17.35}$$

which has, as its solution, the polar equation of an ellispse

$$u = \frac{M}{h^2}(1 + \epsilon \cos \varphi), \tag{17.36}$$

where ϵ is the eccentricity of the ellipse (Figure 17.1a). The extra term $6M^2u/h^2$ is a correction to Newtonian theory. By transposing it, one sees that

$$\frac{d^2u}{d\varphi^2} + \left(1 - \frac{6M^2}{h^2}\right)u = \frac{M}{h^2} \tag{17.37}$$

has the solution

$$u = \frac{M}{h^2}(1 + \epsilon \cos \rho\varphi), \tag{17.38}$$

$$\rho = \sqrt{1 - 6M^2/h^2} \simeq 1 - 3M^2/h^2.$$

Thus the additional term $6M^2u/h^2$ corresponds to an advance in the perihelion (Figure 17.1b). For one revolution of the planet, this advance amounts to $2\pi(1 - \rho)$; that is,

$$\Delta\dot{\varphi} = \frac{6\pi M^2}{h^2}. \tag{17.39}$$

When evaluated numerically, this correction turns out to be extremely small for all planets except mercury, in which case it amounts to 43 seconds of arc per century. This is exactly the amount observed experimentally for the orbit of Mercury, a precession which could

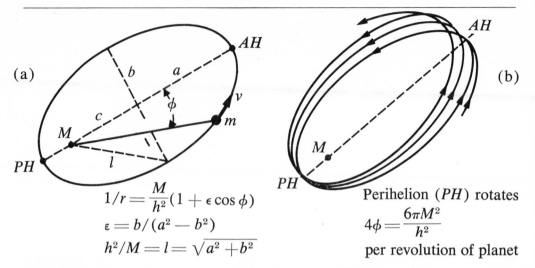

$$1/r = \frac{M}{h^2}(1 + \epsilon \cos \phi)$$

$$\epsilon = b/(a^2 - b^2)$$

$$h^2/M = l = \sqrt{a^2 + b^2}$$

Perihelion (*PH*) rotates

$$4\phi = \frac{6\pi M^2}{h^2}$$

per revolution of planet

FIGURE 17.1 *Newtonian theory gives a perfect ellipse for the trajectory of a planet. The relativistic theory gives approximately an ellipse but the ellipse rotates and its perihelion or aphelion advances slowly in time.*

not be explained by the Newtonian theory or by the special relativistic theory of gravitation. In recent years, with the help of electronic computers, the advances of the perihelions of Venus and of the earth have also been separated from the effects of other perturbing agents, and it has been seen that the theoretical formula (17.39) is well substantiated, also in these cases. We may thus conclude that the theory leads as zero, first, and second-order approximations, respectively, to the Galilean principle of inertia, the Newtonian theory of gravitation, and the advance of the perihelions of the planets and satellites.

17.4. The Bending of Light Rays

The propagation of light in a curved space corresponds to $ds^2 = 0$, which with our line element (17.26) gives an apparent velocity of propagation

$$c' = e^{-(\alpha+\beta)}c. \tag{17.40}$$

Thus the propagation in a gravitational field resembles the propagation in a refractive medium of index $n = e^{-(\alpha+\beta)}$. We know how to treat a ray in such a medium. Consider a tube of light passing near the surface of the sun. According to (17.40), the inner and the outer rays propagate with different velocities. This causes a deflection of the ray of light by the amount per unit length of its path (Figure 17.2a)

$$\Delta \gamma = \frac{1}{c'} \frac{\Delta c'}{\Delta x} = -\frac{\partial}{\partial r}(\alpha + \beta). \tag{17.41}$$

The total inward deflection of a light ray coming from $y = -\infty$ and reaching $y = +\infty$ is then given by (Figure 17.2b)

$$\gamma = \int_{-\infty}^{+\infty} \frac{2GM}{c^2 r} \, dy = \frac{4GM}{c^2 R} \tag{17.42}$$

where R is the closest that the ray gets to the sun. For a light ray grazing the surface of the sun, this gives 1.75 seconds of arc, which is the amount observed by astronomers during the many total eclipses of the sun since the year 1919, when the first measurement of the deflection of light was made. The observed results vary between 1.72″ and 1.82″, but these variations are well within the errors of observation.

The bending of light rays can also be obtained from the geodesic equations of motion (17.27) by setting $ds = 0$. This leads to $h \to \infty$ in (17.28) and (17.29). But

$$\frac{d\varphi}{dt} = \lambda \frac{e^{-2(\alpha+\beta)}}{r^2}, \tag{17.43}$$

where the constant $\lambda = h/k$ is finite. In fact $r^2(d\varphi/dt) = \lambda e^{-2(\alpha+\beta)}$ is the Keplerian rate of sweeping of area, which for a light ray grazing the surface of the sun is given by $\lambda \simeq (d\varphi/dt) \simeq Rc$. Putting $\lambda = h/k$ into (17.30) and evaluating to orders zero and one in M, we get, instead of (17.34),

$$\frac{d^2u}{d\varphi^2} + u = \frac{2MG}{\lambda^2}. \tag{17.44}$$

Here the second-order terms are neglected because, for a very fast particle moving with the velocity of light, the first order effect is already very small. Equation (17.44) is similar to the Newtonian equation except for a factor of 2 in front of M. The solution has the form of a hyperbola, as was mentioned in Chapter 9.

$$u = \frac{1}{r} = \frac{2MG}{\lambda^2}(1 + \epsilon \cos \varphi). \tag{17.45}$$

Now, for $r \to \infty$ we have $dr/dt = c$ and $r^2(d\varphi/dt) = \lambda$. Differentiating equation (17.45) and putting the results in at $r \to \infty$

$$\epsilon = \frac{\lambda c}{2M \sin \varphi_\infty} = \frac{\lambda c}{2M} = \frac{Rc^2}{2MG}. \tag{17.46}$$

Since, from the figure, $\gamma = \pi - 2\varphi_\infty$, φ_∞ being a small angle, we have, for $r = \infty$, that is, for $1/r = 0 = (1 + \epsilon \cos \varphi_\infty)$

$$\frac{\gamma}{2} = \frac{\pi}{2} - \varphi_\infty \simeq \cos \varphi_\infty = \frac{1}{\epsilon}.$$

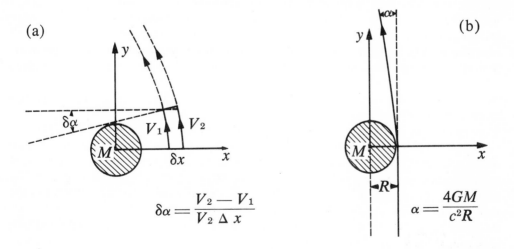

$$(a) \qquad \delta\alpha = \frac{V_2 - V_1}{V_2\,\Delta\,x} \qquad (b) \qquad \alpha = \frac{4GM}{c^2R}$$

FIGURE 17.2 *Light rays passing near the sun are deflected by the gravitational field of the sun.*

Therefore

$$\gamma = \frac{2}{\epsilon} = \frac{4MG}{Rc^2},$$ (17.47)

in agreement with the earlier result (Figure 17.26). The special theory of relativity, which leads to Newtonian form of (17.44) without the factor of 2, gives half of this amount. In fact (17.47) can immediately be inferred from (17.44) and the Coulomb scattering formula of Chapter 9.

17.5. Gravitational Red Shift

One of the motivations for the curved-geometry concept in Chapter XV was the gravitational red shift. We now ask whether the theory accounts numerically for the observed red shift. Consider a *stationary* clock A in the gravitational field of a heavy star. The line element corresponding to this clock with respect to an observer connected to it is

$$ds^2 = e^{-2\alpha} \, dt^2.$$ (17.48)

Now, consider a second clock in a gravitation-free part of space. Let this clock be relatively at rest with respect to the star. The line element for this stationary clock A' is

$$ds^2 = dt'^2$$ (17.49)

and due to the invariance of the line element, ds, we have

$$dt' = e^{-\alpha} \, dt.$$ (17.50)

Thus a periodic phenomenon in the gravitational field of the star will appear to an observer outside the field as slowed down. This causes a red shift for the spectral lines of light emitted by an atom situated in a gravitational field when this light is observed in a gravitation-free part of space. Hence

$$\delta\nu/\nu = - \frac{GM}{c^2 r}.$$ (17.51)

For the sun, this shift is qualitatively observable and the amount agrees with (17.51) within the errors of observation. In the case of the companion of Sirius, a dense heavy star, it reaches to the amount $\delta\nu/\nu = 6.3 \times 10^{-5}$ which is in good agreement with the observation. The red shift was recently measured in the gravitational field of the earth. Two clocks separated by a height Δh in the gravitational field will have a frequency difference

$$\frac{\delta\nu}{\nu} = \frac{\Delta\phi}{c^2} = \frac{\gamma \, \Delta h}{c^2}.$$ (17.52)

Now this is very small. For a height of $\Delta h = 10$ meters, it amounts to $\sim 10^{-15}$. Until a few years ago it was technically impossible to reach such accuracies by use of any time-keeping device, including atomic clocks. In 1960 Mössbauer discovered that under certain circumstances certain nuclei, such as Fe^{57}, emit γ-rays of extremely sharply defined frequency. The absorption of such γ-rays by the same crystals is also extremely sharply defined. In other words, if two such crystals are placed in a gravitational field with a height Δh between them, the ray emitted by the one is not absorbed by the other because of the slight frequency shift caused by the gravitation. Now, one of the crystals can be moved with a velocity v relative to the other to compensate this shift by a Doppler shift and then the absorption will take place. If the theory is right, this velocity must be given by

$$v = \frac{\gamma \, \Delta h}{c} . \tag{17.53}$$

For the above example, $v \simeq 3 \times 10^{-5}$ cm/sec. The experiment was successfully carried out and the shift is found to exist to within 3 per cent of the predicted value. The experiment was performed by R. V. Pound and G. A. Rebka (1960) of Harvard University. The same method was also used to test the consequences of the principle of equivalence in kinematically accelerated reference frames by T. E. Cranshaw, J. P. Schiffer, and A. B. Whitehead of the Harwell Laboratories, England (1960). In this experiment, kinematical acceleration was achieved by rotating the experimental apparatus and not by linear acceleration.

We may note in concluding this section that the gravitational red shift provides the basis for resolving the so-called clock paradox of the special theory of relativity (for this, see problem 17.3). The red shift is one of the major features of the general theory of relativity. As was mentioned earlier, its existence indicates that the theory of gravitation cannot be formulated in a flat space-time. Thus, the flat space theories of gravitation, such as those of Birkhoff or Whitehead, may be ruled out.[†]

17.6. Further Predictions

The advance of the perihelion, the bending of light rays, and the red shift are usually considered as the three crucial tests of the general theory of relativity. The theory has, however, further predictions which are not experimentally tested as yet. These are extremely small effects which at present seem beyond the accuracies of experimental techniques; but it is hoped that in the not-distant future they will be accessible to experimental test. One of these is the so-called Lense-Thirring effect.

In order to understand the Lense-Thirring effect, we first note that when the central body is spherically symmetric and not rotating, the orbital plane of the planet or satellite does not change. If the central body rotates, we must consider in (17.11) other components of $T_{\mu\nu}$ as well as $T_{44} = \sigma$. This results in the existence of g_{i4} and g_{ik} terms besides $g_{\mu\mu}$ in (17.9). With a more elaborate calculation than is given in Section 17.2, one finds that, to the desired accuracy, the line element (17.24) goes over into

$$ds^2 = \left(\frac{1 - \dfrac{M}{2r}}{1 + \dfrac{M}{2r}} \right)^2 dt^2 - \left(1 + \frac{M}{2r} \right)^4 (dx^2 + dy^2 + dz^2) + 2g_{14} \, dx \, dt + 2g_{24} \, dy \, dt \tag{17.54}$$

$$g_{14} = g_{24} = \omega I / c^2 r^2, \qquad r = \sqrt{x^2 + y^2 + z^2}.$$

where ω is the angular velocity of the Earth in the z-direction and I is the moment of inertia about the z-axis. From the geodesic equations of motion we now find that the rotation of the earth produces additional terms which are small compared to those considered in the earlier equations. These *additional* terms in the acceleration are of the form

$$\gamma_\mu \rightarrow -2 \left(\frac{\partial g_{4\alpha}}{\partial x^\mu} - \frac{\partial g_{4\mu}}{\partial x^\alpha} \right) u^\alpha. \tag{17.55}$$

† A. Schild, *Evidence for Gravitational Theories*, Varenna Lectures, Academic Press (1962).

This expression is "similar" to the acceleration which would be experienced by a charged satellite in the magnetic field of the earth, that is, $(\partial_\mu A_\alpha - \partial_\alpha A_\mu)$. This analogy helps to clarify the physical situation.

The rotating earth generates the additional "magnetic analogue" gravitational field, which, including the constant λ to adjust the units, is of the form

$$H_r = \lambda \frac{2I\omega}{r^3} \cos\theta, \qquad H_h = \lambda \frac{I\omega}{r^3} \sin\theta. \tag{17.56}$$

This gives a force $mH_h v$ in the plane of the trajectory and $mH_r v$ perpendicular to the plane of the trajectory. The latter force gives rise to an overall torque on the orbit and will therefore cause a gyroscopic precession of the orbit (Figure 17.3). A rather simple-minded calculation gives for the rate of precession

$$\dot{\Omega} = \lambda I\omega/c^2 r^3 \simeq 54'' \text{ per century}. \tag{17.57}$$

Thus the predicted amount of the precession of a satellite's orbit is of the same order of magnitude as the advance of the perihelion of Mercury. If the effect can be adequately separated from those due to other perturbing agents such as the quadrupole moment of the earth, atmospheric friction, perturbations caused by the moon, et cetera, the effect may well be within reach of satellite measurement techniques in a few years. We would like to emphasize that the satellite experiment is of fundamental importance because it touches on the very nature of the interaction, and we cannot hope to make much significant progress in the physical theory of gravity if we do not know the nature of the interaction causing the phenomena of gravitation.

An effect closely related to the above is the variation of the direction of angular rotation of a satellite as it moves along its orbit. To understand this effect we note first that in the calculation performed above the satellite would also apply a force on the rotating Earth and cause variations in the angular velocity of the Earth (its direction). A similar situation arises if the satellite is rotating. Since the satellite is much smaller the deviation of the

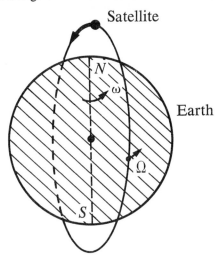

FIGURE 17.3 *According to the general theory of relativity, the precession of the orbit of a satellite is $\Omega = 54''$ per century.*

direction of its angular momentum is larger and it may be hoped that in the future this can be separated from other effects and observed.

Another effect which appears promising for experimental inquiry is the detection of gravitational radiation. Gravitational radiation corresponds to gravitational waves far distant from the radiating bodies. The magnitude of the field components being weak at such distances, the $g_{\mu\nu}$ will differ only slightly from its special relativistic values. Let us therefore write

$$g_{\mu\nu} = g_{\mu\nu}^{(0)} + h_{\mu\nu}, \qquad (17.58)$$

where $g_{\mu\nu}^{(0)}$ is the metric tensor of the Lorentz space. By constructing the field equations (17.8) for this metric and neglecting second and higher order terms in $h_{\mu\nu}$ we obtain

$$\partial_\mu \partial^\mu \psi_\alpha^\beta = - \frac{16\pi}{c^4} \kappa T_\alpha^\beta \qquad (17.59)$$

where

$$\psi_\alpha^\beta = h_\alpha^\beta - \tfrac{1}{2}\delta_\alpha^\beta h. \qquad (17.60)$$

Thus, when at a point where $T_\alpha^\beta = 0$, h_α^β, and $h = h_\alpha^\alpha$ separately satisfy the wave equation while in the space where the radiating system is located, (17.59) is valid. One can solve the equation for ψ_α^β in a fashion similar to the electromagnetic field, and then evaluate the radiated energy from this solution. However, here the situation is more complicated since in the gravitational field the analogue of the stress-energy tensor for the field is not strictly a tensor, but behaves as a tensor only under linear transformations (see chapter 18). For this reason some authors object to this calculation. Nevertheless, a formula for the assumed gravitational radiation may be obtained by this means, and is given by

$$-\frac{d\mathscr{E}}{dt} = \frac{G}{45c^5} \dddot{Q}^2 \qquad (17.61)$$

where

$$\dddot{Q}^2 = \dddot{Q}_{\alpha\beta} \dddot{Q}^{\alpha\beta} \qquad (17.62)$$

$$Q_{ik} = \int \sigma(3x_i x_k - \delta_{ik} r^2)\, dV \qquad (17.63)$$

is the quadrupole moment of the mass distribution. In the monopole and dipole approximations the gravitational radiation vanishes. Due to the c^5 in the denominator and due to the smallness of the gravitational constant G, the gravitational radiation is extremely small. Recently, it was proposed by J. Weber of Maryland University that by vibrating two quartz crystals it may be possible to carry out a coincidence detection of the gravitational radiation of distant stars, double stars or sun flares. If carried out successfully this would be the analogue of Hertz' experiment in electrodynamics.

17.7. The Question of Isotropy of Space

Consider two light waves on the earth, one propagating in a vertical direction and the other in a horizontal direction. Do these two waves propagate with the same velocity? If there is any appreciable difference between the two, it could be detected by experiment.†

† H. Yilmaz, *Phys. Rev. Letters*, **3** (1959), 320.

To give an idea of what kinds of accuracies are needed, consider the nonisotropic Schwarzchild line element

$$ds^2 = \left(1 - \frac{2M}{r}\right) dt^2 - r^2\, d\theta^2 - r^2 \sin^2\theta\, d\varphi^2 - \left(1 - \frac{2M}{r}\right)^{-1} dr^2. \qquad (17.64)$$

If space is isotropic as in (17.24), light propagates with the same speed in all directions, whereas for the nonisotropic case (17.21), from $ds^2 = 0$, we find that the horizontal velocity is larger by the magnitude.

$$\Delta c = GM/cr. \qquad (17.65)$$

This is very small, amounting to $\Delta c = 21$ cm/sec at the surface of the earth, but with refined techniques it may be possible to measure the velocity of light accurately enough to detect an effect of this kind. The interpretation of this kind of an experiment, however, is rather difficult. Since the line element may be put "kinematically" into either the isotropic or nonisotropic form, one would feel that this experiment cannot tell anything. On the other hand if we assume that the experiment were carried out and showed, say, isotropy to be true, then what is the meaning of the nonisotropic solution? The answer to this question would depend on the physical arrangement in which the isotropy is proved. We perform our experiments with equipment constructed out of rigid bodies. Therefore the experiment would mean that relative to a rigid reference frame, the kinematical and dynamical relationships are isotropic. Recently, V. W. Hughes of Yale University carried out experiments on the Zeeman splitting of atomic electrons and proved that, to one part out of 10^{20}, the inertia of an electron (more precisely, its angular momentum) is isotropic. This indicates *indirectly* that space is dynamically isotropic, to the same accuracy. We could, therefore, also count this experiment in favor of the theory of relativity although here there is some difficulty in the interpretation of the reference frame. The experiment seems to show that (here the interpretation is vague) the nonisotropic solution (17.21) should be interpreted as a frame which is not rigid in the usual sense. In the usual experimental set-ups, the isotropy prevails to a very high accuracy.

Summary

(a) Material objects produce curvatures in the space surrounding them and this manifests itself as the familar phenomenon of gravitation.

(b) The laws governing space curvatures in Einstein's theory of gravitation are given by the equation

$$R_{\mu\nu} - \tfrac{1}{2} g_{\mu\nu} R = 8\pi \kappa T_{\mu\nu}$$

where $T_{\mu\nu}$ is the stress-energy tensor of matter.

(c) By solving these equations one can test the theory. The calculations show that one obtains correctly the Newtonian theory of gravitation as a first-order approximation. Also, first-order theory leads to the bending of light rays and the shift of spectral lines. In a second-order approximation, one obtains the observed advance of the perihelion for planetary orbits.

(d) The theory makes further predictions which are being examined for possible future experimental tests.

SELECTED TOPICS IN GENERAL RELATIVITY

18.1. Geodesic Postulate Versus Field Equations

The reader might already have noticed that the geodesic postulate (16.14) and the field equations (17.8) are introduced independently of each other. From the way we have developed the theory, there seems to be no logical necessity that one should depend on the other. In reality, this is not so. Those two assumptions are believed to be not quite independent as we will now explain. Consider the field equations

$$R_\mu^\nu - \tfrac{1}{2}\delta_\mu^\nu R = 8\pi\kappa T_\mu^\nu. \tag{18.1}$$

We may regard the right-hand side, T_μ^ν, of this equation not as representative of something physical but, rather, simply as the result of the computation of the purely "geometrical" tensor of the left-hand side. This would amount to a redefinition of energy tensor solely in terms of geometry. In particular, the point concentrations of energy (particles) would now be regarded as singularities of the geometrical field $g_{\mu\nu}$. It follows, then, that the purely geometrical equation (18.1) should determine how these energy concentrations move. If the theory of the previous chapters is wholly consistent, the motion of energy must turn out to be identical with the geodesic equation of motion. The rigorous proof of this consistency requirement turns out to be quite difficult, especially if the energy concentrations are not exactly point-like. In (1938), Einstein, Infeld, and Hoffmann carried out a series of successive approximations and proved, to third order in M/r, that the geodesic equations follow from the field equations. Since then, the calculations have been carried to sixth order by Infeld and his associates, who have found that the geodesic postulate still holds good. It is now generally believed that for small energy concentrations the field equations (17.8) necessarily lead to geodesic equations of motion without any further assumptions. A number of "rigorous proofs" have also been offered by various authors to the effect that when the energy concentration tends to a point the equations of motion tend to become the geodesic equations. However, these proofs make use of further implicit assumptions, such as the vanishing of pressures and shears at the point singularity.

18.2. The Possibility of a Scalar Field Theory of Gravitation

From the results of the previous chapter, it becomes justifiable to assume that any energy distributions T_μ^ν can be introduced into (17.8) and that the equations will produce the corresponding space-time structure (see also Section 18.4). Can we substitute the stress-energy tensor of a field (say, a scalar field ϕ) and construct a theory of gravitation? Such an approach would in fact be desirable for the following reason: Einstein's theory of gravitation is a purely geometric construct. It does not have anything in common with other branches of physics, such as the electromagnetic or meson fields. It is in a class by itself. Furthermore, the electromagnetic field, electron field, et cetera have made great advances in the past 35 years, whereas gravitation has remained obscure, resisted quantization, and proved almost sterile as far as questions of the elementary constituents of matter are concerned. A different approach such as this one, might be useful at least in trying to find new ways of thinking about gravitation.†

Let the stress-energy tensor corresponding to the scalar field be substituted into (17.8):

$$T_\mu^\nu = \frac{1}{4\pi} (\partial_\mu \phi \partial^\nu \phi - \tfrac{1}{2}\delta_\mu^\nu \partial_\sigma \phi \partial^\sigma \phi) = \frac{1}{8\pi\kappa} (R_\mu^\nu - \tfrac{1}{2}\delta_\mu^\nu R). \tag{18.2}$$

The equations can be solved and the question of whether or not they make physical sense may be investigated. The equations (18.2) have been solved exactly for a time-independent field $\phi(x, y, z)$ and it has been found that the line element is given by (we use the system of units $c = G = 1$)

$$ds^2 = e^{-2\phi} dt^2 - e^{2\phi}(dx^2 + dy^2 + dz^2) \tag{18.3}$$

where ϕ is any solution of the Poisson equation,

$$\left(\frac{\partial^2}{\partial x^2} + \frac{\partial^2}{\partial y^2} + \frac{\partial^2}{\partial z^2}\right)\phi = -4\pi\sigma. \tag{18.4}$$

This is a remarkable feature, because it solves the ten nonlinear, coupled partial differential equations (18.2) at one stroke in terms of the linear and familiar equation (18.4). Furthermore, considering the central force problem where

$$\phi(r) = M/r \tag{18.5}$$

it is seen that (18.3) gives, to third order in M/r, the same $g_{\mu\nu}$ tensor as in (17.23) and therefore correctly satisfies the three experimental tests of the Einstein theory. Even if it is not physically correct, for its ease of obtaining solutions and for the simplicity of its form, the line element (18.3) should prove very useful in practical calculations.

From the outset, this kind of a theory is objectionable since it introduces a new independent variable, ϕ. From the Newtonian analogy, the equation (18.4) describes the interaction between a source $\sigma(x)$ and the field $\phi(x)$. In Chapter 8 we have seen that, for such an interaction, the equation of motion of the source is not a geodesic, but that it satisfies the Newtonian equations of motion (8.11). This is due to the fact that when the source $\sigma(x)$ is introduced, the divergence of T_μ^ν is no longer zero,

$$\partial_\nu T_\mu^\nu = \sigma \frac{\partial\phi}{\partial x^\mu} \neq 0.$$

Therefore, one might feel that in general relativity this feature will persist and that the equation of motion will become nongeodesic. Curiously enough, the scalar theory gets out of this difficulty in a very capricious way: We compute the Einstein tensor

$$R_\mu^\nu - \tfrac{1}{2}\delta_\mu^\nu R$$

for the geometry (18.3), and obtain *identically* the energy tensor of the scalar field

$$T_\mu^\nu = \frac{1}{4\pi} e^{-2\phi} \begin{pmatrix} \alpha^2 - \xi^2/2 & \alpha\beta & \alpha\gamma & 0 \\ \beta\alpha & \beta^2 - \xi^2/2 & \beta\gamma & 0 \\ \gamma\alpha & \gamma\beta & \gamma^2 - \xi^2/2 & 0 \\ 0 & 0 & 0 & -\nabla^2\phi - \xi^2/2 \end{pmatrix} \tag{18.6}$$

† H. Yilmaz, *Phys. Rev.*, **111**, (1958), 1417.

where

$$\alpha = \partial\phi/\partial x, \quad \beta = \partial\phi/\partial y, \quad \gamma = \partial\phi/\partial z, \quad \text{and} \quad \xi = \alpha^2 + \beta^2 + \gamma^2.$$

First of all, on account of the properties of the Einstein tensor this expression must have zero divergence. Secondly, for the geometry given by (18.3) the field equation of $\phi(x)$ is the generalized Laplace equation,

$$D_\mu D^\mu \phi = e^{-2\phi}\left(\frac{\partial^2}{\partial x^2} + \frac{\partial^2}{\partial y^2} + \frac{\partial^2}{\partial z^2}\right) = -4\pi\sigma e^{-2\phi}. \tag{18.7}$$

Note that if $\sigma(x)$ tends to a point concentration, that is, if

$$\phi(x) \rightarrow M/r, \tag{18.8}$$

then this equation is not at all the analogue of the Poisson equation (18.4). In fact, in this case the right-hand side vanishes at the singularity as well and we have, even at the source,

$$D_\mu D^\mu \phi = 0. \tag{18.9}$$

Therefore no energy transfer can take place through the source and the field energy (18.6) follows a geodesic. The theory requires strictly point sources although the energy is embedded entirely in the accompanying field. This result is in keeping with the general attitude towards fields and sources assumed in modern quantum field theory. Another interesting feature of the theory is that the simple functional dependence $g_{\mu\nu} = g_{\mu\nu}(\phi)$ is realized only for isotropic coordinate systems. In nonisotropic systems the dependence of $g_{\mu\nu}$ on ϕ may be a very complicated functional. In this case the simple identification of ϕ as a potential would be lost. Isotropic coordinates are thus selected as specially meaningful for physical interpretation in this theory. Despite these nice features the scalar theory is conceptually more complicated than the Einstein theory because it introduces an extra field equation for ϕ. For this reason its validity must be seriously doubted.

18.3. Stress-Energy Tensoroid

According to Einstein's theory, the gravitational field can be transformed away at any locality by a coordinate transformation. This is in contrast to the electromagnetic field, where no Lorentz transformation will transform, say, a static electric field to zero. Thus the gravitational field does not have the physical character of a physical field like the electromagnetic or meson fields. It is purely geometrical and it can be created or reduced to zero by coordinate transformations. Nevertheless, it would be useful to find an analogue of the stress-energy tensor for the gravitational field, so that the customary ways of thinking about various problems from the point of view of a physical field may be employed. For this purpose we define a quantity, $t_{\mu\nu}$, which behaves as a stress-energy tensor with respect to linear transformations of the coordinates.

Note first that certain quantities which are not tensors may behave as tensors under linear transformations. The Christoffel symbol is an example. We may call such a quantity a "tensoroid." Let the true tensor $T_{\mu\nu}$ be split into two tensoroids

$$T_{\mu\nu} = \tau_{\mu\nu} + t_{\mu\nu} \tag{18.10}$$

such that $\tau_{\mu\nu}$ involves only second-order derivatives of $g_{\mu\nu}$ and $t_{\mu\nu}$ involves only its first-order derivatives. Under a linear transformation, the quantity $\tau_{\mu\nu}$ will then behave somewhat as does matter, and may be identified as the "matter" part, with $t_{\mu\nu}$ as the "field" part.

The tensor $t_{\mu\nu}$ may be called the stress-energy tensor of the gravitational field. It will not be a true tensor, however, unless $\tau_{\mu\nu}$ can be shown to vanish, as in the case of (18.6). For this reason we call $t_{\mu\nu}$ the stress-energy "tensoroid" of the gravitational field. The usual name is the stress-energy pseudo tensor. (Since we have used this nomenclature in connection with space inversion, in Chapter 6, we prefer the name tensoroid.)

In order to make the separation more realistically, let us imagine a coordinate system which reduces to the Lorentz form

$$ds^2 = -dx^2 - dy^2 - dz^2 + dt^2 = g^0_{\mu\nu} \, dx^\mu \, dx^\nu \tag{18.11}$$

when the gravitational effects vanish. Then, in the presence of gravitation we have

$$ds^2 = g_{\mu\nu} \, dx^\mu \, dx^\nu \tag{18.12}$$

where

$$g_{\mu\nu} = g^0_{\mu\nu} + \eta_{\mu\nu}. \tag{18.13}$$

Now, as $y_{\mu\nu} \to 0$ we have

$$R_{\mu\nu} \to -\tfrac{1}{2}\partial_\sigma\partial^\sigma \eta_{\mu\nu} \tag{18.14}$$

$$8\pi\kappa T_{\mu\nu} = R_{\mu\nu} - \tfrac{1}{2}g_{\mu\nu}R \to -\tfrac{1}{2}\partial_\sigma\partial^\sigma U_{\mu\nu} \to 8\pi\kappa\tau_{\mu\nu}$$

where

$$U_{\mu\nu} = \eta_{\mu\nu} - \tfrac{1}{2}g_{\mu\nu}\eta. \tag{18.15}$$

Thus, starting from a weak field $\eta_{\mu\nu} \ll g_{\mu\nu}$, we can identify $T_{\mu\nu}$ in terms of second-order derivatives of $U_{\mu\nu}$. Then, if we remove $\tau_{\mu\nu}$ the remaining part will behave, under any linear transformation of coordinates, as a field tensor,

$$t_{\mu\nu} = T_{\mu\nu} - \tau_{\mu\nu}. \tag{18.16}$$

It is possible to put $t_{\mu\nu}$ into the following compact form

$$t^\beta_\alpha = -\frac{1}{16\pi}\left(\bar{g}^{\mu\nu}_{,\alpha}\frac{\partial \mathcal{L}}{\partial \bar{g}^{\mu\nu}_{,\alpha}} - \delta^\beta_\alpha \mathcal{L}\right), \tag{18.17}$$

where

$$\bar{g}^{\mu\nu} = \sqrt{-g}\, g^{\mu\nu}, \qquad \bar{g}^{\mu\lambda}_{,\alpha} = \partial_\alpha \bar{g}^{\mu\nu} \tag{18.18}$$

$$\mathcal{L} = \bar{g}^{\mu\nu}[\{^\beta_{\mu\,\alpha}\}\{^\alpha_{\nu\,\beta}\} - \{^\alpha_{\mu\,\nu}\}\{^\beta_{\alpha\,\beta}\}]. \tag{18.19}$$

Note that $\mathcal{L}$ plays the role of a Lagrangian function in the derivation of $t_{\mu\nu}$ [compare this with (12.15)]. This expression is not a true scalar, but it can be calculated in any given coordinate frame. Thus, although $t_{\mu\nu}$ is not a true tensor, the separation of $T_{\mu\nu}$ into $\tau_{\mu\nu}$ and $t_{\mu\nu}$ is physically meaningful. However, due to the tensoroid nature of $t_{\mu\nu}$ the definition of energy and the formulation of the conservation laws become rather difficult in general relativity.

18.4. Cosmological Theories

Einstein's theory of gravitation provides a space-time structure whenever the matter distribution is given. It follows that, if the average distribution of matter in the universe is put into the field equations, the average space-time structure for the whole cosmos may be deduced. This is a very interesting program because certain large scale properties of the universe are experimentally known and capable of comparison with such a theory.

We first summarize the most important of these properties: (a) On the average, matter is distributed in a fairly uniform manner in the universe, with a density of approximately $\rho \sim 10^{-27}$ gm/cm³. (b) The universe appears to be fairly isotropic from where we are—the solar system. (c) Light reaching us from distant nebulae is shifted towards the red in proportion to the distance traversed, according to the law

$$\frac{\delta\lambda}{\lambda} = kr, \quad k = 6 \times 10^{-28} \text{ cm}^{-1}. \tag{18.20}$$

Assuming that this is a Doppler shift, we would infer that distant nebulae are receding from us with speeds proportional to their distance from us. (e) According to measurements of their radioactive remains, some rocks in the crust of the earth are at least 3.5 to 4 billion years old. Hence the universe is older than 4 billion years.

We note, first, that it is possible to add to the Einstein tensor a cosmological constant Λ, in the form

$$8\pi\kappa T_\mu^\nu = R_\mu^\nu - \tfrac{1}{2}\delta_\mu^\nu R + \Lambda. \tag{18.21}$$

This simply means that, in the absence of matter, the universe could have everywhere a constant curvature

$$R = 4\Lambda. \tag{18.22}$$

Earlier, this possibility was disregarded and Λ was assumed to be zero, in accordance with the boundary condition that space becomes flat at infinity.

By combining various values of Λ with various possibilities for T_μ^ν, different models of the universe may be constructed. For example, if we put $T_4^4 = 8\pi\rho_0$ and $T_i^i = 8\pi p_0$, constant everywhere (all other T_μ^ν being zero) then, under the assumption that the line element is of the form

$$ds^2 = e^\nu \, dt^2 - r^2 \, d\theta^2 - r^2 \sin^2\theta \, d\varphi^2 - e^\lambda \, dr^2, \tag{18.23}$$

we obtain three possibilities for a static, homogeneous universe

(a) Einstein's Universe: $\nu' = 0$

$$ds^2 = dt^2 - r^2 \, d\theta^2 - r^2 \sin^2\theta \, d\varphi^2 - \frac{dr^2}{1 - \dfrac{r^2}{R^2}} \tag{18.24}$$

where

$$1/R^2 = \Lambda - 8\pi p_0. \tag{18.25}$$

(b) De Sitter's Universe: $\rho_0 + p_0 = 0$

$$ds^2 = \left(1 - \frac{r^2}{R^2}\right) dt^2 - r^2 \, d\theta^2 - r^2 \sin^2\theta \, d\varphi^2 - \frac{dr^2}{1 - \dfrac{r^2}{R^2}} \tag{18.26}$$

where

$$1/R^2 = (\Lambda + 8\pi\rho_0)/3. \tag{18.27}$$

(c) Special relativity: $\nu' = 0$, $\rho_0 + p_0 = 0$.

These static models do not predict the cosmological red shift (18.20) and therefore are only of mathematical interest. It is possible to introduce an expansion into Einstein's model by assuming a gradual thinning out of matter. The rate of expansion and of thinning out is then fitted to the red-shift formula.

H. Bondi and T. Gold postulated that the universe should be the same everywhere, always, and in all directions. For example, the density of matter must not thin out but must stay constant as the universe expands according to formula (18.20). It follows that matter must be *continuously created* to maintain the constant density. From purely kinematical arguments they have arrived at the conclusion that the line element must have the isotropic form

$$ds^2 = dt^2 - e^{2kt}(dx^2 + dy^2 + dz^2). \tag{18.28}$$

It is seen that for $ds^2 = 0$ (light waves) we have

$$v = \frac{dr}{dt} = e^{-kr} \tag{18.29}$$

leading to a Doppler shift

$$\frac{\delta\lambda}{\lambda} \simeq kr. \tag{18.30}$$

The conflict with the age of the earth is avoided by observing that, as new matter is created, new nebulae are being continually formed among the old ones. Therefore, a given nebula can be of any age.

It is a remarkable fact that F. Hoyle was able to drive the same line element by postulating a rate of creation in the Einstein field equations. The surprising fact is that the kinematically constructed line element (18.28) should turn out to be an exact solution of Einstein's ten nonlinear field equations, with exactly the rate of creation originally assumed, and that the field equations, originally conceived by Einstein on the basis of $D_\mu T^\nu_\mu = 0$ should now accommodate a situation which requires $dT^{44}/dt =$ rate of creation. The universe described by the line element (18.28) is called *steady state* in contrast to static or time varying universes.

18.5. Geometrodynamics

Recently, the amazing wealth contained in Einstein's field equations (17.8) was brought to light by the development of a new branch of general relativity, *Geometrodynamics*. After many unsuccessful attempts to unify gravitation and the electromagnetic field by a generalization of these equations (the so-called unified field theories), physicists started to realize that perhaps no generalization is necessary; the equations might already have sufficient room to accommodate the electromagnetic field and charge. This development is based on the following facts: (a) The energy tensor, $T_{\mu\nu}$, in the gravitational equations can represent any form of energy whatsoever: matter, field, electromagnetic, et cetera. (b) Once

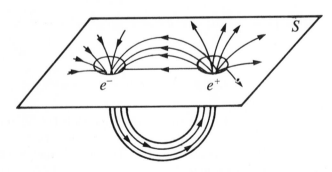

FIGURE 18.1 *A multiply-connected region intended to describe electron and positron.*

introduced into the equations, the energy, and the physical phenomenon corresponding to it, takes on a geometric meaning and its equations of motion are determined by Einstein's field equations. (c) The geometrical concepts of multiple-connectedness and other topological properties may correspond to physical properties such as charge (Figure 18.1). According to this line of thought, physics is essentially geometry. The dynamics of physical objects (curvatures, topologies, singularities) are assumed to follow from the geometrical tensor equations (17.8).

After these preliminaries we may now outline the treatment of the electromagnetic field according to this approach.

J. A. Wheeler and C. Misner, and much earlier G. Y. Rainnch, noticed that the Einstein tensor $R_\mu^\nu - \frac{1}{2}\delta_\mu^\nu R$ can be put into a form which has formally the same structure as the electromagnetic energy tensor $T_{\mu\nu}$ such that its trace is zero. Then one can write

$$R_{\mu\nu} - \tfrac{1}{2}g_{\mu\nu}R = 2f_{\mu\sigma}f_\nu^\sigma - \tfrac{1}{2}g_{\mu\nu}f_{\sigma\tau}f^{\sigma\tau}. \tag{18.31}$$

Taking the divergence we obtain

$$\sqrt{-g}\,\frac{\partial}{\partial x^\nu}\,(\sqrt{-g}\,f^{\mu\nu}) = 0 \tag{18.32}$$

and, from the definition of $f_{\mu\nu}$

$$f_{\mu\nu} = \partial_\mu A_\nu - \partial_\nu A_\mu, \tag{18.33}$$

we have

$$\partial^\mu f_{\sigma\nu} + \partial^\sigma f_{\nu\mu} + \partial^\nu f_{\mu\sigma} = 0. \tag{18.34}$$

Here (18.33) and (18.34) are the eight Maxwell equations. Due to the identical vanishing of the Einstein tensor, however, these fields cannot have sources. A very interesting device was therefore invented. Consider the two-dimensional tube of Figure 18.1 (an example of so-called "wormholes"). There is nowhere a source; but from the surface S, the tube could appear as though due to two oppositely charged sources! Taking advantage of this analogy, it is assumed that sources are multiply connected regions of space-time.

Another interesting feature of the theory is that, given the Einstein tensor with the requisite properties to describe an electromagnetic energy,

$$R_\mu^\mu = R = 0, \qquad R_\mu^\sigma R_\sigma^\nu = R_{\sigma\tau}R^{\sigma\tau}\delta_\mu^\nu/4, \tag{18.35}$$

the field $f_{\mu\nu}$ is not uniquely determined. Any new field, obtained from the old by use of the angle α

$$f'_{\mu\nu} = f_{4\nu}\cos\alpha + f_{ik}\sin\alpha, \qquad i, k = 1, 2, 3. \tag{18.36}$$

is another solution. The angle α can be thought of as an integral over a vector field, a_μ

$$\alpha(x) = \int a_\mu\, dx^\mu + \alpha_0 \tag{18.37}$$

and it can be proved that a_μ can be geometrically constructed out of the curvature tensor. In a source-free region, we will have

$$\partial_\mu a_\nu - \partial_\nu a_\mu = 0. \tag{18.38}$$

Thus the usual source-free electromagnetic field may be thought of being equivalent to (18.35) and (18.38) whereas source is introduced, through (18.37), entirely as a topological property of space. Further generalizations of this approach to other fields border on the purely speculative. Hence, we shall stop here, wishing good luck and a pleasant journey to the reader in his further explorations of these and other fascinating new fields of relativity.

In concluding the book, we wish to emphasize again that in modern physics general relativity did not find important applications. For this reason we have devoted more space to special relativity which had a profound influence on the present state of physics. Such topics as unified field theory, quantization of geometry, and Mach's principle are left out because these subjects, up to now, did not show much promise in the way of experimental verification. Some important theoretical discussions, such as the initial value problem of general relativity, are not included because such a discussion is beyond the purpose of the book. Perhaps a discussion of electrodynamics in refractive media and thermodynamics from a relativistic point of view would have been desirable. Since we intended to deal only with the microscopic laws of physics, we had to sacrifice these topics also. In quantum field theory discussion of interacting fields is not carried to completion. The new and fascinating field of elementary particles and dispersion relations are also left out since this would carry us too far afield from our primary aim and into a subject which is not as yet sufficiently crystallized. We hope, however, that the essential tools are provided to aid the reader who desires to go further in these matters.

THE GREEN'S FUNCTION

In mechanics the equation of motion of a particle is a differential equation of second order. Consequently, the solution must contain two integration constants. These two constants may be determined by giving the initial position and the initial velocity of the particle. Hence, giving the values of $x(t)$ and $\dot{x}(t)$ at a time $t = t'$ fixes the two integration constants and the subsequent motion of the particle is completely determined.

Now mathematically the wave equation (8.14) or its more general form (8.35) are also second-order equations in time and a similar approach should apply. Here, of course, the situation is more complicated because there are also space derivatives and the equations are partial differential equations. This should not bother us much, however, because according to the theory of relativity, space and time variables are symmetrical.

Having reminded the reader of these simple facts, let us now look for the solutions of equation (8.35)

$$(\partial_\mu \partial^\mu - \kappa^2)\phi(x) = -4\pi\rho(x), \tag{A.1}$$

where $\phi(x)$ and $\partial_\mu\phi(x)$ correspond to the initial values $x(t)$ and $x'(t)$ of the mechanical problem. For example, $\phi(x', y', z', t)$ at $t = t'$ is called the initial value of the field at the space point x', y', z'. Likewise, $\phi(x, y, z, t')$ at $x = x', y = y', z = z'$ is called the boundary value of the field at the instant t'. These are simple generalizations of the initial value concept to fit the relativistic symmetry.

We now claim that a general solution of (A.1) can be written as†

$$\phi(x) = -4\pi\int\rho(x')G(x - x')\,dx' + \int[G(x - x')\partial'_\mu\phi(x') + \phi(x')\partial'_\mu G(x - x')]\,dS'^\mu. \tag{A.2}$$

From equation (A.1) and the requirement that $\phi(x)$ satisfy the initial and the boundary conditions we can find the necessary equations defining $G(x - x')$, the so-called *Green's function*.

(a) Since $\phi(x)$ satisfies the wave equation (A.1), $G(x - x')$ must also satisfy the same equation in its x variable. Forming the equation (A.1) by differentiation under the integral sign in (A.2), we see from the first term that

$$(\partial_\mu\partial^\mu - \kappa^2)G(x - x') = \delta(x - x'). \tag{A.3}$$

(b) Since $\phi(x) \to \phi(x')$ at $x = x'$ we must have

$$\partial'_\mu G(x - x') = \delta_\mu(x - x'), \tag{A.4}$$

$$G(x - x') = 0 \qquad \text{at} \qquad x = x'. \tag{A.5}$$

† This form is suggested by the following theorem in mathematics: The general solution of a linear inhomogeneous differential equation can be obtained by forming a linear combination of the solution of its homogeneous part and one of its particular solutions.

(c) By differentiating (A.2) under the integral sign, one sees then that $\partial_\mu \phi(x) \to \partial'_\mu \phi(x')$ at $x = x'$ is automatically satisfied.

(d) Note that (A.5) essentially contains the principle of causality. For $t = t'$ defines a space-like distance and $G(x - x')$ is an invariant function. Since by Lorentz transformations a space-like distance is transformed into $(x - x')^2 < 0$, $G(x - x')$ will continue to vanish due to its invariant character. Thus, we may extend equation (A.5) to satisfy the more general situation

$$G(x - x') = 0, \qquad (x - x')^2 \leqslant 0. \tag{A.6}$$

Putting all these together, we get the set of defining equations

$$\left.\begin{aligned}(\partial_\mu \partial^\mu - \kappa^2)G(x - x') &= \delta(x - x') \\ \partial'_\mu G(x - x') &= \delta_\mu(x - x') \\ G(x - x') &= 0 \quad \text{for} \quad (x - x')^2 \leqslant 0\end{aligned}\right\}. \tag{A.7}$$

The problem then is to find a function $G(x - x')$ satisfying these conditions. Once this function is determined and the manipulation of the integral form (A.2) is mastered, there is no serious difficulty in solving field problems. The function $G(x - x')$ is sometimes called "the fundamental solution" of the wave equation. It is a solution of the wave equation with the boundary conditions given in (A.7).

We may now proceed to show that the function defined by the integral representation

$$G(x - x') = \frac{1}{(2\pi)^4} \int_c \frac{dk e^{-ik(x-x')}}{\kappa^2 - k^2} \tag{A.8}$$

satisfies all these conditions.

It is important to note here that the form of (A.8) is consistent with our earlier conclusion that any solution of the wave equation can be obtained by a superposition of the transforms of a single solution. Here the solution being transformed is $e^{-ik(x-x')}$ in its x variable. It is a simple plane wave. If we transform it, we will get another solution with a different k. If we take a linear combination of all such solutions, we have $G(x - x') = \sum_k c_k e^{-ik(x-x')}$. When the summation is over a continuous variable k this can be written as an integral,

$$G(x - x') = \frac{1}{(2\pi)^4} \int dk c(k) e^{-ik(x-x')}. \tag{A.9}$$

From this the first condition of (A.7) will lead to $c(k) = 1/(\kappa^2 - k^2)$ consistent with (A.8).

Now take $\mu = 4$. We have

$$\frac{\partial}{\partial t} G(x - x') = \frac{1}{(2\pi)^3} \int e^{-i\vec{k}(\vec{x}-\vec{x}')} d^3k \frac{1}{2\pi i} \int \frac{e^{i\omega(t-t')}\omega \, d\omega}{(\omega + a)(\omega - a)} \tag{A.10}$$

where $a = c\sqrt{\kappa^2 + k^2}$. If we integrate the ω part along the path shown in Figure A.1, we see that the contour must be closed in the *upper* part of the complex ω-plane when $t > t'$ (otherwise $G(x - x')$ will become infinite at $t \to \infty$). This gives

$$\tfrac{1}{2}[e^{ia(t-t')} + e^{-ia(t-t')}] = \cos a(t - t') \tag{A.11}$$

which is unity for $t = t'$. We then have

$$\partial_4 G(x - x') = \frac{1}{(2\pi)^3} \int e^{-i\vec{k}(\vec{x}-\vec{x}')} d^3k = \delta_4(x - x'). \tag{A.12}$$

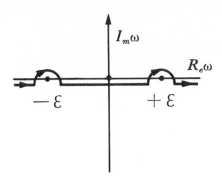

FIGURE A.1

For $G(x - x')$ a similar process of integration gives

$$G(x - x') = \frac{1}{(2\pi)^3} \int e^{-i\vec{k}(\vec{x}-\vec{x}')} \, d^3k \, \frac{1}{2\pi} \int \frac{e^{i\omega(t-t')} \, d\omega}{(\omega + a)(\omega - a)} \tag{A.13}$$

$$\frac{1}{2ai} [e^{ia(t-t')} - e^{-ia(t-t')}] = \frac{1}{a} \sin a(t - t'). \tag{A.14}$$

This is zero for $t = t'$ and leads to $G(x - x') = 0$ for $t = t'$.

Thus, the causality principle, Huygens' principle, the effect of initial conditions ($t = t'$), and space boundaries ($x_i = x_i'$) are all contained in the Green's function (A.8) and the integral (A.2).

From the integral form (A.9), one sees that the *Fourier transform*, $G(k)$, of Greens' function is formally given by

$$G(k) = \frac{1}{k^2 - \kappa^2}. \tag{A.15}$$

This is usually called Green's function in momentum space.

The method of the Green's function is general. For a scalar field with vanishing rest mass, we let $\kappa = 0$. In this case the Green's function is denoted by $D(x - x')$.

$$D(x) = \frac{1}{(2\pi)^4} \int_c \frac{dk e^{-ikx}}{k^2}; \qquad D(k) = \frac{1}{k^2}. \tag{A.16}$$

For the electromagnetic field, (A.2) may be simply taken over for each component $A_\mu(x)$, with $\kappa = 0$.

We note here that a very interesting concept is introduced in the course of integration on the complex ω-plane. Namely, we have assumed implicitly that the Green's function is analytic in the upper half plane. This condition is equivalent to saying that no field problem will lead to catastrophic situations for $t > t'$, which is yet another expression of the principle of causality.

MATRICES AND OPERATORS

A rectangular matrix is an array of numbers a_{ij}

$$A = \begin{pmatrix} a_{11} & a_{12} & \cdots & a_{1l} \\ a_{21} & a_{22} & \cdots & a_{2l} \\ \cdots & \cdots & \cdots & \cdots \\ a_{k1} & a_{k2} & \cdots & a_{kl} \end{pmatrix}, \tag{B.1}$$

where the elements a_{ij} are, in general, complex. The horizontal lines are called rows and the vertical lines are called columns. The elements a_{11}, a_{22}, a_{33}, ... are called *diagonal elements*. A matrix is called diagonal if all off-diagonal elements are zero,

$$D = \begin{pmatrix} a_{11} & & & 0 \\ & a_{22} & & \\ & & a_{33} & \\ 0 & & & \cdots \end{pmatrix}. \tag{B.2}$$

If all elements of a diagonal matrix are equal, $a_{ii} = \lambda$, it is called spherical. If in addition $\lambda = 1$, then the matrix is called the *unity*, or *identity* matrix.

$$I = \begin{pmatrix} 1 & & & 0 \\ & 1 & & \\ & & 1 & \\ 0 & & & 1 \end{pmatrix}. \tag{B.3}$$

Addition of two matrices, $S = A + B$, corresponds to the addition of their elements

$$s_{ik} = a_{ik} + b_{ik}. \tag{B.4}$$

Multiplication $R = AB$ is defined by

$$r_{ik} = \sum_l a_{il} b_{lk} \tag{B.5}$$

when the number of rows of B is equal to the number of columns of A. Note that in general BA is not equal to AB so that matrix multiplication is *not* necessarily commutative. However, two diagonal matrices always commute and they can be treated as ordinary numbers. Also, a spherical or identity matrix commutes with all matrices. The matrix

$$C = AB - BA \tag{B.6}$$

is called the commutator of A and B.

The inverse B of a matrix A is defined as

$$AB = BA = I \tag{B.7}$$

where I is the identity matrix. We may write

$$B = A^{-1}. \tag{B.8}$$

This is possible only if the number of rows and columns of A are equal and if its determinant is not zero. In other words, A possesses an inverse only if it is *square* and *nonsingular*. We can then also write $A = B^{-1}$.

If a matrix, A, is reflected relative to its diagonal (that is, its rows and columns are interchanged) we obtain its *transpose*, $\tilde{A}$.

$$\tilde{a}_{ij} = a_{ji} \tag{B.9}$$

The adjoint $A^\dagger$ of a matrix A is the complex conjugate of the transposed matrix

$$A^\dagger = \tilde{A}^*. \tag{B.10}$$

If a matrix is equal to its own adjoint, it is called *Hermitian*. A Hermitian matrix, $A = A^\dagger$, has the property that the elements symmetrical about its diagonal are complex conjugates of each other. If the adjoint of a matrix is equal to its inverse, then the matrix is called *unitary*. This is defined by

$$UU^\dagger = U^\dagger U = I. \tag{B.11}$$

If a matrix S is nonsingular, the transformation

$$A' = S A S^{-1} \tag{B.12}$$

is called a *similarity* transformation of A. Similarity transformations have the property that they leave matrix equations invariant.

A *unitary* transformation is affected by a unitary matrix

$$\bar{A} = U A U^{-1} = U A U^\dagger. \tag{B.13}$$

A unitary transformation also leaves matrix equations form-invariant and in addition it does not alter the eigenvalues of Hermitian operators.

If a matrix has only one column, it is called a *column matrix*.

$$\Phi = \begin{pmatrix} \alpha_1 \\ \alpha_2 \\ \cdot \\ \cdot \\ \cdot \\ \alpha_l \end{pmatrix} \tag{B.14}$$

The transpose of a column matrix is a *row matrix*. When a column matrix is multiplied by a rectangular matrix a linear transformation is produced.

$$A\Phi = \sum_k a_{ik}\alpha_k = b_i \tag{B.15}$$

We conceive of this as an operation and sometimes call A an *operator* and $\Phi = | \ )$ an *operand*. Two successive operations A and B are equivalent to a single operation $C = BA$. The operation AB is not in general the same as BA due to the possible lack of commutation.

The operand $\Omega = |\ )$ may be conceived of as a state formed by the superposition of individual states,

$$|0) = \begin{pmatrix} 1 \\ 0 \\ 0 \\ \cdot \\ \cdot \end{pmatrix}, \qquad |1) = \begin{pmatrix} 0 \\ 1 \\ 0 \\ \cdot \\ \cdot \end{pmatrix}, \qquad |2) = \begin{pmatrix} 0 \\ 0 \\ 1 \\ \cdot \\ \cdot \end{pmatrix}, \qquad \dots \tag{B.16}$$

such that

$$|\ ) = \alpha_1|0) + \alpha_2|1) + \dots . \tag{B.17}$$

Therefore each state is itself an operand. An operator, in general, carries a state into another state. If an operator reproduces the state as in

$$O|o') = o'|o') \tag{B.18}$$

where o' is a number, then $|o')$ is called an *eigenstate* of 0, and o' is called its *eigenvalue* belonging to the state $|o')$. Eigenvalues do not have to be real. But if they are, the corresponding operator is Hermitian. All these considerations are assumed to be valid even in the case of infinite matrices, which often arises in physics.

In quantum mechanics, the characterization of the states of a system is made in terms of their real eigenvalues. An observation is conceived of as a Hermitian operation such that the eigenvalues belonging to its eigenstates are extracted. Since observation is in principle acquiring information from a system, it would be difficult to understand how this could be done without actually changing the state. We must therefore conceive of an observable operator in two steps. First, the state $|o_k')$ is actually carried into other states by an operator b. Then another operator, a, transforms all $|o_l')$ back into $|o_k')$.

$$b|o_k') = \sum_l \xi_{kl}|o_l'), \qquad a|o_l') = \eta_{lk}|o_k'), \tag{B.19}$$

$$ab|o_k') = \sum_l \xi_{kl}\eta_{lk}|o_k') \tag{B.20}$$

where by a redefinition

$$o_k' = \sum_l \xi_{kl}\eta_{lk}.$$

If o_k' is real, $O = ab$ is Hermitian. This leads to $b = \omega a^\dagger$ where ω is a real number. Therefore observables can be expanded as

$$O = \omega_1 aa^\dagger + \omega_2 a^\dagger a + \omega_3 aaa^\dagger a^\dagger + \dots . \tag{B.21}$$

where a and $a^\dagger$ are elementary (or fundamental) operators. Since the main difference between ordinary numbers and operators is the lack of commutativity of operators, we expect that the laws of quantum mechanics will be formulated by providing the commutation properties of the fundamental operators like a and $a^\dagger$. In Chapter XIII we see that this is actually the case.

PROBLEMS

1.1. A motor boat is moving upstream in a river with full speed. A woman drops a small box opposite to a tree. Half an hour later, she informs the captain that her jewels are in the box. They immediately turn around and find the box five miles downstream from where it was dropped. What is the velocity of the river? (Mileage marks were read on the land.) (Figure P.1.)

1.2. Two sailboats are moving uniformly in two different directions with velocities u and v. Suppose that at the initial instant $t = 0$, they are at a distance $l = AB$ apart. Find the minimum distance the two boats will ever achieve. (Figure P.2.)

1.3. In a train moving with a velocity $a = 2$ meters per second, a stone is thrown vertically with a velocity $b = 10$ meters per second. Find the trajectory of the stone with respect to the earth. The gravitational acceleration of the earth is $g = 981$ cm/sec.

2.1. Assuming that light is composed of small elastic particles, show that the Michelson-Morley experiment can be explained on the basis of classical relativity. Also, show that such particles, by reflecting them repeatedly from moving mirrors, could, according to classical relativity, be made to travel with much higher velocities than c. This result could be tested experimentally.

2.2. The device shown in the text (Figure 2.1) is set up in a ship. The sea and the air are calm. The times t_1 and t_2 are measured to be $t_1 = 0.01$ sec and $t_2 = 0.0102$ sec. Find the velocity of the ship. Why don't we interpret this result as a violation of the principle of relativity? (Velocity of sound is $V = 340$ meters/sec.)

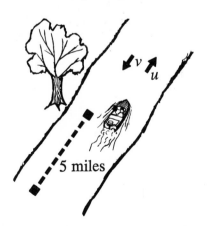

FIGURE P.1

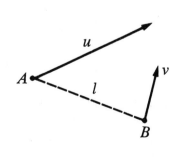

FIGURE P.2

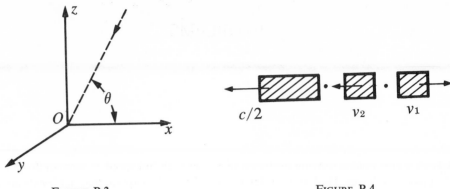

FIGURE P.3   FIGURE P.4

2.3. Consider a light ray in a reference frame S in the x–z plane. The ray makes an angle $\theta = 60°$ with the x axis. What will be the new angle when the system is moving in the x direction with a velocity $c/2$. Do the problem classically. (Figure P.3.)

3.1. Show that two reference frames having the same acceleration, γ, move with constant relative velocity with respect to each other. Can one use Lorentz transformations between such frames?

3.2. Using (3.24) show that the operator

$$\frac{\partial^2}{\partial x^2} + \frac{\partial^2}{\partial y^2} + \frac{\partial^2}{\partial z^2} - \frac{1}{c^2}\frac{\partial^2}{\partial t^2} = \kappa^2$$

is invariant. This is the analogue of the invariance of

$$dx^2 + dy^2 + dz^2 - c^2\,dt^2 = ds^2.$$

3.3. Prove that the requirement of symmetry between x and ct in (3.5) and the requirement that the transformation be *unimodular* lead to the Lorentz transformation. (Unimodular means that the determinant of the transformation is unity.)

4.1. A huge missile explodes and divides into two equal parts. The two pieces take off with velocities $c/2$, one to the right and the other to the left. The piece which moves to the right again divides into two by an explosion such that with respect to its own rest frame the resulting two pieces take off with velocities $c/2$ to the right and left. Calculate the velocities of these last two pieces with respect to the earth. (Figure P.4.)

4.2. A man on a station platform sees two trains approaching each other at the rate $(\frac{7}{8})c$, but the observer on one of the trains sees the other train approaching him with a velocity $(\frac{35}{37})c$. What are the velocities of the trains with respect to the station? (Figure P.5.)

4.3. Applying equations (3.24), obtain the Doppler effect and the aberration formulas.

4.4. Solve problem 2.3 relativistically.

4.5. How fast must you be driving your car to see a red light as green? Wavelengths of red and green light are 6300 Å and 5400 Å, respectively.

5.1. Two explosions, one on the earth and one on the polar star are observed to be simultaneous (by an observer midway between them). What would be the time difference between receiving the two waves by an observer on a rocket ship moving towards the polar star with the velocity v?

5.2. A young man goes to the Polar star and comes back to earth on a rocket. Calculate the age difference between him and his twin brother who stayed on the earth. The velocity of the rocket is $v = (\frac{4}{5})c$ and the distance between the earth and the Polar star is 40 light years.

5.3. A man starts on a space trip in a rocket. A spring balance inside the rocket shows a constant acceleration $\gamma = 100$ meters/sec². What is the velocity of his rocket with respect to the earth after two years have elapsed on his own clock? What is the total distance travelled according to an observer on the earth?

5.4. Show that under space-inversion, the momentum changes sign but the angular momentum is unaltered.

5.5. Solve problem 1.1 using special relativity.

5.6. We know that a man is not symmetric under mirroring. This is evident, for we are predominantly right-handed (or left-handed) and our heart is on the left side. Would you think that neutrinos produce this asymmetry? If not, how would you explain it?

6.1. Show that if a tensor is symmetric in one coordinate frame, it is symmetric in all frames. Do the same for antisymmetry.

6.2. Prove that, in (6.19), we can redefine $\gamma_\mu \to S\gamma_\mu S^{-1}$ where S is any matrix with an inverse (nonsingular). This is called a similarity transformation. Under a similarity transformation $\Psi \to S\Psi$, a spinor stays a spinor, and (6.19) is not altered.

6.3. From (6.25) derive the spinor transformations corresponding to

$$z' = \frac{z - vt}{\sqrt{1 - v^2/c^2}}, \qquad t' = \frac{t - \frac{v}{c^2}z}{\sqrt{1 - v^2/c^2}}.$$

7.1. A particle of rest mass m_0 and velocity $v = 3c/5$ collides with a particle at rest of rest mass m_0. Assuming that, after the collision, the two particles coalesce, compute the velocity and the rest mass of the resulting particle

7.2. Assume that in a thermonuclear reactor, one pound of hydrogen is fused into helium every second. Compute the power of the reactor in units of horsepower. The atomic weights of hydrogen and helium are H $= 1.0086$, He $= 4.003$.

7.3. A rocket is propelled by emitting light. Its mass is $M = 5$ tons and it emits an intense beam of light energy, $W = 1.8 \times 10^{20}$ ergs/sec. It starts from rest and after twenty-three days the operator shuts off the oven. Neglecting heat and other radiation, compute the final velocity and the remaining rest mass of the rocket. (Figure P.6.)

7.4. If a right-angled lever appears in equilibrium to an observer at rest, prove that to an observer in a moving system the lever will appear to be in equilibrium. (A right-angled lever is shown in the figure above. It is free to rotate around the pivot, O, if the torques due to the forces f_1 and f_2 do not balance.) (Figure P.7.)

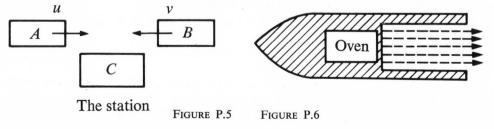

The station   FIGURE P.5   FIGURE P.6

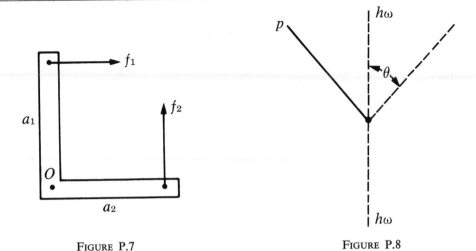

7.5. Consider the collision of an electron at rest with a photon of energy $\mathscr{E} = \hbar\omega$. After the collision, the electron has momentum p and the photon has energy $\mathscr{E}' = \hbar\omega'$. Find the relation between ω and ω'. (Figure P.8.)

8.1. (a) Evaluate the stress-energy tensor of a point source at rest for $\kappa = 0$.
(b) Prove that, in this case, two such sources interact according to the Newtonian law, Q^2/r^2.
8.2. Evaluate the stress-energy tensor of a plane wave $\phi = ae^{ikx} + a^*e^{-ikx}$. Construct the energy and momentum of the wave.
8.3. Find the plane wave superposition of waves which gives the static Yukawa solution (8.31). Identify the Green's function.

10.1. Prove the identity (10.9) by writing it out.
10.2. For the plane wave $A_\mu = a_\mu \cos(\omega t - kz + \alpha_\mu)$, evaluate the energy, momentum, and spin angular momentum.
10.3. In a reference frame, S, consider an electron at rest in a static magnetic field H_z. In a reference frame S' moving with the velocity V relative to S, evaluate the Lorentz force acting on the electron. Find the trajectory of the electron in S'.
10.4. In a reference frame S, the static electric and magnetic fields E and H make an angle θ with each other. Find the velocity and direction of the system in which they are parallel.
10.5. Find the field of a uniformly moving electric charge.
10.6. Prove that the Lorentz condition $\partial_\mu A^\mu = 0$ guarantees the positive definiteness of energy in all frames if it is so in one particular frame.
10.7. Compute the field energy of a uniform spherical charge Q of radius a.

11.1. Take the two solutions (11.48) and construct the energy, momentum, angular momentum, and charge for these solutions.
11.2. Prove that (11.55) is gauge invariant under the combined gauge invariance principles of the first and second kind.

11.3. Evaluate the energy, momentum, and left- or right-handedness of the two fields (11.61).

12.1. Derive formulas (12.7) and (6.25).

12.2. Prove that the transformation (12.32) of a Lagrangian

$$\mathscr{L}' = \mathscr{L} + \partial_\mu h^\mu(\phi)$$

does not alter the variational problem, if $h^\mu(\phi)$ vanishes at spatial infinity.

12.3. Prove equation (12.21).

12.4. Prove that the orbital angular momentum and spin angular momentum are not separately gauge invariant, but that the total angular momentum is.

16.1. The string of a hydrogen balloon is tied to the floor of a car. The windows and doors are closed and the car is standing still on a horizontal road. The driver steps on the gas and causes a 200 cm/sec² uniform acceleration. Find the angle of the string of the balloon with the vertical after transients have died down.

16.2. What happens to a lighted cigarette in an elevator when the rope of the elevator is cut?

16.3. Given the space-time geometry

$$ds^2 = e^{-2\phi}\,dt^2 - e^{2\phi}(dx^2 + dy^2 + dz^2),$$

find the geodesic equations of motion.

16.4. Show that Newton's equations of motion lead to an elliptic orbit for a planet or a satellite.

17.1. Show that outside of a spherically symmetric mass distribution the line element has the same form as (17.9). In other words, a spherically symmetric mass and a point mass have the same line element outside the mass distribution.

17.2. By an appropriate transformation, express the Schwarzchild line element

$$ds^2 = \left(1 - \frac{2M}{c}\right)dt^2 - r^2\,d\theta^2 - r^2\sin^2\theta\,d\varphi^2 - \left(1 - \frac{2M}{r}\right)^{-1}dr^2$$

in isotropic form.

17.3. Resolve the clock paradox of special relativity by using the line element (17.24).

18.1. Show that the Nordström line element

$$ds^2 = e^{-2\phi}(dt^2 - dx^2 - dy^2 - dz^2)$$

where

$$\phi = A\exp\left[2\pi i\nu\left(t - \frac{\alpha x + \beta y + \gamma z}{c}\right)\right]$$

is a solution of equations (17.8).

18.2. For the isotropic line element given by

$$ds^2 = e^{-2\phi}\,dt^2 - e^{2\phi}(dx^2 + dy^2 + dz^2)$$

evaluate the general d'Alembertian $\phi^\mu_{;\mu}$.

18.3. Compute T^ν_μ and G^ν_μ in an 8-dimensional space given by

$$ds^2 = e^{-2\phi}(d\alpha^2 + d\beta^2 + d\gamma^2) - e^{2\phi}(dx^2 + dy^2 + dz^2 + dt^2 + d\omega^2)$$

where $\phi = \phi(x, y, z, t, \omega)$; α, β, γ being inert variables.

SOLUTIONS TO PROBLEMS

1.1. To attack this problem frontally would lead to two algebraic equations with three unknowns. The problem becomes trivial if we choose a coordinate system attached to the water. In this system the box is stationary but the earth with everything on it is moving with a velocity u in the opposite direction. The boat takes, on the stationary water, half an hour to go and half an hour to come back to the box. During that time the tree moves five miles. The velocity of the river is thus 5 miles an hour. (Figure S.1.)

1.2. Let us choose a coordinate system attached to the boat B. From this coordinate system the sea and everything on it will appear to be moving in the opposite direction with a velocity $-\vec{v}$, and therefore A will have a velocity which is $\vec{u} - \vec{v}$. The problem of finding the minimum distance reduces to finding the perpendicular from B to the new direction of A. (Figure S.2.)

1.3. With respect to a man in the train (Figure S.3), the motion of the stone takes place on a vertical line according to the equations

$$y = bt - \tfrac{1}{2}gt^2; \qquad x = 0.$$

If we look at the stone from the earth, which is moving with respect to the train with the velocity $\vec{a}$, the stone will also have a horizontal velocity component $\vec{a}$ so that

$$y' = bt - \tfrac{1}{2}gt^2; \qquad x' = at.$$

Eliminating t from these, we get the equation of a parabola

$$y' = \frac{b}{a}x' - \frac{1}{2}\frac{g}{a^2}x'^2 = 50x' - 12.26x'^2.$$

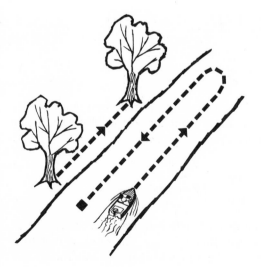

FIGURE S.1

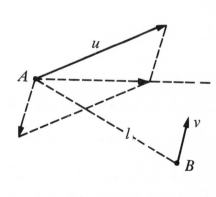

FIGURE S.2

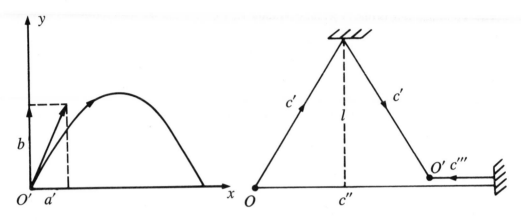

2.1. According to the reflection of elastic bodies, the relative velocity with respect to the mirror is preserved. Also the incident and the reflected particles make the same angle with the normal of the reflecting surface (Figure S.4). Thus, according to classical relativity, the various velocities are

$$c' = \sqrt{c^2 + v^2}; \qquad c'' = c + v; \qquad c''' = c - v$$

and the respective distances traveled by these velocities are

$$l' = l\sqrt{1 + v^2/c^2}; \qquad l'' = l\left(1 + \frac{v}{c}\right); \qquad l''' = l\left(1 - \frac{v}{c}\right)$$

dividing, respectively,

$$t_1 = \frac{2l'}{c'} = \frac{2l}{c}; \qquad t_2 = \frac{l''}{c''} + \frac{l'''}{c'''} = \frac{2l}{c}.$$

Since relative velocity with respect to the mirror is preserved in the reflection of a particle, a particle moving with the velocity c after being reflected from a mirror will have a velocity $c \pm 2v$. This can be repeated and after n reflections we get $c \pm 2nv$.

2.2. From the formulas (2.2) and (2.3),

$$\frac{t_2}{t_1} = \sqrt{1 - v^2/V^2}; \qquad v = \frac{2V}{100} = 7.8 \text{ meters/sec.}$$

Here the air is a substance and it can serve as a material reference frame. The velocity of the ship is thus measured relative to this reference frame, the air. The result is therefore consistent with the classical relativity. In the case of light rays Michelson's experiment has shown that the classical relativity is wrong or that there is no such substance as the ether which can serve as a reference frame.

2.3. In the new system the vertical and the horizontal components of the velocity are according to Galileo's transformations (1.9).

$$u'_z = \frac{\sqrt{3}}{2} c; \qquad u'_x = \tfrac{1}{2}c + \tfrac{1}{2}c = c; \qquad \tan \theta' = \frac{\sqrt{3}}{2}; \qquad \theta' = 41°.$$

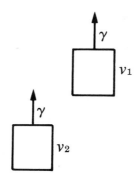

FIGURE S.5

3.1. Let the two velocities be v_1 and v_2 (Figure S.5),

$$\frac{dv_1}{dt} - \frac{dv_2}{dt} = \gamma - \gamma = 0.$$

Therefore

$$d(v_1 - v_2) = 0, \qquad v_1 - v_2 = V = \text{constant}.$$

However, one cannot use Lorentz transformations between these frames because neither is inertial.

3.2. Use formulas (3.24).

3.3. The symmetry between x and ct requires (3.5) to be written

$$x' = \alpha\left(x - \frac{V}{c} ct\right)$$

$$ct' = \alpha\left(ct + \frac{\gamma c}{\alpha} x\right) = \alpha\left(ct - \frac{V}{c} x\right)$$

so that $\gamma c/\alpha = -V/c$ or $\gamma = -\alpha \dfrac{V}{c^2}$.

Then the unimodularity means

$$\begin{vmatrix} \alpha & -\dfrac{\alpha V}{c} \\ -\dfrac{\alpha V}{c} & \alpha \end{vmatrix} = \alpha^2\left(1 - \frac{V^2}{c^2}\right) = 1,$$

that is,

$$\alpha = \frac{1}{\sqrt{1 - \dfrac{V^2}{c^2}}}.$$

4.1. Applying the formula for the combinations of velocities

$$w_1 = \frac{\frac{c}{2} + \frac{c}{2}}{1 + \frac{c^2}{4c^2}} = \frac{4}{5}c; \qquad w_2 = \frac{\frac{c}{2} - \frac{c}{2}}{1 - \frac{c^2}{4c^2}} = 0.$$

4.2. Let the velocities of the two trains with respect to the station be u and v. We have

$$u + v = \frac{7}{5}c.$$

On the other hand from the combination of velocities the man on the train sees

$$w = \frac{u + v}{1 + \frac{uv}{c^2}} = \frac{35}{37}c.$$

Solving these two equations, we find

$$u = \frac{3}{5}c; \qquad v = \frac{4}{5}c.$$

4.3. By differentiating (4.20) and (4.21), we see that, formally

$$\frac{\partial}{\partial t} = 2\pi v, \qquad \frac{\partial}{\partial x} = -2\pi v \frac{\alpha}{c} \qquad \frac{\partial}{\partial y} = -2\pi v \frac{\beta}{c};$$

$$\frac{\partial}{\partial t'} = 2\pi v', \qquad \frac{\partial}{\partial x'} = -2\pi v' \frac{\alpha'}{c}, \qquad \frac{\partial}{\partial y'} = -2\pi v' \frac{\beta'}{c}.$$

Then combining them according to (3.24), the desired formulas follow.

4.4. To solve the problem relativistically, we use the equations (4.18)

$$u'_x = \frac{u_x + v}{1 + \frac{u_x v}{c^2}}; \qquad u'_z = \frac{u'_z \sqrt{1 - v^2/c^2}}{1 + \frac{u_x v}{c^2}};$$

$$\tan \theta' = \frac{u'_z}{u'_k} = \frac{u_y \sqrt{1 - v^2/c^2}}{u_x + v} = \frac{3}{2}; \qquad \theta' = 37°$$

4.5. Using the relativistic Doppler formula (4.22) we find

$$\frac{\lambda_1}{\lambda_2} = \frac{1 + \frac{v}{c}}{\sqrt{1 - \frac{v^2}{c^2}}} = \frac{7}{6}; \qquad v = 0.15c.$$

5.1. Let the distance between Earth and the Star be $2a$ (Figure S.6). We have

$$x + y + \xi = 2a.$$

The time difference in Earth-Star System is

$$\Delta t = \frac{y - x}{c} = \frac{\xi}{V}.$$

If we eliminate y, ξ, we obtain

$$\Delta t = 2(a - x)/(c + v).$$

Therefore,

$$\Delta t' = \Delta t \sqrt{1 - \frac{v^2}{c^2}} = \frac{2(a - x)}{c} \sqrt{\frac{1 - \dfrac{v}{c}}{1 + \dfrac{v}{c}}}.$$

(Note here that if $x = a$, both Δt and $\Delta t'$ would vanish, since both observers then are observing a coincidence.)

5.2. To the man who stays on the earth the journey takes $t = 2 \times 40 \dfrac{c}{v} = 80 \times \frac{5}{4} = 100$ years. For the man who makes the journey we have $\tau = t\sqrt{1 - v^2/c^2} = 60$ years. Thus the latter is 40 years younger than his twin brother.

5.3. Since in the rest frame of the rocket $d\alpha = \gamma \, d\tau/c$, we have

$$\alpha = \int_0^\tau \gamma \, d\tau/c = \frac{\gamma\tau}{c} = 21; \qquad v = c \tanh \alpha = c \frac{1 - e^{-42}}{1 + e^{-42}}.$$

According to an observer on earth, the total distance covered is

$$l = \int_0^t v \, dt = \int_0^\tau v \cosh \alpha \, d\alpha = \frac{c^2}{\gamma} \int_0^\alpha \sinh \alpha \, d\alpha = \frac{c^2}{\gamma}\left[\frac{1}{\sqrt{1 - v^2/c^2}} - 1 \right].$$

5.4. Under space inversion $x_k \to -x_k$, $t \to t$; the x component of momentum, for example, behaves as (see Chapter 7)

$$p_x = \frac{m_0 \, dx/dt}{\sqrt{1 - v^2/c^2}} \to \frac{m_0(-dx/dt)}{\sqrt{1 - v^2/c^2}} \to -p_x;$$

whereas

$$M_x = zp_y - yp_z \to (-z)(-p_y) - (-y)(-p_z) \to M_x.$$

The same follows for the other components of p and M.

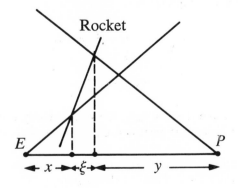

FIGURE S.6

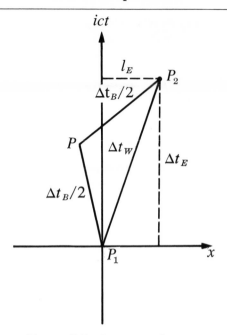

FIGURE S.7   *Space-time diagram.*

5.5. The process cannot be described from the boat (not inertial). Let us describe it from the earth (Figure S.7). We know only the earth distance l_E and boat time Δt_B which is represented by the path $\overline{P_1}\overline{PP_2}$. Let the boat-water relative velocity be u. Then

$$\Delta t_W = \Delta t_B / \sqrt{1 - u^2/c^2}.$$

Since

$$c^2 \Delta t_W^2 = c^2 \Delta t_E^2 - l_E^2,$$

$$\Delta t_E = \sqrt{\Delta t_W^2 + \frac{l_E^2}{c^2}}.$$

Therefore, the Earth-water velocity v is

$$v = \frac{l_E}{\Delta t_E} = \frac{l_E}{\sqrt{\dfrac{\Delta t_B}{1 - \dfrac{u^2}{c^2}} + \dfrac{l_E^2}{c^2}}}.$$

We see that, in contrast to the classical case, the river velocity depends on the boat-river velocity (artificially) since distance is measured on the earth while time is measured on the boat.

5.6. According to the present view, macroscopic physics can develop asymmetries which microscopic physics does not have. Thus, at the beginning of evolution, absorption of a right-polarized light beam may have started a trend which persisted throughout the evolutionary process.

6.1. Use the tensor transformations (6.11).

6.2. Notice first that

$$S\delta_{\mu\nu}S^{-1} = \delta_{\mu\nu}.$$

Now multiply equation (6.19) by S on the left and S^{-1} on the right. Also put $SS^{-1} = 1$ between the γ_μ's.

6.3. See equation (11.27).

7.1. Applying the laws of conservation of energy and momentum, we have the equations

$$\frac{m_0 v}{\sqrt{1 - v^2/c^2}} = \frac{M_0 V}{\sqrt{1 - V^2/c^2}};$$

$$m_0 + \frac{m_0}{\sqrt{1 - v^2/c^2}} = \frac{M_0}{\sqrt{1 - V^2/c^2}}.$$

solving for V and M_0, we get

$$V = \frac{v}{1 + \sqrt{1 - v^2/c^2}} = c/3; \qquad M_0 = \sqrt{9/2}\,m_0.$$

Notice that the rest mass of the resulting particle is larger than the sum of the rest masses of the two original particles.

7.2. We assume four hydrogen nuclei combine into one helium nucleus. Therefore the mass loss per unit time is $445 \times (4 \times 1.0086 - 4.003)/1.0086 \simeq 3.33$ grams sec. Then the power of the reactor is $W = 3.33 \times c^2 \simeq 400$ billion horsepower.

7.3. The amount W is given with respect to the rest frame of the rocket. Therefore inside the rocket an acceleration

$$\gamma = \frac{dv}{d\tau} = \frac{c \, d\alpha}{d\tau} = W/c(M - W\tau/c^2)$$

is measured. Here τ is the proper time of the rocket. Now by analogy to problem 5.3, we see that

$$\alpha = \int_0^\tau (\gamma/c) \, d\tau.$$

Introducing $\xi = W/Mc^2$, we find

$$\alpha = \int_0^\tau \frac{\xi \, d\tau}{1 - \xi\tau} = \log \frac{1}{1 - \xi\tau}.$$

Therefore the velocity is

$$v = c \tan h\alpha = c \frac{e^\alpha - e^{-\alpha}}{e^\alpha + e^{-\alpha}} \simeq \frac{9}{41} c.$$

The remaining rest mass of the rocket is simply $M' = M(1 - \xi\tau) = 4$ tons.

7.4. For the rest observer

$$a_1 f_1 = a_2 f_2.$$

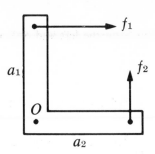

FIGURE S.8

For the observer in the moving frame (Figure. S.8), we have

$$a_1' = a_1, \qquad f_2' = f_2$$

$$a_2' = a_2\sqrt{1 - \frac{v^2}{c^2}}, \qquad f_1' = f_1 \Big/ \sqrt{1 - \frac{v^2}{c^2}}.$$

Since, however, the force f_1' is moving with the velocity V, it carries a flow of energy $f_1'V$. This flow of energy represents a change of momentum per unit time

$$\frac{\Delta P}{\Delta t} = \left(\frac{Vf_1'}{c^2}\right)V$$

which is an additional force. Thus

$$a_1'f_1' + a_1'f_1'\frac{V^2}{c^2} = a_2'f_2'$$

from the above expressions, the torques again balance. The proof could actually be made far easier and more general by noticing that the result is a consequence of the conservation of angular momentum. This follows as a consequence of the symmetry of $T_{\mu\nu} = T_{\nu\mu}$. Since symmetry is preserved (problem 6.1) under a Lorentz transformation, the system will have no angular momentum in the new frame if it has none in the original one.

7.5. This is the famous Compton Effect. See any atomic physics book dealing with elementary particles. The answer is:

$$\frac{1}{\omega'} - \frac{1}{\omega} = \frac{h}{mc^2}(1 - \cos\theta).$$

8.1(a). From (8.31) we have, for $\kappa = 0$, the form

$$\phi = \frac{Q}{r} = \frac{Q}{\sqrt{x^2 + y^2 + z^2}}$$

where Q is the source strength (Figure S.9). Then from (8.6) we compute the stress-energy tensor to be

$$
T_{\mu\nu} = \frac{1}{4\pi} \frac{Q^2}{r^6}
\begin{pmatrix}
x^2 - y^2 - z^2 & 2yx & 2zx & 0 \\
2xy & y^2 - x^2 - z^2 & 2zy & 0 \\
2xz & 2yz & z^2 - x^2 - y^2 & 0 \\
0 & 0 & 0 & x^2 + y^2 + z^2
\end{pmatrix}.
$$

(b) Consider the two sources, Q, at a distance $R = 2a$ apart. If we orient the z-axis along $\overline{QQ}$ and select the midway point as the origin we have this time as our potential,

$$
\phi = \frac{Q}{\sqrt{x^2 + y^2 + (z - a)^2}} + \frac{Q}{\sqrt{x^2 + y^2 + (z + a)^2}}.
$$

We are interested in the stresses on the plane. We can calculate the total force transmitted across the plane, especially if we know T_{zz}. Now at the surface $z = 0$,

$$
\frac{\partial \phi}{\partial x} = \frac{2Qx}{(x^2 + a^2)^{\frac{3}{2}}}, \qquad \frac{\partial \phi}{\partial y} = \frac{2Qy}{(x^2 + a^2)^{\frac{3}{2}}},
$$

$$
\frac{\partial \phi}{\partial z} = 0,
$$

so that

$$
T_{xz} = 0, \qquad T_{yz} = 0, \qquad T_{zz} = + \frac{Q^2 r^2}{2\pi(x^2 + a^2)^{\frac{3}{2}}}.
$$

The stress T_{zz} implies a force per unit area. Therefore, by integrating over the whole

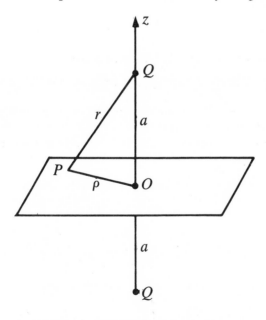

FIGURE S.9

surface, we have the magnitude (the $+$ sign actually indicates that it is a pressure, therefore the force is repulsive).

$$f = \iint T_{zz}\, dS = \frac{Q^2}{2} \int_0^\infty \int_0^{2\pi} \frac{r^3\, dr\, d\phi}{(r^2 + a^2)^{\frac{3}{2}}} = \frac{Q^2}{R^2}.$$

8.2. See equation (8.43).

8.3. In the superposition (8.20) we will have no time dependence, and $\phi(x) = Ae^{-\kappa r}/r$. But then the integral can be evaluated from 0 to ∞.

$$\int_0^\infty a(k) e^{i\vec{k}\cdot\vec{x}} d^3 k = \frac{Ae^{-\kappa r}}{r}$$

Applying to both sides the operator $(\nabla^2 - \kappa^2)$,

$$\int_0^\infty -a(k)(k^2 + \kappa^2) e^{i\vec{k}\cdot\vec{x}} d^3 k = -4\pi A\delta(r),$$

but since

$$\frac{1}{2\pi} \int_0^\infty e^{i\vec{k}\cdot\vec{x}} d^3 k = \delta(r)$$

we have

$$a(k) = \frac{A}{2\pi^2} \frac{1}{k^2 + \kappa^2}.$$

The Green's function in momentum space is thus

$$G(k) = \frac{1}{2\pi^2} \frac{1}{k^2 + \kappa^2},$$

whereas in actual space-time,

$$G(x) = \frac{e^{-\kappa r}}{r}.$$

10.1. Take the permutation $\mu\nu\sigma = 123$ as an example:

$$\partial^3(\partial^1 A^2 - \partial^2 A^1) + \partial^2(\partial^3 A^1 - \partial^1 A^3) + \partial^1(\partial^2 A^3 - \partial^3 A^2) \equiv 0.$$

Since the operations $\partial^\mu \partial^\nu = \partial^\nu \partial^\mu$ are interchangeable, the terms cancel two by two.

10.2. See problem (8.2) and Section (10.5).

10.3. In S the force on the electron is zero. In S' the field is given as (transformation law for an antisymmetric tensor)

$$H'_x = 0 \qquad H'_y = 0, \qquad H'_z = \frac{H_z}{\sqrt{1 - v^2/c^2}};$$

$$E'_x = 0, \qquad E'_y = \frac{\dfrac{v}{c} H_z}{\sqrt{1 - v^2/c^2}}, \qquad E'_z = 0.$$

Therefore the Lorentz force is

$$\vec{F}' = e\left(\vec{E}' + \frac{\vec{v} \times \vec{H}'}{c}\right) = e\left(\frac{\dfrac{v}{c} H_z}{\sqrt{1 - v^2/c^2}} - \frac{v}{c} \frac{H_z}{\sqrt{1 - v^2/c^2}}\right) = 0,$$

and hence in S' the electron moves according to

$$m_0 \frac{d^2x'}{d\tau^2} = 0$$

which leads to

$$x' = \frac{vt - x_0}{\sqrt{1 - v^2/c^2}} \; ; \qquad y' = y_0; \qquad z' = z_0.$$

This result could be obtained from the condition that the electron is at rest in S. The Lorentz transformation then leads directly to the answer.

10.4. In this reference frame

$$\sin \theta = \frac{\vec{E} \times \vec{H}}{|H| \cdot |E|} .$$

Now the transformation law for an antisymmetric tensor leads for E and H to

$$E'_x = E_x \qquad\qquad H'_x = H_x$$

$$E'_y = \frac{E_y + \frac{V}{c} H_z}{\sqrt{1 - v^2/c^2}} \qquad H'_y = \frac{H_y - \frac{V}{c} E_z}{\sqrt{1 - v^2/c^2}}$$

$$E'_z = \frac{E_z - \frac{V}{c} H_y}{\sqrt{1 + v^2/c^2}} \qquad H'_z = \frac{H_z + \frac{V}{c} E_y}{\sqrt{1 - v^2/c^2}} .$$

Let E and H be in the (yz) plane (Figure S.10). Then the condition that in the new frame, they are parallel,

$$\vec{E}' \times \vec{H}' = 0,$$

leads to

$$\frac{V}{c}(E^2 + H^2) = \left(1 - \frac{V^2}{c^2}\right) E \times H.$$

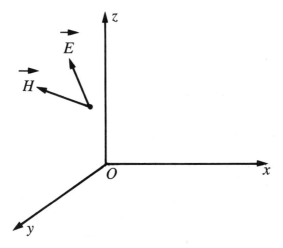

FIGURE S.10

Thus we find V from the equation

$$V^2 + \alpha V - c^2 = 0, \quad \text{where} \quad \alpha = c\left(\frac{H}{E} + \frac{E}{H}\right) \Big/ \sin \theta$$

10.5. We can find the field first for a static charge, then transform to the moving frame

$$A_1 = A_2 = A_3 = 0, \qquad A_4 = i\phi = \frac{ie}{r},$$

$$r = \sqrt{x^2 + y^2 + z^2}$$

In the moving frame

$$A_4' = \frac{ie}{\sqrt{1 - \dfrac{v^2}{c^2}} \sqrt{(x - vt)^2 + y^2 + z^2}},$$

$$A_1' = \frac{(v/c)e}{\sqrt{1 - \dfrac{v^2}{c^2}} \sqrt{(x - vt)^2 + y^2 + z^2}}.$$

From this we can calculate the E and H fields (Lenard-Wiechert problem).

10.6. The energy, as given by the stress-energy tensor (10.13), is

$$T_{44} = \frac{1}{4\pi}\left(\partial_4 A^\mu \partial_4 A_\mu - \tfrac{1}{2}\partial_\lambda A^\mu \partial^\lambda A_\mu\right)$$

$$= \frac{1}{8\pi}\left(\partial_k A^\alpha \partial^k A_\alpha + \partial_4 A^\alpha \partial^4 A_\alpha\right)$$

where $k = 1, 2, 3$. This can be negative on account of $A_4 = i\phi$ if $\partial_4 A^4 \neq 0$. Thus, if we guarantee that in the rest frame $\partial\phi/\partial t = 0$, we would eliminate the difficulty in that frame. In general coordinates, this condition translates into the covariant form $\partial_\mu A^\mu = 0$.

10.7. The field strength inside and outside the sphere are, respectively,

$$\nabla\phi = \frac{Q}{a^3} r \qquad \text{for} \qquad r < a,$$

$$\nabla\phi = \frac{Q}{r^2} \qquad \text{for} \qquad r > a.$$

Therefore, by integrating we have

$$E = -(1/8\pi)\int_0^a \left(\frac{Qr}{a^3}\right)^2 dv - (1/8\pi)\int_a^\infty \left(\frac{Q}{r^2}\right)^2 dv = -\frac{3}{5}\frac{Q^2}{a}$$

11.1. They are given in (11.49). (The negative ones.)

11.2. See section (12.4).

11.3. Using the expressions (11.63) and solutions of the form (11.66), we have for $(+)$ frequencies

	$\mathcal{E}$	P	η
u:	$\Lambda\omega$	Λk	$-k/|k|$
v:	$\Lambda'\omega$	$\Lambda'k$	$+k/|k|$

Thus the v-field represents a right-handed neutrino.

12.1. These arise from the properties of fields under Lorentz transformations, $x' = Lx$.

$$\phi_r'(Lx) = S_r^\sigma \phi_\sigma(x).$$

Under an infinitesimal (homogeneous) Lorentz transformation $x_\mu \rightarrow x_\mu + \alpha_{\mu\nu} x^\mu$ where $\alpha_{\mu\nu}$ are small quantities, we have

$$S_r^\sigma \rightarrow \delta_r^\sigma + \Sigma_r^{\sigma\mu\nu} \alpha_{\mu\nu},$$
$$\delta\phi_r \rightarrow \tfrac{1}{2} \Sigma_r^{\sigma\mu\nu} \phi_\sigma \alpha_{\mu\nu}.$$

The factor $\tfrac{1}{2}$ is introduced because of a double counting of terms due to the antisymmetry between μ and ν. For a scalar $S_r^\sigma \equiv 1$ so that $S \rightarrow 1 + 0$, $\Sigma_r^{\sigma\mu\nu} = 0$. For a vector S_r^σ is the Lorentz transformation itself,

$$S_r^\sigma = a_r^\sigma \rightarrow g_r^\sigma + \alpha_r^\sigma \rightarrow g_r^\sigma + g_r^\mu g^{\sigma\nu} \alpha_{\mu\nu}.$$

Due to the antisymmetry of $\alpha_{\mu\nu}$ we may write this as

$$g_r^\sigma + \tfrac{1}{2}(g_r^\mu g^{\sigma\nu} - g_r^\nu g^{\sigma\mu}).$$

For Spinors let $\phi = \alpha_{\alpha\beta}$ be small in (11.21). $S_\rho^\sigma \rightarrow \delta_\rho^\sigma + \tfrac{1}{4}(\gamma^\mu \gamma^\nu)_\rho^\sigma \alpha_{\mu\nu}$. Again, because of the antisymmetry, we may write $\Sigma_\rho^{\sigma\mu\nu} = \tfrac{1}{4}(\gamma^\mu \gamma^\nu - \gamma^\nu \gamma^\mu)_\rho^\sigma$. By successive application of infinitesimal unitary transformations we obtain

$$S_\rho^\sigma = \{e^{\tfrac{1}{4}\gamma^{\mu\nu} \alpha_{\mu\nu}}\}_\rho^\sigma$$

where σ and ρ are matrix indices.

12.2. The change in the action integral can be expressed as a surface integral

$$\Lambda = \int_\Omega \partial_\mu h^\mu \, d\Omega = \int_\sigma h^\mu(\phi) \, dS_\mu.$$

If h^μ vanishes at spatial infinity, the contribution to the action is zero.

12.3. Taking the divergence, we have

$$\partial_\mu j^\mu = \partial_\mu \bar\psi \gamma^\mu \psi + \bar\psi \gamma^\mu \partial_\mu \psi.$$

Now adding and substracting $\kappa \bar\Psi \Psi$ we see, from (11.2) and (11.14), that the divergence is zero.

12.4. First it is easy to see that the spin part (10.18) is nongauge invariant (just evaluate with $A_\mu \rightarrow A_\mu + \partial_\mu \Phi$). If we prove that under a gauge transformation the Lagrangian transforms as (12.22) then $M^{\mu\nu} = L^{\mu\nu} + N^{\mu\nu}$ which is derived from it is also gauge invariant. Consider the infinitesimal gauge transformation $A_\mu \rightarrow A_\mu + \epsilon \partial_\mu \Phi$ where ϵ is infinitesimal. We find $\mathscr{L} \rightarrow \mathscr{L} + \epsilon \partial_\mu \partial^\alpha \Phi \partial^\mu A_\alpha$, which can be written

$$\mathscr{L} \rightarrow \mathscr{L} + \epsilon \partial^\alpha(\partial_\mu \Phi \partial^\mu A_\alpha) - \epsilon \partial_\mu \Phi \partial^\mu(\partial^\alpha A_\alpha).$$

We see that the last term is zero on account of the Lorentz condition whereas the second term has the form (12.22).

16.1. Due to the acceleration, everything inside the car is pushed backward with the acceleration γ. This is equivalent to an additional uniform gravitational field. Therefore we can think of the car (after transients die down) as at rest if we add to the gravitational field $\vec{g}$ the acceleration $\vec{\gamma}$. The new gravitational field is $\vec{g}' = \vec{g} + \vec{\gamma}$. In such a gravitational field, the hydrogen balloon will point opposite to the resultant gravitational field $\vec{g}'$.

$$\tan \theta = \frac{\gamma}{g} = \frac{200}{981}, \qquad \theta = 11°.3.$$

Note: What would happen if the windows of the car were open?

16.2. When the elevator is freely falling, there is no gravitational field in the elevator. The reason a cigarette keeps itself lit is the air circulation, due to the difference of specific weights between warm and cold air. Since weight does not exist in a falling elevator, the resulting air circulation stops and the cigarette is soon extinguished.

16.3. Using the Christoffel symbols for the line element, we obtain

$$\ddot{x} = \frac{\partial \phi}{\partial x} e^{-4\phi} + \frac{\partial \phi}{\partial x} v^2 - 2v_x(\vec{\nabla}\phi \cdot \vec{v}),$$

$$\ddot{y} = \frac{\partial \phi}{\partial y} e^{-4\phi} + \frac{\partial \phi}{\partial y} v^2 - 2v_y(\vec{\nabla}\phi \cdot \vec{v}),$$

$$\ddot{z} = \frac{\partial \phi}{\partial z} e^{-4\phi} + \frac{\partial \phi}{\partial z} v^2 - 2v_z(\vec{\nabla}\phi \cdot \vec{v}),$$

where

$$\ddot{x} = \frac{d^2x}{dt^2}; \qquad v_x = dx/dt \dots \text{etc.}$$

16.4. From the expression for the energy, $dE = F_x\, dx + F_y\, dy + F_z\, dz$, and using Newton's equations we find

$$\tfrac{1}{2}mv^2 - \frac{Mm}{r} = E = \text{constant.}$$

Second, confining the motion to the (xy) plane, we see that

$$dA = x\, dy - y\, dx = r^2\, d\varphi.$$

By using equations (6.3), we have

$$\frac{d}{dt}\left(\frac{dA}{dt}\right) = \frac{d}{dt}\left(x\frac{dy}{dt} - y\frac{dx}{dt}\right) = x\frac{d^2y}{dt^2} - y\frac{d^2x}{dt^2} = 0,$$

so that

$$\frac{dA}{dt} = r^2\frac{d\varphi}{dt} = h = \text{constant.}$$

(For the rest of the problem, see Section 9.4.)

17.1. This follows from the fact that in (17.14) we do not have to consider mass as a δ-function at $r \to 0$. We may distribute it spherically. Then, outside this distribution, the equations (17.15) and (17.16) are still valid. The mass enters into the solution only through the integration constant $k_2 = -2\kappa M$. Outside the mass this constant is therefore the same, whether the mass is distributed spherically or concentrated at a point.

17.2. Substitute

$$r = \left(1 + \frac{M}{2r}\right)^2 \bar{r}$$

into the Schwarzschild line element. After some simple calculations and dropping the bar, we obtain

$$ds^2 = \left(\frac{1 - \dfrac{M}{2r}}{1 + \dfrac{M}{2r}}\right)^2 dt^2 - \left(1 + \frac{M}{2r}\right)^2 (dr^2 + r^2\, d\theta^2 + r^2 \sin^2\theta\, d\varphi^2).$$

17.3. The essence of the linear clock paradox can be related to problem 5.2, where we found that the man who made the rocket trip is younger than his twin brother. The paradox is this: With respect to the rocket, the earth has undergone a similar motion. Therefore, using the same reasoning a completely opposite conclusion can be reached. The resolution of this paradox lies in the fact that the earth stayed inertial (that is, no observer on earth has felt any acceleration) whereas the rocket was decelerated while reversing its velocity. Thus, the special theory of relativity is applicable to the earth's observer but not to the observer in the rocket. The latter must take into consideration the effects of acceleration, which are equivalent to a gravitational field all over the space. Here we will take this into account only in first order.

For the observer on earth, let the journey take the time $T = t_1 + t_2 + t_3$, where t_2 is the time spent during the turning around. He has the relations $t_1 = t_3 = l/v$, $t_2 = 2v/\gamma$, γ being the acceleration. Thus for him $T = 2l/v + 2v/\gamma$. But his brother will measure

$$T' = \frac{2l}{v}\sqrt{1 - v^2/c^2} + \frac{2v}{\gamma}.$$

By choosing l and γ rather large, the time of turning around may be made negligible compared to the total time of the journey and we may write

$$T = T'/\sqrt{1 - v^2/c^2} \simeq T'\left(1 + \frac{v^2}{2c^2}\right).$$

From the point of view of the rocket, an analogous reasoning applies to t_1 and t_2 so that

$$t_1' + t_2' = \frac{2l'}{v}\sqrt{1 - v^2/c^2}$$

but t_2' is completely different. Indeed when the rocket is being decelerated, the earth appears to the man on the rocket to be in a gravitational field $\phi = -\gamma x'/c^2$. This causes a gravitational time dilation

$$t_2' = \frac{2v}{\gamma} e^{-\phi} - \frac{2v}{\gamma}\left(1 + \frac{\gamma l'}{c^2}\right).$$

Putting this in,

$$T = \frac{2l'}{v}\sqrt{1 - v^2/c^2} + \frac{2v}{\gamma}\left(1 + \frac{\gamma l'}{c^2}\right) \simeq \frac{2l'}{v} + \frac{l'v}{c^2} + \frac{2v}{\gamma}.$$

Since $2v/\gamma$ is negligible compared to $2l/v$, we see that

$$T \simeq \frac{2l'}{v}\left(1 + \frac{v^2}{2c^2}\right) \simeq T'\left(1 + \frac{v^2}{2c^2}\right)$$

which is the same as the above result. Thus the introduction of general relativity resolves the clock paradox.

18.1. The general wave equation for the Nordström line element is

$$\phi^{\mu}_{;\mu} = -e^{2\phi}\left(\nabla^2 - \frac{1}{c^2}\frac{\partial^2}{\partial t^2}\right)\phi + e^{2\phi}\left[(\nabla\phi)^2 - \frac{1}{c^2}\left(\frac{\partial\phi}{\partial t}\right)^2\right] = 0$$

which is satisfied by

$$\phi = A\exp\left[2\pi i\nu\left(t - \frac{\alpha x + \beta y + z}{c}\right)\right]$$

where $\alpha^2 + \beta^2 + \gamma^2 = 1$. On the other hand, if we calculate the G^{ν}_{μ}, we see that, due to the above equation

$$G^{\nu}_{\mu} = 2(\phi_{\mu}\phi^{\nu} - \phi^{\nu}_{;\mu}) = 8\pi T^{\nu}_{\mu} - 2\phi^{\nu}_{\mu}.$$

Upon contraction, the second term gives (here we used the notation $\phi_{\mu} = \partial_{\mu}\phi$, $\phi^{\nu}_{\mu} = \partial_{\mu}\partial^{\nu}\phi$)

$$e^{2\phi}\left(\nabla^2 - \frac{1}{c^2}\frac{\partial^2}{\partial t^2}\right)\phi;$$

and due to the solution assumed, this can be put into the form $\phi^{\mu}_{;\mu}$. Thus the second term adds to the Lagrangian,

$$\mathscr{L} = -(\tfrac{1}{2})T^{\mu}_{\mu} = -(T/2),$$

the divergence of a vector ϕ^{μ}. Such a term does not disturb the dynamical theory. The line element is therefore a solution.

18.2. The general d'Alembertian is given by

$$\phi^{\mu}_{;\mu} = \frac{1}{\sqrt{-g}}\frac{\partial}{\partial x^{\nu}}\left(g^{\mu\nu}\sqrt{-g}\frac{\partial}{\partial x^{\mu}}\right)\phi.$$

From the given line element,

$$g^{11} = g^{22} = g^{33} = -e^{-2\phi}; \qquad g^{44} = e^{2\phi}; \qquad \sqrt{-g} = e^{2\phi},$$

We therefore obtain

$$\phi^{\mu}_{;\mu} = e^{-2\phi}\left(\frac{\partial}{\partial t}e^{4\phi}\frac{\partial}{\partial t} - \nabla^2\right)\phi.$$

In a time-independent case, this reduces to $\phi^{\mu}_{;\mu} = -e^{-2\phi}\nabla^2\phi$.

18.3. The method is similar to the previous problem. The answer is, in terms of the curvature tensor (using the symbol $\square_n$ for n-dimensional d'Alembertian)

$$R_{\mu\nu} = 2m\phi_{\mu}0_{\nu} + \delta_{\mu\nu}\square^2_n\phi, \qquad \mu, \nu = 1, 2, 3, 4, 5.$$

$$R_{ik} = \begin{cases} -\square^2_n\phi e^{-4\phi} - (m-1)\phi_{\mu}\phi^{\mu}e^{-4\phi} & \text{if} \quad i = k \\ 0 & \text{if} \quad i \neq k \end{cases}$$

$$R_{iv} = R_{vi} = 0 \qquad i, k = 6, 7, 8.$$

Here $n = 5$, $m = 3$. The result is general. It holds for an N dimensional geometry if $N = n$, $n = m + 2$. In this problem and in 16.3, 18.1, and 18.2 we made use of line elements which depend on scalar fields not because we have a preference but because they are easier as exercises.

INDEX

ABOUT THE AUTHOR

Huseyin Yilmaz received a B.S. degree in 1950 and an M.S. in 1951, both in electrical engineering, from Technical University of Istanbul. He was awarded the "Student University Prize" for being the most outstanding graduate of his class. In 1952 he entered the Massachusetts Institute of Technology as a doctoral candidate and research assistant. In 1954 he received his Ph.D. in theoretical Physics from M.I.T.

From 1954 to 1956 he held an assistant professorship in physics at Stevens Institute of Technology, and in 1956 he was employed by the National Research Council of Canada. In 1957 he joined Sylvania Electric Products, Inc. In 1959 he was invited to the Institute for Advanced Study in Princeton, where he received a prize from the Gravity Research Foundation for his work on two MASER experiments to test general relativity. In 1960 he developed a mathematical theory of color perception based on the Darwinian theory of evolution. This theory rejects the so-called Von Kries' law and proposes a new law of color transformation. It was stimulated by and is in agreement with the work of Dr. Edwin H. Land on two-color perception. Recently he has generalized the theory to include other sense perceptions.

Dr. Yilmaz joined Arthur D. Little, Inc., in the spring of 1962 as a senior staff member of the Research and Development division. He is also on the staff of the Department of Biology, M.I.T., and has been appointed recently as an honorary Professor of Physics at Northeastern University. He is a member of the American Physical Society and Sigma Xi.

THIS BOOK WAS SET

IN TIMES ROMAN TYPE BY

THE UNIVERSITIES PRESS

IT WAS DESIGNED BY THE STAFF OF

BLAISDELL PUBLISHING COMPANY